lu

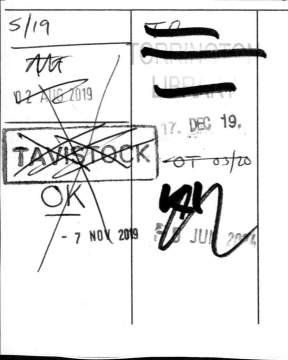

A famous, creatively-blocked, novelist faces exile or execution unless he can write a new story in the title novella of this collection, and the theme of writing threads through the pages of the entire book.

As well as eleven dazzling stories that explore strange pasts and new futures, there are pieces drawn from the writer's life, substantial commentaries on the origins and development of each of the stories, and a major new essay on how ideas are developed.

Both a magnificent gathering of fiction and a penetrating examination of the craft of writing, *Frost on Glass* memorably showcases and analyses the storytelling genius of Ian R. MacLeod.

FROST
ON
GLASS

IAN R. MACLEOD

2015

Published in July 2015 by PS Publishing Ltd. by
arrangement with the author. All rights reserved by the author.

FIRST EDITION

ISBN
978-1-84863-888-4
978-1-84863-889-1 (Signed Edition)

Story credits appear at the end of the book.

Design and layout by Alligator Tree Graphics.

Printed and bound in England by T.J. International.

PS Publishing Ltd
Grosvenor House
1 New Road
Hornsea, HU18 1PG
England

editor@pspublishing.co.uk
www.pspublishing.co.uk

Contents

Introduction *Don't Look Back*

You should never look back, especially when it comes to short stories. They're like flings or affairs rather than the marriages of novels, and it's all too easy to get drawn away from the road ahead by picking over old joys, regrets and what-might-have-beens. Still, any collection such as this cannot help but cast a glance over its shoulder, and I, both as a reader and a writer, have an abiding interest in how fiction is written—something I intend to explore in this book.

Writing is at least as much a craft as it is an art, and one of the things I aim to do in these pages is to offer some insight into how various aspects of my stories came about. I've written a long new story, "Frost on Glass," which gives this collection its name and is itself about writing, and the frustrations of trying to master and control something so evanescent, along with a substantial new essay "I've Got This Idea For a Story . . ." which is both an examination and a spirited defence of that most fundamental and tricky of writerly subjects. I've also included various other non-fiction pieces I've written here and there over the years, which touch in one way or another on the process of writing.

As for the stories, and despite all the things I say about them, I hope that they speak for themselves.

FROST
ON
GLASS

The Discovered Country

THE trees of Farside are incredible. Fireash and oak. Greenbloom and maple. Shot through with every colour of autumn as late afternoon sunlight blazes over the Seven Mountains' white peaks. He'd never seen such beauty as this when he was alive.

The virtual Bentley takes the bridge over the next gorge at a tyrescream, then speeds on through crimson and gold. Another few miles, and he's following the coastal road beside the Westering Ocean. The sands are burnished, the rocks silver-threaded. Every new vista a fabulous creation. Then ahead, just as purple glower sweeps in from his rear-view over those dragon-haunted mountains, come the silhouette lights of a vast castle, high up on a ridge. It's the only habitation he's seen in hours.

This has to be it.

Northover lets the rise of the hill pull at the Bentley's impetus as its headlights sweep the driveway trees. Another turn, another glimpse of a headland, and there's Elsinore again, rising dark and sheer.

He tries to refuse the offer to carry his luggage made by the neat little creature that emerges into the lamplit courtyard to greet him with clipboard, sharp shoes and lemony smile. He's encountered many chimeras by now. The shop assistants, the street cleaners, the crew on the steamer ferry that brought him here. All substantially humanoid, and invariably polite, although amended as necessary to perform their tasks, and far stranger to his mind than the truly dead.

He follows a stairway up through rough-hewn stone. The thing's name is Kasaya. Ah, now. The east wing. I think you'll find what we have here more than adequate. If not . . . Well, you *must* promise to let me know. And this is called the Willow Room. And *do* enjoy your stay . . .

Northover wanders. Northover touches. Northover breathes. The interior of this large high-ceilinged suite with its crackling applewood fire and narrow, deep-set windows is done out in an elegantly understated arts-and-craftsy style. Amongst her many attributes, Thea Lorentz always did have excellent taste.

What's struck him most about Farside since he jerked into new existence, on the bed in the cabin of that ship bound for New Erin, is how unremittingly *real* everything seems. But the slick feel of this patterned silk bedthrow . . . The spiky roughness of the teasels in the flower display . . . He's given up telling himself that everything he's experiencing is just some clever construct. The thing about it, the thing that makes it all so impossibly overwhelming, is that *he's* here as well. Dead, but alive. The evidence of his corpse doubtless already incinerated, but his consciousness—the singularity of his existence, what philosophers once called "the conscious I", and theologians the soul, along with his memories and personality, the whole sense of self which had once inhabited pale jelly in his skull—transferred.

The bathroom is no surprise to him now. The dead do so many things the living do, so why not piss and shit as well? He strips and stands in the shower's warm blaze. He soaps, rinses. Reminds himself of what he must do, and say. He'd been warned that he'd soon become attracted to the blatant glories this world, along with the new, young man's body he now inhabits. Better just to accept rather than fight. All that matters is that he holds to the core of his resolve.

He towels himself dry. He slips on his watch—seemingly a Rolex, but a steel model, neatly unostentatious—and winds it carefully. He dresses. Hangs up his clothes in a walnut panelled wardrobe that smells faintly of mothballs, and hears a knock at the door just as he slides his case beneath the bed.

"Yes? Come in . . ."

When he turns, he's expecting another chimera servant. But it's Thea Lorentz.

This, too, is something they'd tried to prepare him for. But encountering her after so long is much less of a shock than he's been expecting. Thea's image is as ubiquitous as that of Marilyn Munroe or the Virgin Mary back on Lifeside, and she really hasn't changed. She's dressed in a loose-fitting shirt. Loafers and slacks. Hair tied back. No obvious evidence of any make-up. But the crisp white shirt with its rolled up cuffs shows her dark brown skin to perfection, and one loose strand of her tied back hair plays teasingly at her sculpted neck. A tangle of silver bracelets slide on her wrist as she steps forward to embrace him. Her breasts are unbound and she still smells warmly of the patchouli she always used to favour. Everything about her feels exactly the same. But why not? After all, she was already perfect when she was alive.

"Well . . . !" That warm blaze is still in her eyes, as well. "It really *is* you."

"I know I'm springing a huge surprise. Just turning up from out of nowhere like this."

"I can take these kind of surprises any day! And I hear it's only been—what?—less than a week since you transferred. Everything must still feel so very strange to you."

It went without saying that his and Thea's existences had headed off in different directions back on Lifeside. She, of course, had already been well on her way toward some or other kind of immortality when they'd lost touch. And he . . . Well, it was just one of those stupid lucky breaks. A short, ironic keyboard riff he'd written to help promote some old online performance thing—no, no, it was nothing she'd been involved in—had ended up being picked up many years later as the standard message-send fail signal on the global net. Yeah, that was the one. Of course, Thea knew it. Everyone, once they thought about it for a moment, did.

"You know, Jon," she says, her voice more measured now, "you're the one person I thought would never choose to make this decision. None of us can pretend that being Farside isn't a position of immense privilege, when most of the living can't afford food, shelter, good health. You always were a man of principle, and I sometimes thought you'd just fallen to . . . Well, the same place that most performers fall to, I suppose, which is no particular place at all. I even considered trying to find you and get in touch, offer you . . . " She gestures around her. "Well, this. But you wouldn't have taken it, would you? Not on those terms."

He shakes his head. In so many ways she still has him right. He detested—no, he quietly reminds himself—*detests* everything about this vast vampiric sham of a world that sucks life, hope and power from the living. But she hadn't come to him, either, had she? Hadn't offered what she now so casually calls *this*. For all her fame, for all her good works, for all the aid funds she sponsors and the good causes she promotes, Thea Lorentz and the rest of the dead have made no effort to extend their constituency beyond the very rich, and almost certainly never will. After all, why should they? Would the gods invite the merely mortal to join them on Mount Olympus?

She smiles and steps close to him again. Weighs both his hands in her own. "Most people I know, Jon—most of those I have to meet and talk to and deal with, and even those I have to call friends—they all think that I'm Thea Lorentz. Both Farside and Lifeside, it's long been the same. But only you and a few very others really know who I am. You can't imagine how precious and important it is to have you here . . . "

He stands gazing at the door after she's left. Willing everything to dissolve, fade, crash, melt. But nothing changes. He's still dead. He's still standing here in this Farside room. Can still even breathe the faint patchouli of Thea's scent. He finishes dressing—a tie, a jacket, the same supple leather shoes he arrived in—and heads out into the corridor.

Elsinore really is *big*—and resolutely, heavily, emphatically, the ancient building it wishes to be. Cold gusts pass along its corridors. Heavy doors groan and creak. Of course, the delights of Farside are near-infinite. He's passed through forests of mist and silver. Seen the vast, miles-wide back of some great island of a seabeast drift past when he was still out at sea. The dead can grow wings, sprout gills, spread roots into the soil and raise their arms and become trees. All these things are not only possible, but visibly, virtually, achievably real. But he thinks they still hanker after life, and all the things of life the living, for all their disadvantages, possess.

He passes many fine-looking paintings as he descends the stairs. They have a Pre-Raphaelite feel and, from the little he knows of art, seem finely executed, but he doesn't recognise any of them. Have these been created by virtual hands, in some virtual workshop, or have they simply sprung into existence? And what would happen if he took that sword which also hangs on display, and slashed it through a canvas? Would the painting be gone forever? Almost certainly not. One thing he knows for sure about Farside's vast database is that it's endlessly backed up, scattered, diffused and re-collated across many secure and heavily armed vaults back in what's left of the world of the living. There are very few guaranteed ways of permanently destroying anything, least of all the dead.

Farther down, there are holo-images, all done in stylish black and white. Somehow, even in a castle, they don't look out of place. Thea, as always, looks like she's stepped out of a fashion-shoot. The dying jungle suits her. As does this war-zone, and this flooded hospital, and this burnt-out shanty town. The kids, and it is mostly kids, who surround her with their pot bellies and missing limbs, somehow manage to absorb a little of her glamour. On these famous trips of hers back to view the suffering living, she makes an incredibly beautiful ghost.

Two big fires burn in Elsinore's great hall, there's a long banqueting table, and the heads of many real and mythic creatures loom upon the walls. Basilisk, boar, unicorn . . . Hardly noticing the chimera servant who rakes his chair out for him, Northover sits down. Thea's space at the top of the table is still empty.

In this Valhalla where the lucky, eternal dead feast forever, what strikes Northover most strongly is the sight of Sam Bartleby sitting beside Thea's vacant chair. Not that he doesn't know that the man has been part of what's termed *Thea Lorentz's inner circle* for more than a decade. But, even when they were all still alive and working together on *Bard On Wheels*, he'd never been able to understand why she put up with him. Of course, Bartleby made his fortune with those ridiculous action virtuals, but the producers deepened his voice so much, and enhanced his body so ridiculously, that it was a wonder to Northover they bothered to use him at all. Now, though, he's chosen to bulk himself out and cut his hair in a Roman fringe. He senses Northover's gaze, raises his glass and gives an ironic nod. He still has the self-regarding manner of someone who thinks himself far better looking and cleverer than he actually is.

Few of the dead, though, choose to be beautiful. Most elect for the look that expresses themselves at what they thought of as the most fruitful and self-expressive period of their lives. Amongst people this wealthy, this often equates to late middle age. The fat, the bald, the matronly and the downright ugly rub shoulders, secure in the knowledge that they can become young and beautiful whenever they wish.

"So? What are you here for?"

The woman beside him already seems flushed from the wine, and has a homely face and a dimpled smile, although she sports pointed teeth, elfin ears and her eyes are cattish slits.

"For?"

"Name's Wilhelmina Howard. People just call me Will . . . " She offers him a claw-nailed hand to shake. "Made my money doing windfarm recycling in the non-federal states. All that lovely superconductor and copper we need right here to keep our power supplies as they should be. Not that we ever had much of a presence in England, which I'm guessing is where you were from . . . ?"

He gives a guarded nod.

"But isn't it just so *great* to be here at Elsinore? *Such* a privilege. Thea's everything people say she is, isn't she, and then a whole lot more as well? *Such* compassion, and all the marvellous things she's done! Still, I know she's invited me here because she wants to get hold of some of my money. Give back a little of what we've taken an' all. Not that I won't give. That's for sure. Those poor souls back on Lifeside. We really have to do something, don't we, all of us . . . ?"

"To be honest, I'm here because I used to work with Thea. Back when we were both alive."

"So, does that make you an *actor*?" Wilhelmina is looking at him more closely now. Her slit pupils have widened. "Should I *recognise* you? Were you in any of the famous—"

"No, no." As if in defeat, he holds up a hand. Another chance to roll out his story. More a musician, a keyboard player, although there wasn't much he hadn't turned his hand to over the years. Master of many trades, and what have you—at least, until that message-fail signal came along.

"So, pretty much a lucky break," murmurs this ex take-no-shit business-woman who died and became a fat elf, "rather than any kind of lifetime endeavour . . . ?"

Then Thea enters the hall, and she's changed into something more purposefully elegant—a light grey dress that shows her fine breasts and shoulders without seeming immodest—and her hair is differently done, and Northover understands all the more why most of the dead make no attempt to be beautiful. After all, how could they, when Thea Lorentz does it so unassailably well? She stands waiting for a moment as if expectant silence hasn't already fallen, then says a few phrases about how pleased she is to have so many charming and interesting guests. Applause follows. Just as she used to do for many an encore, Thea nods and smiles and looks genuinely touched.

The rest of the evening at Elsinore passes in a blur of amazing food and superb wine, all served with the kind of discreet inevitability which Northover has decided only chimeras are capable of. Just like Wilhelmina, everyone wants to know who he's with, or for, or from. The story about that jingle works perfectly; many even claim to have heard of him and his success. Their curiosity only increases when he explains his and Thea's friendship. After all, he could be the route of special access to her famously compassionate ear.

There are about twenty guests here at Elsinore tonight, all told, if you don't count the several hundred chimeras, which of course no one does. Most of the dead, if you look at them closely enough, have adorned them-selves with small eccentricities; a forked tongue here, an extra finger there, a crimson badger-stripe of hair. Some are new to each other, but the inter-actions flow on easy rails. Genuine fame itself is rare here—after all, entertainment has long been a cheapened currency—but there's a relaxed feeling-out between strangers in the knowledge that some shared acquaintance or interest will soon be reached. Wealth always was an exclusive club, and it's even more exclusive here.

Much of the talk is of new Lifeside investment. Viral re-programming of food crops, all kinds of nano-engineering, weather, flood and even birth control—although the last strikes Northover as odd considering how rapidly the human population is decreasing—and every other kind of plan imaginable to make the earth a place worth living in again is discussed. Many of these schemes, he soon realises, would be mutually incompatible, and potentially incredibly destructive, and all are about making money.

Cigars are lit after the cheeses and sorbets. Rare, exquisite whiskeys are poured. Just like everyone else, he can't help but keep glancing at Thea. She still has that way of seeming part of the crowd yet somehow apart—or above—it. She always had been a master of managing social occasions, even those rowdy parties they'd hosted back in the day. A few words, a calming hand and smile, and even the most annoying drunk would agree that it was time they took a taxi. For all her gifts as a performer, her true moments of transcendent success were at the lunches, the less-than-chance-encounters, the launch parties. Even her put-downs or betrayals left you feeling grateful.

Everything Farside is so spectacularly different, yet so little about her has changed. The one thing he does notice, though, is her habit of toying with those silver bangles she's still wearing on her left wrist. Then, at what feels like precisely the right moment, and thus fractionally before anyone expects, she taps her wineglass as she stands up to say a few words. From anyone else's lips, they would sound like vague expressions of pointless hope. But, coming from her, it's hard not to be stirred.

Then, with a bow, a nod, and what Northover was almost sure is a small conspiratorial blink in his direction—which somehow seems to acknowledge the inherent falsity of what she has just done, but also the absolute need for it—she's gone from the hall, and the air suddenly seems stale. He stands up and grabs at the tilt of his chair before a chimera servant can get to it. He feels extraordinarily tired, and more than a little drunk.

In search of some air, he follows a stairway that winds up and up. He steps out high on the battlements. He hears feminine chuckles. Around a corner, shadows tussle. He catches the starlit glimpse of a bared breast, and turns the other way. It's near-freezing on these battlements. Clouds cut ragged by a blazing sickle moon. Northover leans over and touches the winding crown of his Rolex watch and studies the distant lace of waves. Then, glancing back, he thinks he sees another figure behind him. Not the lovers, certainly. This shape bulks far larger, and is alone. Yet the dim outlines of the battlements gleam though it. A malfunction? A premonition? A genuine ghost? But then, as Northover moves, the figure moves with him, and he realises that he's seeing nothing but his own shadow thrown by the moon.

He dreams that night that he's alive again, but no longer the young and hopeful man he once was. He's mad old Northy. Living, if you call it living, so high up in the commune tower that no one else bothers him much, and with nothing but the old piano he's somehow managed to restore for company. Back in his old body, as well, with his old aches, fatigues and irritations. But for once, it isn't raining, and frail sparks of sunlight cling to shattered glass in the ruined rooms, and the whole flooded, once-great city of London is almost beautiful, far below.

Then, looking back, he sees a figure standing at the far end of the corridor that leads through rubble to the core stairs. They come up sometimes, do the kids. They taunt him and try to steal his last few precious things. Northy swears and lumbers forward, grabbing an old broom. But the kid doesn't curse or throw things. Neither does he turn and run, although it looks as if he's alone.

"You're Northy, aren't you?" the boy called Haru says, his voice an adolescent squawk.

He awakes with a start to new light, good health, comforting warmth. A sense, just as he opens his eyes and knowledge of who and what he is returns, that the door to his room has just clicked shut. He'd closed the curtains here in the Willow Room in Elsinore, as well, and now they are open. And the fire grate has been cleared, the applewood logs restocked. He reaches quickly for his Rolex, and begins to relax as he slips it on. The servants, the chimeras, will have been trained, programmed, to perform their work near-invisibly, and silently.

He showers again. He meets the gaze of his own eyes in the mirror as he shaves. Whatever view there might be from his windows is hidden in a mist so thick that the world beyond could be the blank screen of some old computer from his youth. The route to breakfast is signalled by conversation and a stream of guests. The hall is smaller than the one they were in last night, but still large enough. A big fire crackles in a soot-stained hearth, but steam rises from the food as cold air wafts in through the open doors.

Dogs are barking in the main courtyard. Horses are being led out. Elsinore's battlements and towers hover like ghosts in the blanketing fog. People are milling, many wearing thick gauntlets, leather helmets and what look like padded vests and kilts. The horses are big, beautifully groomed but convincingly skittish in the way that Northover surmises expensively pedigreed beasts are. Or were. Curious, he goes over to one as a chimera stable boy fusses with its saddle and reins.

The very essence of equine haughtiness, the creature tosses its head and does that lip-blubber thing horses do. Everything about this creature is impressive. The flare of its nostrils. The deep, clean, horsy smell. Even, when he looks down and under, the impressive, seemingly part-swollen heft of its horsey cock.

"Pretty spectacular, isn't he?"

Northover finds that Sam Bartleby is standing beside him. Dressed as if for battle, and holding a silver goblet of something steaming and red. Even his voice is bigger and deeper than it was. The weird thing is, he seems more like Sam Bartleby than the living Sam Bartleby ever did. Even in those stupid action virtuals.

"His name's Aleph—means alpha, of course, or the first. You may have heard of him. He won, yes didn't you . . . ?" By now, Bartleby's murmuring into the beast's neck. "The last ever Grand Steeple de Paris."

Slowly, Northover nods. The process of transfer is incredibly expensive, but there's no reason in principle why creatures other than humans can't join Farside's exclusive club. The dead are bound to want the most presti-

gious and expensive toys. So, why not the trapped, transferred consciousness of a multi-million dollar racehorse?

"You don't ride, do you?" Bartleby, still fondling Aleph—who,
Northover notices, is now displaying an even more impressive erection—
asks.

"It wasn't something I ever got around to."

"But you've got plenty of time now, and there are few things better than
a day out hunting in the forest. I suggest you start with one of the lesser,
easier, mounts over there, and work your way up to a real beast like this.
Perhaps that pretty roan? Even then, though, you'll have to put up with a
fair few falls. Although, if you really want to cheat and bend the rules, and
know the right people, there are shortcuts . . . "

"As you say, there's plenty of time."

"So," Bartleby slides up into the saddle with what even Northover has
to admit is impressive grace. "Why are you here? Oh, I don't mean getting
here with that stupid jingle. You always were a lucky sod. I mean, at Elsinore. I suppose you want something from Thea. That's why most people
come. Whether or not they've got some kind of past with her."

"Isn't friendship enough?"

Bartleby is now looking down at Northover in a manner even more
condescending than the horse.

"You should know better than most, Jon, that friendship's just another
currency." He pauses as he's handed a long spear, its tip a clear, icy
substance that could be diamond. "I should warn you that whatever it is
you want, you're unlikely to get it. At least, not in the way you expect. A
favour for some cherished project, maybe?" His lips curl. "But that's not *it*
with you, is it? We know each other too well, Jon, and you really haven't
changed. Not one jot. What you really want is Thea, isn't it? You want her
wrapped up and whole, even though we both know that's impossible. Thea
being Thea just as she always was. And, believe me, I'd do anything to
defend her. Anything to stop her being hurt . . . "

With a final derisory snort and a spark of cobbles, Bartley and Aleph
clatter off.

———

The rooms, halls and corridors of Elsinore are filled with chatter and bustle. Impromptu meetings. Accidental collisions and confusions that have surely been long planned. Kisses and business cards are exchanged. Deals are brokered. Promises offered. The spread of the desert which has now consumed most of north Africa could be turned around by new cloud-seeding technologies, yet still, there's coffee, or varieties of herb tea if preferred.

No sign of Thea, though. In a way she's more obvious Lifeside, where you can buy as much Thea Lorentz tat as even the most fervent fanatic could possibly want. Figurines. Candles. Wallscreens. Tee shirts. Some of it, apparently, she even endorses. Although always, of course, in a good cause. Apart from those bothersome kids, it was the main reason Northover spent so much of his last years high up and out of reach of the rest of the commune. He hated being reminded of the way people wasted what little hope and money they had on stupid illusions. Her presence here at Elsinore is palpable, though. Her name is the ghost at the edge of every conversation. Yes, but Thea . . . Thea . . . And Thea . . . Thea . . . Always, always, everything is about Thea Lorentz.

He realises this place she's elected to call Elsinore isn't any kind of home at all—but he supposes castles have always fulfilled a political function, at least when they weren't under siege. People came from near-impossible distances to plead their cause, and, just as here, probably ended up being fobbed off. Thea's chimera servants mingle amid the many guests. Northover notices Kasaya many times. A smile here. A mincing gesture there.

He calls after him the next time he sees him bustling down a corridor.

"Yes, Mister Northover . . . ?" Clipboard at the ready, Kasaya spins round on his toes.

"I was just wondering, seeing as you seem to be about so much, if there happen to be more than one of you here at Elsinore?"

"That isn't necessary. It's really just about good organisation and hard work."

"So . . . " Was that *really* slight irritation he detected, followed by a small flash of pride? " . . . you can't be in several places at once?"

"That's simply isn't required. Although Elsinore does have many short cuts."

"You mean, hidden passageways? Like a real castle?"

Kasaya, who clearly has more important things to see to, manages a smile. "I think that that would be a good analogy."

"But you just said think. You *do* think?"

"Yes." He's raised his clipboard almost like a shield now. "I believe I do."

"How long have you been here?"

"Oh . . . " He blinks in seeming recollection. "Many years."

"And before that?"

"Before that, I wasn't here." Hugging his clipboard more tightly than ever, Kasaya glances longingly down the corridor. "Perhaps there's something you need? I could summon someone . . . "

"No, I'm fine. I was just curious about what it must be like to be you, Kasaya. I mean, are you always on duty? Do your kind ever *sleep*? Do you change out of those clothes and wash your hair and—"

"I'm sorry sir," the chimera intervenes, now distantly firm. "I really can't discuss these matters when I'm on duty. If I may . . . ?"

Then, he's off without a backward glance. Deserts may fail to bloom if the correct kind of finger food isn't served at precisely the right moment. Children blinded by onchocerciasis might not get the implants that will allow them to see grainy shapes for lack of a decent meeting room. And, after all, Kasaya is responding in the way that any servant would—at least, if a guest accosted them and started asking inappropriately personal questions when they were at work. Northover can't help but feel sorry for these creatures, who clearly seem to have at least the illusion of consciousness. To be trapped forever in crowd scenes at the edges of the lives of the truly dead . . .

Northover comes to another door set in a kind of side-turn that he almost walks past. Is this where the chimera servants go? Down this way, Elsinore certainly seems less grand. Bright sea air rattles the arrowslit glass. The walls are raw stone, and stained with white tidemarks of damp. This, he imagines some virtual guide pronouncing, is by far the oldest part of the castle. It certainly feels that way.

He lifts a hessian curtain and steps into a dark, cool space. A single barred, high skylight fans down on what could almost have been a dungeon. Or a monastic cell. Some warped old bookcases and other odd bits of furniture, all cheaply practical, populate a roughly paved floor. In one corner, some kind of divan or bed. In another, a wicker chair. The change of light is so pronounced that it's a moment before he sees that someone is sitting there. A further beat before he realises it's Thea Lorentz, and that she's seated before a mirror, and her fingers are turning those bangles on her left wrist. Frail as frost, the silver circles tink and click. Otherwise, she's motionless. She barely seems to breathe.

Not a mirror at all, Northover realises as he shifts quietly around her, but some kind of tunnel or gateway. Through it, he sees a street. It's raining, the sky is reddish with windblown earth, and the puddles seem bright as blood. Lean-to shacks, their gutters sluicing, line something too irregular to be called a street. A dead power pylon leans in the mid-distance. A woman stumbles into view, drenched and wading up to the knee. She's holding something wrapped in rags with a wary possessiveness that suggests it's either a baby or food. This could be the suburbs of London, New York or Sydney. That doesn't matter. What does matter is how she falls to her knees at what she sees floating before her in the rain. Thea . . . ! The woman almost drops whatever she's carrying as her fingers claw upward and her ruined mouth shapes the name. She's weeping, and Thea is weeping as well—two silver trails that follow the perfect contours of her face. Then, the scene fades in another shudder of rain, and Thea Lorentz is looking out at him from the reformed surface of a mirror with the same soft sorrow that poor, ruined woman must have seen in her gaze.

"Jon."

"This, er . . . " he gestures.

She stands up. She's wearing a long tweed skirt, rumpled boots, a loose turtleneck woollen top. "Oh, it's probably everything people say it is. The truth is that, once you're Farside, it's too easy to forget what Lifeside is really like. People make all the right noises—I'm sure you've heard them already. But that isn't the same thing."

"Going there—being seen as some virtual projection in random places like that—aren't you just perpetuating the myth?"

She nods slowly. "But is that really such a terrible thing? And that cat-eyed woman you sat next to yesterday at dinner. What's her name,

Wilhelmina? Kasaya's already committed her to invest in new sewerage processing works and food aid, all of which will be targeted on that particular area of Barcelona. I know she's a tedious creature—you only have to look at her to see that—but what's the choice? You can stand back, and do nothing, or step in, and use whatever you have to try to make things slightly better."

"Is that what you really think?"

"Yes. I believe I do. But how about *you*, Jon? What do you think?"

"You know me," he says. "More than capable of thinking several things at once. And believing, or not believing, all of them."

"Doubting Thomas," she says, taking another step forward so he can smell patchouli.

"Or Hamlet."

"Here of all places, why not?"

For a while, they stand there in silence.

"This whole castle is designed to be incredibly protective of me," she says eventually. "It admits very few people this far. Only the best and oldest of friends. And Bartleby insists I wear these as an extra precaution, even though they can sometimes be distracting . . . " She raises her braceletted wrist. "As you've probably already gathered, he's pretty protective of me, too."

"We've spoken. It wasn't exactly the happiest reunion."

She smiles. "The way you both are, it would have been strange if it was. But look, you've come all this incredible way. Why don't we go out somewhere?"

"You must have work to do. Projects—I don't know—that you need to approve. People to meet."

"The thing about being in Elsinore is that things generally go more smoothly when Thea Lorentz isn't in the way. You saw what it was like last night at dinner. Every time I open my mouth people expect to hear some new universal truth. I ask them practical questions and their mouths drop. Important deals fall apart when people get distracted because Thea's in the room. That's why Kasaya's so useful. He does all that's necessary—joins up the dots and bangs the odd head. And people scarcely even notice him."

"I don't think he likes it much when they do."

"*More* questions, Jon?" She raises an eyebrow. "But everything here on Farside must still seem so strange to you, when there's so much to explore . . . "

Down stairways. Along corridors. Through storerooms. Perhaps these are the secret routes Kasaya hinted at, winding through the castle like Escher tunnels in whispers of sea-wet stone. Then, they are down in a great, electric-lit cavern of a garage. His Bentley is here, along with lines of other fine and vintage machines long crumbled to rust back on Lifeside. Maseratis. Morgans. Lamborghinis. Other things that look like Dan Dare spaceships or Faberge submarines. The cold air reeks of new petrol, clean oil, polished metal. In a far corner and wildly out of place, squatting above a small black pool, is an old VW Beetle.

"Well," she says. "What do you think?"

He smiles as he walks around it. The dents and scratches are old friends. "It's perfect."

"Well, it was never *that*. But we had some fun with it, didn't we?"

"How does this work? I mean, creating it? Did you have some old pictures of it? Did you manage to access—"

"Jon." She dangles a key from her hand. "Do you want to go out for a drive, or what?"

"The steering even *pulls* the same way. It's amazing . . . "

Out on roads that climb and camber, giving glimpses of flanks of forest through the slowly thinning mist, deep drops. Headlights on, although it makes little difference and there doesn't seem to be any other traffic. She twiddles the radio. Finds a station that must have stopped transmitting more than fifty years ago. Van Morrison, Springsteen and Dylan. So very, very out of date—but still good—even back then. And even now, with his brown-eyed girl beside him again. It's the same useless deejay, the same pointless adverts. As the road climbs higher, the signal fades to a bubbling hiss.

"Take that turn up there. You see, the track right there in the trees . . . ?"

The road now scarcely a road. The Beetle a jumble of metallic jolts and yelps. He has to laugh, and Thea laughs as well, the way they're being bounced around. A tunnel through the trees, and then some kind of clearing, where he stops the engine and squawks the handbrake, and everything falls still.

"Do you remember?"

He climbs out slowly, as if fearing a sudden movement might cause it all to dissolve.

"Of course I do . . . "

Thea, though, strides ahead. Climbs the sagging cabin steps.

"This is . . . "

"I know," she agrees, testing the door. Which—just as it had always been—is unlocked.

This, he thinks as he stumbles forward, is what it really means to be dead. Forget the gills and wings and the fine wines and the spectacular food and the incredible scenery. What this is, what it means . . .

Is *this.*

The same cabin. It could be the same day. Thea, she'd called after him as he walked down the street away from an old actors' pub off what was still called Covent Garden after celebrating—although that wasn't the word—the end of *Bard On Wheels* with a farewell pint and a spliff. Farewell and fuck off as far as Northover was concerned, Sam Bartleby and his stupid sword fights especially. Shakespeare and most other kinds of real perform-ance being well and truly dead, and everyone heading for well-deserved obscurity. The sole exception being Thea Lorentz, who could sing and act and do most things better than all the rest of them combined, and had an air of being destined for higher things that didn't seem like arrogant bull-shit even if it probably was. Out of his class, really, both professionally and personally. But she'd called to him, and he'd wandered back, for where else was he heading? She'd said she had a kind of proposal, and why didn't they go out for a while, out in her old VW? All the bridges over the Thames hadn't yet been down then, and they'd driven past the burnt-out cars and abandoned shops until they came to this stretch of woodland where the trees were still alive, and they'd ended up exactly here. In this clearing, inside this cabin.

There's an old woodburner stove that Northover sets about lighting, and a few tins along the cobweb shelves, which he inspects and settles on a tin of soup. He nearly cuts his thumb struggling to open it, and sets it to warm on the top of the stove as it begins to send out amber shadows. He goes to the window, clears a space in the dust, pretending to check that he turned the VW's lights off, but in reality trying to grab a little thinking time. He didn't, doesn't, know Thea Lorentz that well at this or any point. But he knows her well enough to understand that her spontaneous suggestions are nothing if not measured.

"Is this how it was, do you think?" she asks, shrugging off her coat and coming to stand behind him. Again, that smell of patchouli. She slides her arms around his waist. Nestles her chin against his shoulder. "I wanted you to be what I called producer and musical director for my Emily Dickinson thing. And you agreed."

"Not before I'd asked if you meant roadie and general dogsbody."

He feels her chuckle. "That as well . . . "

"What else was I going to do, anyway?" Dimly, in the gaining glow of the stove, he can see their faces in reflection.

"And how about now?"

"I suppose it's much the same."

He turns. It's he who clasps her face, draws her mouth to his. Another thing about Thea is that, even when you know it's always really her, it somehow seems to be you.

Their teeth clash. It's been a long time. This is the first time ever. She draws back, breathless, pulls off that loose-fitting jumper she's wearing. He helps her with the shift beneath, traces, remembers, discovers or redis-covers, the shape and weight of her breasts. Thumbs her hardening nipples. Then, she pulls away his shirt, undoes his belt buckle. Difficult here to be graceful, even if you're Thea Lorentz, struggle-hopping with zips, shoes and panties. Even harder for Northover with one sock off and the other caught on something or other, not to mention his young man's erection, as he throws a dusty blanket over the creaky divan. But laughter helps. Laughter always did. That, and Thea's knowing smile as she takes hold of him for a moment in her cool fingers. Then, Christ, she lets go of him again. A final pause, and he almost thinks this isn't going to work, but all she's doing is pulling off those silver bracelets, and then, before he can realise what else it is she wants, she's snapping off the bangle of his Rolex as well and pulling him down, and now there's nothing else to be done, for they really are naked.

Northover, he's drowning in memory. Greedy at first, hard to hold back, especially with the things she does, but then trying to be slow, trying to be gentle. Or, at least, a gentleman. He remembers, anyway—or is it now happening?—that time she took his head between her hands and raised it to her gaze. *You don't have to be so careful,* she murmurs. Or murmured. *I'm flesh and blood, Jon. Just like you . . .*

He lies back. Collapsed. Drenched. Exhausted. Sated. He turns from the cobweb ceiling and sees the Rolex lies cast on the gritty floor. Softly ticking. Just within reach. But already, Thea is stirring. She scratches, stretches. Bracelet hoops glitter as they slip back over her knuckles. He stands up. Pads over to a stained sink. There's a trickle of water. What might pass for a towel. Dead or living, it seems, the lineaments of love remain the same, although he notices how the untouched soup remains cold despite the stove's apparent heat.

"You never were much of a one for falling asleep after," Thea comments, straightening her sleeves as she dresses.

"Not much of a man, then."

"Some might say that . . . " She laughs as she fluffs her hair. "But we had something, didn't we, Jon? We really did. So why not again?"

There it is. Just when he thinks the past's finally over and done with. Not Emily Dickinson this time, or not only that project, but a kind of greatest hits. Stuff they did together with *Bard On Wheels*, although this time it'll be just them, a two-hander, a proper double act, and, yes Jon, absolutely guaranteed no Sam fucking Bartleby. Other things as well. A few songs, sketches. Bits and bobs. Fun, of course. But wasn't the best kind of fun always the stuff you took seriously? And why not start here and see how it goes? Why not tonight, back at Elsinore?

As ever, what can he say but yes?

Thea drives. He supposes she did before, although he can't really remember how they got back to London. The mist has cleared. She, the sea, the mountains, all look magnificent. That Emily Dickinson thing, the one they did before, was a huge commercial and critical success. Even if people did call it a one-woman show, when he'd written half the script and all of the music. To have those looks, and yet to be able to hold the stage and sing and act so expressively! Not to mention, although the critics generally did, that starlike ability to assume a role, yet still be Thea Lorentz. Audrey Hepburn got a mention. So did Grace Kelly. A fashion icon, too, then. But Thea could carry a tune better than either. Even for the brief time they were actually living together in that flat in Pimlico, Northover sometimes found himself simply looking—staring, really—at Thea. Especially when she was sleeping. She just seemed so angelic. Who are you really? he'd wondered. Where are you from? Why are you here, and with me of all people?

He never did work out the full chain of events that brought her to join *Bard On Wheels*. Of course, she'd popped up in other troupes and performances—the evidence was still to be found on blocky online postings and all those commemorative hagiographies, but remembrances were shaky and it was hard to work on the exact chain of where and when. A free spirit, certainly. A natural talent. Not the sort who'd ever needed instructing. She claimed that she'd lost both her parents to the Hn3i epidemic, and had grown up in one of those giant orphanages they set up at Heathrow. As to where she got that poise, or the studied assurance she always displayed, all the many claims, speculations, myths and stories that eventually emerged—and which she never made any real attempt to quash— drowned out whatever had been the truth.

They didn't finish the full tour. Already, the offers were pouring in. He followed her once to pre-earthquake, pre-nuke Los Angeles, but by then people weren't sure what his role exactly was in the growing snowball of Thea Lorentz's fame. He wasn't her flunky, and he wasn't her toyboy, but it was hard to explain. Not that she was unfaithful. At least, not to his knowledge. She probably never had the time. Pretty clear to everyone, though, that Thea Lorentz was moving on and up. And that he wasn't. Without her, although he tried getting other people involved, the Emily Dickinson poem arrangements sounded like the journeymen pieces they probably

were. Without her, he even began to wonder about the current where-
abouts of his other old sparring partners in *Bard On Wheels*.

It was in old LA, at a meal at the Four Seasons, that he'd met, encountered, experienced—whatever the word for it was—his first dead person.
They were still pretty rare back then, and this one had made its arrival on
the roof of the hotel by veetol just to show that it could, when it really
should have just popped into existence in the newly-installed reality fields
at their table like Aladdin's genie. The thing had jittered and buzzed, and
its voice seemed over-amplified. Of course, it couldn't eat, but it pretended
to consume a virtual plate of quail in puff pastry with foie gras in a truffle
sauce, which it pretended to enjoy with virtual relish. You couldn't fault
the thing's business sense, but Northover took the whole experience as
another expression of the world's growing sickness.

Soon, it was the Barbican and the Sydney Opera House for Thea (and
how sad is was that so many of these great venues were situated next to the
rising shorelines) and odd jobs or no jobs at all for him. The flat in Pimlico
went, and so, somewhere, did hope. The world of entertainment was
careering, lemming-like, toward the cliffs of pure virtuality, with just a few
bright stars such as Thea to give it the illusion of humanity. Crappy fantasy-
dramas or rubbish docu-musicals that she could sail through and do her
Thea Lorentz thing, giving them an undeserved illusion of class. At least,
and unlike that idiot buffoon Bartleby, Northover could see why she was
in such demand. When he thought of what Thea Lorentz had become,
with her fame and her wealth and her well-publicised visits to disaster
areas and her audiences with the Pope and the Dalai Lama, he didn't
exactly feel surprised or bitter. After all, she was only doing whatever it
was that she'd always done.

Like all truly beautiful women, at least those who take care of themselves, she didn't age in the way that the rest of the world did. If anything,
the slight sharpening of those famous cheekbones and the small care lines
that drew around her eyes and mouth made her seem even more breath-
takingly elegant. Everyone knew that she would mature slowly and
gracefully and that she would make—just like the saints with whom she
was now most often compared—a beautiful, and probably incorruptible,
corpse. So, when news broke that she'd contracted a strain of new-variant

septicemic plague when she was on a fact-finding trip in Manhattan, the world fell into mourning as it hadn't done since . . . Well, there was no comparison, although JFK and Martin Luther King got a mention, along with Gandhi and Jesus Christ and Joan of Arc and Marylyn Munroe and that lost Mars mission and Kate and Diana.

Transfer—a process of assisted death and personality uploading—was becoming a popular option. At least, amongst the few who could afford it. The idea that the blessed Thea might refuse to do this thing, and deprive a grieving world of the chance to know that somehow, somewhere, she was still there, and on their side, and sorrowing as they sorrowed, was unthinkable. By now, well ensconced high up in his commune with his broom and his reputation as an angry hermit, left with nothing but his memories and that wrecked piano he was trying to get into tune, even Northover couldn't help but follow this ongoing spectacle. Still, he felt strangely detached. He'd long ago fallen out of love with Thea, and now fell out of admiring her as well. All that will-she won't-she crap that she was doubtless engineering even as she lay there on her deathbed! All she was doing was exactly what she'd always done, twisting the whole fucking world around her fucking little finger. But then maybe, just possibly, he was getting the tiniest little bit bitter . . .

Back at Elsinore, Kasaya has already been at work. Lights, a low stage, decent mikes and pa system, along with a spectacular grand piano, have all been installed at the far end of the great hall were they sat for yesterday's dinner. The long tables have been removed, the chairs rearranged. Or replaced. It really does look like a bijou theatre. The piano's a Steinway. If asked, Northover might have gone for a Bechstein. The action, to his mind, and with the little chance he's even had to ever play such machines, being a tad more responsive. But you can't have everything, he supposes. Not even here.

The space is cool, half-dark. The light from the windows is settling. Bartleby and his troupe of merry men have just returned from their day of tally-ho slaughter with a giant boar hung on ropes. Tonight, by sizzling flamelight out in the yard, the dining will be alfresco. And after that . . .

Well, word has already got out that Thea and this newly arrived guy at Elsinore are planning some kind of reunion performance. No wonder the air in this empty hall feels expectant.

He sits down. Wondrous and mysterious as Thea Lorentz's smile, the keys—which are surely real ivory—gleam back at him. He plays a soft e-minor chord. The sound shivers out. Beautiful. Although that's mostly the piano. Never a real musician, Northy. Nor much of a real actor, either. Never a real anything. Not that much of a stagehand, even. Just got lucky for a while with a troupe of travelling players. Then, as luck tends to do, it ran out on him. But still. He hasn't sat at one of these things since he died, yet it couldn't feel more natural. As the sound fades, and the gathering night washes in, he can hear the hastening tick of his Rolex.

The door at the far end bangs. He thinks it's most likely Kasaya. But it's Thea. Barefoot now. Her feet sip the polished floor. Dark slacks, an old, knotted shirt. Hair tied back. She looks the business. She's carrying loose sheaves of stuff—notes, bits of script and sheet music—some of which he recognises as she slings them down across the gleaming lid of the piano.

"Well," she says, "shall we do this thing?"

Back in his room, he stands for a long time in the steam heat of the shower. Finds he's soaping and scrubbing himself until his skin feels raw and his head is dizzy. He'd always wondered about those guys from al-Qaeda and Hezbollah and the Taliban and New Orthodoxy. Why they felt such a need to shave and cleanse the bodies they would soon be destroying. Now, though, he understands perfectly. The world is ruined and time is out of joint, but this isn't just a thing you do out of conviction. The moment has to be right, as well.

Killing the dead isn't easy. In fact, it's near impossible. But not quite. The great strength of the dead is the sheer overpowering sense of reality they bring to the sick fantasy they call Farside. Everything must work. Everything has to be what it is, right down to the minutest detail. Everything must be what it seems to be. But this is also their greatest weakness. Of course, they told Northy when they took off his blindfold as he sat chained to a chair which was bolted to the concrete floor in that deserted shopping mall, we can try to destroy them by trying to tear everything in Farside apart. We can fly planes into their reactors, introduce viruses into their processing suites, flood their precious data vaults with seawater. But there's always a backup. There's always another power source. We can never wreck enough of Farside to have even a marginal effect upon the whole. But the dead themselves are different. Break down the singularity of their existence for even an instant, and you destroy it forever. The dead become truly dead.

Seeing as it didn't exist as a real object, they had to show him the Rolex he'd be wearing through a set of VR gloves and goggles. Heavy-seeming of course, and ridiculously over-engineered, but then designer watches had been that way for decades. This is what you must put on along with your newly assumed identity when you return to consciousness in a cabin on board a steamer ferry bound for New Erin. In many ways, the watch is what it appears to be. It ticks. It tells the time. You'll even need to remember to wind it up. But carefully. Pull the crown out and turn it backwards—no, no, not now, not even here, you mustn't—and it will initiate a massive databurst. The Farside equivalent of an explosion of about half a pound of semtex, atomising anything within a three metre radius—yourself, of course, included, which is something we've already discussed—and causing damage, depending on conditions, in a much wider sphere. Basically, though, you need to be within touching distance of Thea Lorentz to be sure, to be certain. But that alone isn't enough. She'll be wearing some kind of protection which will download her to a safe backup even in the instant of time it takes the blast to expand. We don't know what that protection will be, although we believe she changes it regularly. But, whatever it is, it must be removed.

A blare of lights. A quietening of the murmurous audience as Northover steps out. Stands centre stage. Reaches in his pocket. Starts tossing a coin. Which, when Thea emerges, he drops. The slight sound, along with her presence, rings out. One thing to rehearse, but this is something else. He'd forgotten, he really had, how Thea raises her game when you're out here with her, and it's up to you to try to keep up.

A clever idea that went back to *Bard On Wheels*, to re-reflect *Hamlet* through some of the scenes of Stoppard's *Rozencrantz and Guildenstern Are Dead*, where two minor characters bicker and debate as the whole famous tragedy grinds on in the background. Northover doubts if this dumb, rich, dead audience get many of the references, but that really doesn't matter when the thing flows as well as it does. Along with the jokes and witty wordplay, all the stuff about death, and life in a box being better than no life at all, gains a new resonance when it's performed here on Farside. The audience are laughing fit to bust by the end of the sequence, but you can tell in the falls of silence that come between that they know something deeper and darker is really going on.

It's the same when he turns to the piano, and Thea sings a few of Shakespeare's jollier songs. For, as she says as she stands there alone in the spotlight and her face glows and those bangles slide upon her arms, The man that hath no music in himself, the motions of his spirit are dull as night. She even endows his arrangement of Under the Greenwood Tree, which he always thought too saccharine, with a bittersweet air.

This, Northover thinks, as they move on to the Emily Dickinson section—which, of course, is mostly about death—is why I have to do this thing. Not because Thea's fake or because she doesn't believe in what she's doing. Not because she isn't Thea Lorentz any longer and has been turned inside out by the dead apologists into some parasitic ghost. Not because what she does here at Elsinore is a sham. I must do this because she is, and always was, the treacherous dream of some higher vision of humanity, and people will only ever wake up and begin to shake off their shackles when they realise that living is really about forgetting such illusions, and looking around them, and picking up a fucking broom and clearing up the mess of the world themselves. The dead take our power, certainly—both physically and figuratively. The reactors that drive the Farside engines use resources and technologies the living can barely afford. Their clever systems subvert and subsume our own. They take our money, too. Masses and masses of it. Who'd have thought that an entirely virtual economy could do so much better than one that's supposedly real? But what they really take from us, and the illusion that Thea Lorentz will continue to foster as long as she continues to exist, is hope.

Because I did not stop for death . . . Not knowing when the dawn will come, I open every door . . . It all rings so true. You could cut the air with a knife. You could pull down the walls of the world. Poor Emily Dickinson, stuck in that homestead with her dying mother and that sparse yet volcanic talent that no one even knew about. Then, and just when the audience are probably expecting something lighter to finish off, it's back to Hamlet, and sad, mad Ophelia's songs—which are scattered about the play just as she is; a wandering, hopeless, hopeful ghost—although Northover has gathered them together as a poignant posy in what he reckons is some of his best work. Thea knows it as well. Her instincts for these things are more honed than his ever were. After all, she's a trouper. A legend. She's Thea Lorentz. She holds and holds the audience as new silence falls. Then, just as she did in rehearsal, she slides the bangles off her arm, and places them atop the piano, where they lie bright as rain circles in a puddle.

"Keep this low and slow and quiet," she murmurs, just loud enough for everyone in the hall to hear as she steps back to the main mike. He lays his hands on the keys. Waits, just as they always did, for the absolute stilling of the last cough, mutter and shuffle. Plays the chords that rise and mingle with her perfect, perfect voice. The lights shine down on them from out of sheer blackness, and it's goodnight, sweet ladies, and rosemary for remembrance, which bewept along the primrose path to the grave where I did go . . .

As the last chord dies, the audience erupts. Thea Lorentz nods, bows, smiles as the applause washes over her in great, sonorous, adoring waves. It's just the way it always was. The spotlight loves her, and Northover sits at the piano for what feels like a very long time. Forgotten. Ignored. It would seem churlish for him not to clap as well. So he does. But Thea knows the timing of these things better than anyone, and the crowd loves it all the more when, the bangles looped where she left them on the piano, she beckons him over. He stands up. Crosses the little stage to join her in the spotlight. Her bare left arm slips easy around his waist as he bows. This could be Carnegie Hall. This could be the Bolshoi. The manacling weight of the Rolex drags at his wrist. Thea smells of patchouli and of Thea, and the play's the thing, and there could not, never could be, a better moment.

There's even Sam Bartleby, sitting grinning but pissed-off right there on the front row and well within range of the blast.

They bow again, *thankyouthankyouthankyou*, and by now Thea's holding him surprisingly tightly, and it's difficult for him to reach casually around to the Rolex, even though he knows it must be done. Conscience doth make cowards of us all, but the time for doubt is gone, and he's just about to pull and turn the crown of his watch when Thea murmurs something toward his ear which, in all this continuing racket, is surely intended only for him.

"What?" he shouts back.

Her hand cups his ear more closely. Her breath, her entire seemingly living body, leans into him. Surely one of those *bon mots* that performers share with each other in times of triumph such as this. Just something else that the crowds love to see.

"Why don't you do it now?" Thea Lorentz says to Jon Northover. "What's stopping you . . . ?"

He's standing out on the moonlit battlements. He doesn't know how much time has passed, but his body is coated in sweat and his hands are trembling and his ears still seem to be ringing and his head hurts. Performance comedown to end all performance come-downs, and surely it's only a matter of minutes before Sam Bartleby, or perhaps Kasaya, or whatever kind of amazing Farside device it is that really works the security here at Elsinore, comes to get him. Perhaps not even that. Maybe he'll just vanish. Would that be so terrible? But then, they have cellars here at Elsinore. Dungeons, even. Put to the question. Matters of concern and interest. Things they need to know. He wonders how much full-on pain a young, fit body such as the one he now inhabits is capable of bearing . . . He fingers the Rolex, and studies the drop, but somehow he can't bring himself to do it.

When someone does come, it's Thea Lorentz. Stepping out from the shadows into the spotlight glare of the moon. He sees that she's still not wearing those bangles, but she keeps farther back from him now, and he knows it's already too late.

"What made you realise?"

She shrugs. Shivers. Pulls down her sleeves. "Wasn't it one of the first things I said to you? That you were too principled to ever come here?"

"That was what I used to think as well."

"Then what made you change your mind?"

Her eyes look sadder than ever. More compassionate. He wants to bury his face in her hair. After all, Thea could always get more out of him than anyone. So he tells her about mad old Northy, with that wrecked piano he'd found in what had once been a rooftop bar up in his eyrie above the commune, which he'd spent his time restoring because what else was there to do? Last working piano in London, or England, most likely. Or the whole fucking world come to that. Not that it was ever that much of a great shakes. Nothing like here. Cheaply built in Mexico of all places. But then this kid called Haru comes up, and he says he's curious about music, and he asks Northy to show him his machine for playing it, and Northy trusts the kid, which feels like a huge risk. Even that first time he sits Haru down at it, though, he knows he's something special. He just has that air.

"And you know, Thea . . . " Northover finds he's actually laughing. "You know what the biggest joke is? Haru didn't even *realise*. He could read music quicker than I can read words, and play like Chopin and Chick Corea, and to him it was all just this lark of a thing he sometimes did with this mad old git up on the fortieth floor . . .

"But he was growing older. Kids still do, you know, back on Lifeside. And one day he's not there, and when he does next turn up, there's this girl downstairs who's apparently the most amazing thing in the history of everything, and I shout at him and tell him just how fucking brilliant he really is. I probably even used the phrase *God-given talent*, whatever the hell that's supposed to mean. But anyway . . . "

"Yes?"

Northover sighs. This is the hard bit, even though he's played it over a million times in his head. "They become a couple, and she soon gets pregnant, and she has a healthy baby, even though they seem ridiculously young. A kind of miracle. They're so proud they even take the kid up to show me, and he plonks his little hands on my piano, and I wonder if he'll come up one day to see old Northy, too. Given a few years, and assuming old Northy is still alive, that is, which is less than likely. But that isn't how it happens. The baby gets sick. It's winter and there's an epidemic of some new variant of the nano flu. Not to say there isn't a cure. But the cure needs money—I mean, you know what these retrovirals cost better than anyone, Thea—which they simply don't have. And this is why I should have kept my big old mouth shut, because Haru must have remembered what I yelled at him about his rare, exceptional musical ability. And he decides his baby's only just starting on his life, and he's had a good innings of eighteen or so years. And if there's something he can do, some sacrifice he can make for his kid . . . So that's what he does . . . "

"You're saying?"

"Oh, come on, Thea! I know it's not legal, either Lifeside or here. But we both know it goes on. Everything has its price, especially talent. And the dead have more than enough vanity and time, if not the application, to fancy themselves as brilliant musicians, just the same way they might want to ride an expensive thoroughbred, or fuck like Casanova, or paint like Picasso. So Haru sold himself, or the little bit that someone here wanted, and the baby survived and he didn't. It's not that unusual a story, Thea, in the great scheme of things. But it's different, when it happens to someone you know, and you feel you're to blame."

"I'm sorry," she says.

"Do you think that's enough?"

"Nothing's ever enough. But do you really believe that whatever arm of the resistance you made contact with actually wanted me, Thea Lorentz, fully dead? What about the reprisals? What about the global outpouring of grief? What about all the inevitable, endless let's-do-this-for-Thea bullshit? Don't you think it would suit the interests of Farside itself far better to remove this awkward woman who makes unfashionable causes fashionable and brings attention to unwanted truths? Wouldn't *they* prefer to extinguish Thea Lorentz and turn her into a pure symbol they can manipulate and market however they wish? Wouldn't that make far better sense than whatever it was you thought you were doing?"

The sea heaves. The whole night heaves with it.

"If you want to kill me, Jon, you can do so now. But I don't think you will. You can't, can you? That's where the true weakness of whoever conceived you and this plan lies. You *had* to be what you are, or were, to get this close to me. You had to have free will, or at least the illusion of it . . . "

"What the hell are you saying?"

"I'm sorry. You might think you're Jon Northover—in fact, I'm sure you do—but you're not. You're not him really."

"That's—"

"No. Hear me out. You and I both know in our hearts that the real Jon Northover wouldn't be here on Farside. He'd have seen through the things I've just explained to you, even if he had ever contemplated actively joining the resistance. But that isn't it, either. Not really. I loved you, Jon Northover. Loved *him*. It's gone, of course, but I've treasured the memories. Turned them and polished them, I suppose. Made them into something clearer and more real than ever existed. This afternoon, for instance. It was all too perfect. You haven't changed, Jon. You haven't changed at all. People, real people, either dead or living, they shift and they alter like ghosts in reflection, but you haven't. You stepped out of my past, and there you were, and I'm so, so, sorry to have to tell you these things, for I fully believe that you're a conscious entity that feels pain and doubt just like all the rest of us. But the real Jon Northover is most likely long dead. He's probably lying in some mass grave. He's just another lost statistic. He's gone beyond all recovery, Jon, and I mourn for him deeply. All you are is something that's been put together from my stolen memories. You're too, too perfect."

"You're just saying that. You don't know."

"But I do. That's the difference between us. One day, perhaps, chimeras such as you will share the same rights as the dead, not to mention the living. But that's one campaign too far even for Thea Lorentz—at least, while she still has some control over her own consciousness. But I think you know, or at least you *think* you do, how to tune a piano. Do you know what inharmonicity is?"

"Of course I do, Thea. It was me who told you about it. If the tone of a piano's going to sound right, you can't tune all the individual strings to exactly the correct pitch. You have to balance them out slightly to the sharp or the flat. Essentially, you tune a piano ever so marginally out of tune,

because of the way the strings vibrate and react. Which is imper-
fectly . . . Which is . . . I mean . . . Which is . . . "

He trails off. A flag flaps. The clouds hang ragged. Cold moonlight pours
down like silver sleet. Thea's face, when he brings himself to look at it,
seems more beautiful than ever.

The trees of Farside are magnificent. Fireash and oak. Greenbloom and
maple. Shot through with every colour of autumn as dawn blazes toward
the white peaks of the Seven Mountains. He's never seen such beauty as
this. The tide's farther in today. Its salt smell, as he winds down the window
and breathes it in, is somehow incredibly poignant. Then the road sweeps
up from the coast. Away from the Westering Ocean. As the virtual Bentley
takes a bridge over a gorge at a tyrescream, it dissolves in a roaring pulse of
flame.

A few machine parts twist jaggedly upward, but they settle as the wind
bears away the sound and the smoke. Soon, there's only the sigh of the
trees, and the hiss of a nearby waterfall. Then, there's nothing at all.

ONE OF THE THINGS I'VE BECOME CONSCIOUS OF AS I PUT THIS collection together, and especially as I've reviewed what I've said and written over the years about writing, is how unsettled I've become about the issue of genre. Most often, when people ask me what I write, I'll say SF and perhaps add that I also write fantasy, but the reality is that I'm not remotely happy with either of those labels. Of course, that's what much of my work is, at least in the sense that that's how it's categorised, and it's hard to imagine how a story such as "The Discovered Country," which is set in the future, and involves downloaded personality and virtual reality, could be thought of as anything other than SF. But still, when I tell people what I write, I want to say, yes, a lot of it's SF, but I wish I could call it something else.

I'm well aware that this is a drift of loyalties that many writers who become "pigeonholed", as they might see it, into a certain area of literature, experience as they get older and more pompous. Writers of thrillers who think their latest work is "more than" a thriller. Or, indeed, so-called main-stream writers who'd very much like their static works to be thought of a beach-book material. Still, as far as I'm concerned, there was a time when SF, or at least a certain kind of SF, was genuinely at the cutting edge of what could be achieved in literature. I grew up, or grew into, reading writers like Ballard and Aldiss and Silverberg and Priest, as well at Fowles and Pynchon, when they were at their most ambitious and experimental, and saw a road ahead where SF wouldn't so much be absorbed into the literary mainstream as become the way ahead for it.

Of course, and although I describe the excitement of that time of discovery farther on in this collection, that didn't happen. Neither did I ever want to become the kind of writer who takes great stylistic and structural risks—the biggest risk of all, of course, being that you become unreadable. But what I did want to become, and still want to be, is a writer who can tell a story which incorporates strangeness and wonder—and, sure, addresses the past, the present and the future—but one who also writes with a sense of style, and creates a vivid sense of place and character, and, above all, engages the reader's emotions. And, if there is a template for that aim, it's *Weihnachtsabend* by Keith Roberts. Which is the story I set out to try to copy when I wrote "The Discovered Country."

I can well remember first reading *Weihnachtsabend* sitting on a coach on a rainy daytrip to Bourton-on-the-Water in the Cotswolds on what must have been my sixteenth birthday, with Hawkwind's Silver Machine riding surprisingly high in the charts. The premise is an alternate Britain which has succumbed to Hitler, and in it a man and a woman arrive through a snowy landscape at a Christmas house party in a grand stately home where they find their loyalty to the regime, and each other, tested. Lamborghinis are offered. A love affair resurfaces. The children of the privileged families of the British Reich are sent on a scary midnight hunt for presents while being stalked by the demon Hans Trapp. The Boxing Day hunt gains a horrible new twist.

Roberts wasn't a writer who surprised with his intellectual or technological insights. He was also often weak on plot, although not in the case of *Weihnachtsabend*, which is probably why it's one of his most fondly remembered works. But he had an artist's eye for words, and, at his best, a Hardyesque insight into both the small tragedies of the human condition and, especially, into his female characters. When it came to depicting women, his later work often veered towards the sort of objectification to which many male writers, from Hardy himself to John Updike, are prone, but at his best he could make them both mysterious and empathetic, incredibly *other*, yet amazingly real. Which is, I suppose, what all people, outside the frail illusion of self that we strive to maintain inside our own heads, truly are. I'll leave you to judge which side of the line I fall with Thea in "The Discovered Country" and the female characters in my other works. As many characters in this collection, from Dottie in "Re-Crossing the Styx" to Gloria in "Frost on Glass" will demonstrate, I certainly write a great deal about beautiful, fateful women.

I know I made a bad job of copying Roberts' story—the woman I tried to put in the car with him when Northover arrives at Ellsinore wouldn't come to life until I combined her with Thea, and the calculations and acceptances he has to make in this world of the dead are perhaps a long way from 1940s alternate-world fascism—but then I always expected to fall short. After all, *Weihnachtsabend* is an acknowledged classic of its kind, so I knew I was taking a clumsy and oblique run-up at a very high bar. One of my favourite writing anecdotes—and a great many of these stem from music—is John Lennon's comment that the Beatles found their original sound through attempting to copy the black R&B records they all loved. Of course, he admitted, they made a hash of it, and what they did came out sounding like something else. Which is how these things work.

Weihnachtsabend ends with the main male character turning against the regime and, effectively, committing suicide. When I reread the story now, I'm still struck by the sense of brooding glamour and menace, and the power of Roberts' descriptive insights; a whole, different, world captured as if in a snowy glass ball. But the style, which I once so loved, creaks in places with a misguidedly thrillerish, Ian Flemingish, tone, and, at the end of the day, it is just another story about a Britain overcome by fascism—a premise so stale and yet so fascinating that I wrote a novel, *The Summer Isles*, using a variation of it. But there's one particular passage of *Weihnachtsabend* which sings to me as much now as when I first read it. It describes the two main characters falling asleep in each other's arms after making love, and they drift toward a perfected world where "spires reared gold and tree leaves moved and dazzled and white cars sang". Wow, I thought, and still think. It's one of those miracles of prose, like Fitzgerald's description of the guests arriving at Jay Gatsby's party, or the last paragraph or so of *A Canticle for Leibowitz*, or the bit in Proust when he writes about imagining Venice before he's been there, which thrill me in ways that even the greatest poetry never can, and made me want to try to write in the first place, and still makes me want to write now.

HECTOR DOUGLAS MAKES A SALE

DUSK was the beginning of Hector's Douglas' favourite time. Up with the lark might be fine and dandy for some salesmen, and middays and afternoons doubtless had their advocates as well, but as far as Hector was concerned you couldn't beat the slow slide into dark.

A puff of his cheeks. A cheery whistle. A jaunt of his straw boater, and he was off to do business with his shiny black case. He'd read all the inspirational books and pamphlets. He'd attended so many correspondence schools he'd thought of setting one up himself. He knew all the tricks and ruses. Knew that every objection was a selling point begging an answer. Knew, as well, that features must be linked to benefits and that product knowledge is the key to success. Even knew how important it was to highlight at least one unique angle, and never to sell on price alone. As for positive thinking—hell, his thinking was so positive it went right off the goddarn scale.

Now here comes Hector once again, he and his shadow striding the lamplit territory of these Los Angeles streets, which he thought of as his home, church, workshop and office combined, with dancing—yet determined—little steps. My, how he loved his work! A few kids still out running and shouting in backyards. The thump of wood on ash and the clap of leather, although it was already getting almost too dark to see. Mums in white aprons calling to their children across dim lawns. Bicycles ticking by like metal swallows heading home to roost, with plates of peanut butter and jelly waiting in bright linoleum kitchens before the final climb to bed.

Hector had worked his way up from nowhere. Apart from maybe icebergs to Eskimos (and he might even have to check his resume on that) there wasn't much that, one time or another, he hadn't been called upon to sell. Brushes—not the Fuller brand, which was all name and no product, but the Dodkins range of brooms, brushes and dusters, which really did give its lucky purchasers that extra edge in the never-ending War Against Dust. Cleaning preparations to put that new-car sparkle inside your home. Permanent life and pet insurance in five no-quibble instalments. Easy-clean gutters. No-clean aluminium siding. Electrical garage doors to make your home the envy of not just your neighbours, but your whole neighbour*hood*. Encyclopaedias, of course—but also the *Modern Library of All the Classics of World Literature*, edited for quick and easy reading, to turn you into a marvel to your friends, with an illus-trated Bible thrown in. Miniature busts of all the great presidents. A different set (this was largely for Roman Catholic communities) of the major saints. The Psiclean—marvellous, marvellous invention, although heavy to carry and difficult to demonstrate—to remove all those lingering pesky traces of psychic dirt from your house. A postal laundry service that meant you never had to wash another sheet. He'd done them all—and successfully, as well. But now—and he was absolutely certain of it—he was selling the genuine, ultimate, final product. Nothing else could ever come close.

The thing about sales, to Hector's way of thinking, was that it wasn't just a job. Sure, you heard people say that kind of thing about driving trucks or pouring concrete, but Hector thought of selling in the way a priest might think about working for God. He'd seen too many hobos and ne'er-do-wells dragging his precious calling through the dog dirt. Seen ragged men with no money, no hope, no shoes and no idea of what they were doing trudging door to door trying to sell useless clothes pegs, or washing-line-stolen rags. Sometimes, apart from desperation and hunger, they weren't selling anything at all. To his mind, they were little better than gypsies. Or worse.

Even in the drive-in hotels and freeway bars that his fellow professionals frequented, Hector often found that the sheer wonder and excitement of the trade had been lost. There were salesmen who drank too much, or groused about their product (and if they didn't buy into its key features and special attractions, who else ever would?). There were many others who didn't keep themselves up to date with the latest techniques. Then there were the sort who weren't that interested in selling at all, and kept panties or who-knew what else as evidence of their filthy conquests. It was all, so very, very wrong.

Always a privilege. Always an opportunity. Always around the next turn was the chance of that sale which would turn things around from the merely better to the absolute best. Not that Hector walked up every drive. No siree. For Lack of Selection and Consideration of Your Target Customer was one of the *Five Basic Selling Errors*. Or was it one of the *Seven Selling Sins*? Either way, you didn't just blunder like some robot up to every house that presented itself, especially when you were selling what Hector was selling. Where would be the intelligence—which was a Good Salesman's Best Ally—in that?

Look for signs. Check for all the little clues, which even in a new whites-only suburb such as this where every house was seemingly identical, spelt out those crucial signs of Customer Need. Then you were already halfway toward that magical Sales Rapport. Although he had no garden himself, or any real place at all where he actually lived, Hector had become quite an expert in the many fragrant bowers he'd stood in over the years while people stared out at him like he was a shoe-scraping. *Ah*, an inbreath of air, *I do so love the scent of the sunset magnolia.* Or *Isn't that a dwarf sabinata?* Didn't matter too much what you said, and so much the better if they replied that that was actually a peony or whatever. For then you already had the beginnings of a conversation. And Conversation led to Sales.

Ah! Here we were. A house. The special one. Not too many lights. Not too few either. But something *defeated* about it. Something lost and waiting. Hector listened and sniffed, testing the air for the sounds and smells of cooking, washing up, running taps, bathfoam bristling, stifled groans and the creak of bedsprings—all the many distracting activities which were barriers to a sale. But no. This house had that special aura that he could taste like sour ozone off the ocean. He chuckled and swung his featherlight black case so high his arm almost did a cartwheel. The best chances, the best opportunities, always had this same anticipatory sense.

Hector saw his ideal customer as someone—a man, a woman, rich or poor, old or young, healthy or ill, already actually dying for all he cared; to him, as with all the best salesmen, it simply didn't matter—whose whole existence had been put on hold in anticipation of his arrival.

Creak of the picket gate. Unoiled. Step-dance along the paving. Clattery; a fraction loose. The lawn a touch unkempt, as well. The whole place clinging to the standards of this suburb by its torn fingernails. There had probably been a few looks and words from the neighbours. Even the car lacked that usual showroom gleam, and the hood felt dusty and dirty as Hector ran his fingers along it to check for warmth. And that tree over in the corner of the plot . . . A sorry thing, indeed. Ragged with climbing ivy gone so rampant that the kids' treehouse which had once inhabited its middle branches was now almost drowned in waves of greenish black.

Nothing at the doorstep but lovely, looming silence. Until . . . *ding dong.* A sound, along with *knock, knock,* to set any salesman's pulse thrilling. Then a pause so delicious he had to stop himself from crying out. Followed, equally deliciously, by a shadow thrown against the mottled glass from inside the hall. Somewhere, in a different house, a baby was crying. But not here. No, no. Not now, anyway. The frosted glass door swings inward from its cobweb corners. Hector bit his lip and blinked back a single tear. Oh. Yes. The moment so perfect as he stood poised on tippy-toes with thighs clamped tight—a plump, boater-wearing ballerina waiting for the signal to dance.

"Ah! Good *evening*! And what a *good* evening it is."

"Yeah." Not agreement. Not even a question. Almost a noise. But every sound and every look and every word, up to and including, *fuck off buddy,* was the beginning of dialogue. And without dialogue, there would never have been a single sale since the serpent sold Eve that apple. And where would we be then?

A guy in a hair-sprouting vest studied Hector through the screen door mesh, unlit cigarette in the corner of a mouth drawn down in stubbly disregard. Hector caught beer smells, old cooking smells . . . Misery, and B.O. and dirty carpets—so many, many products that this customer, if they did but know it, needed! The man worked in engineering—most probably aviation. Hector could see it in the scarring of his hands and in the oiled dirt beneath his ruined nails, just as he could see the scars of grief and defeat around his eyes.

"What *is* that?" Another voice called from along the hallway. Quavery. Female. Half-drunk.

"It's just some . . . " The guy looked Hector up and down again. Though a door half open, Hector glimpsed a corner filled with the same boy's face in many different photographs—school and camp, pageboy at a wedding—along with framed finger-smeared paintings of square houses and smiley suns, newscuttings, ribbon rosettes, school reports . . .

"What I'd really like to share with you this evening—"

"Can't you see we're done!"

Already, the door slamming shut.

Oh well. Hector unclamped his thighs, spun on his toes. The street-lamps shone and the sky was streaked with crimson, laying a Golden Pathway to Success which blazed right ahead of him along the sidewalk. Another turn, another street, another door, another look, both grumpy and puzzled, although this one from a woman with red streaks down her face in a stained nylon shift. Not there, perhaps. But close. Oh, so close! Another slam. And then another. And another. The most words he'd exchanged so far involved some instructions as to where he could shove his case, and sideways first.

So many of the salesmen he'd talked to over the years would have already been discouraged. But not Hector Douglas, no siree. He'd tried to explain this sometimes—his irrepressible philosophy, his religion, his life. He'd gone back with some of these same sad and lost men to their motel rooms on nights when the freeway traffic roared and the thin drapes pulsed like a neon headache. He'd sat knee to knee with them between twin beds as they nursed their umpteenth whisky, or maybe just swigged the stuff straight from the bottle.

For what *was* it all about? What was the point, the fucking, pissing, point, buddy, if you couldn't meet the ridiculous targets set by those douchebags at regional office, or believe for one moment in the gimcrack shit you're supposed to be pushing? The wife long gone, and that girlfriend nothing but a cheap cunt who'd run off with all your cash at the first available opportunity. Only one step ahead of the repo guys who wanted your car and probably all the blood out of your veins with it. A life in ruins, buster. Fucking ruins. That's what you're looking at here. Don't try to tell me different, although you don't seem to have drunk much of this whisky, and what the hell is there left to sell . . . ?

Now. A street of bigger houses, off in the meandering dark. The cars bigger, as well. Caddies and Buicks instead of Chevys and Fords, although that in itself meant little to Hector, for did not everyone from the lowest sewer rat deserve the same opportunity to buy what he longed to sell? But the house which caught his eye and snagged his senses didn't have a car in the drive. Fact was, a less skilled salesman than Hector Douglas might even have assumed the place was empty and walked right past. Fully dark now. All the windows here dark as well. But no. Not entirely. They breathed out that special sense of waiting. They moved like mouths and begged him to come.

Up the drive. Up the steps. Mmm. Loved that thing the builders had done with the wood pillars. Loved that perfect, perfect sweep of dark-edged, immaculately bordered lawn. Crisp chimes of the doorbell filling him with ice-cream shivers. The silence and absence which followed, even more. Again, then? Yes, why not. *Ding, dong* . . . This time, Hector really couldn't help himself. He clamped his thighs to stop the small circle of damp that might otherwise arrive and gave a small, ecstatic yelp. For good salesmen had to be Persistent and Indomitable.

Now, they came. And he was certain right away that this was it. The door drawing back, slow and grand and revelatory as the Pearly Gates themselves. There they stood. The one. Hector was sure, and he was walking toward her and holding out his hand to clasp hers even before she had edged back the screen door.

Smell of new carpets. New paint. New everything. A fine, fine house. Of that there was no doubt. The woman had been sitting alone in her immaculate kitchen. Drew him back that way with a vague beckon past photos of a Hawaii honeymoon and real paintings that were almost as good as photos except you actually see the marks of the artist's brush. Into all that fitted Formica and wood and steel and light. Cigarettes on the table. Ashtray brimming with stubs. Had the customer been drinking? Not exactly. No. But her voice and her manner was slow and slurred.

"Suppose you may as well sit down . . . "

"Much obliged."

Hector gave his straw boater, which of course he'd already doffed, a little twirl as he set it down on the tabletop. Then, with a quick but gleeful spin, he settled himself into his chair.

"My . . . " He looked around again. Breathed in the air. Which, even without the booze, was ripe with potentiality. " . . . this is *wonderful.*"

"Think so?" She sat down facing him. Lit a fresh cigarette even though the one at the side of the ashtray still floated lazy grey curls. "You really do?"

"Well, of course."

"You're selling something, I suppose?" A bitter chuckle. "Why the hell else would anyone want to come visit this dump . . . ?" A frown. She'd once been pretty. Belle of the prom. Gleaming lovely and near-naked beside her parent's pool. Not now. Grey at roots, tattered at the corners. Nails pink and bloody crescents. Skin worn through to tendril veins. "Bit late, isn't it?"

"It's never too late to make a sale."

She almost chuckled at that. Which was good.

Her tired eyes travelled and focussed briefly, and not without a little difficulty, on the black case he'd left propped beside the chair. "And what exactly are you supposed to be selling?"

Hard not to bridle at that *supposed.* But Hector Douglas didn't bridle. Hector Douglas kept his cool.

"Maybe . . . " He smiled. His eyes, he knew, were glittering. "We could get to know each other a little first?"

"What is there to know?" She gestured with her cigarette, ash settling unnoticed on her ashen arm. But Hector waited. Hector was patient. Soon, just like all the very best customers, she began to talk.

She was lovely to him now. Lovely in a way he guessed she or any other customer never saw. Even more than the actual sale itself, it was this sharing, this dialogue, as, like lovers, they prepared for the inevitable consummation, which was the best time of all. She spoke, at first, so vividly of her upbringing that Hector could almost hear the arguments and the shatter of ornaments going on in the room next door. She'd wanted out.

Had wanted out quickly. Had hated the school—*academy*, they called it, can you believe that?—with its sneering bullies and bruised knuckles for every slip in deportment almost as much as she had hated home. Couldn't wait to grow up. Couldn't wait to be married and *out*.

Out.

You understand what I'm saying, mister?

Out . . . ?

Hector nodded. Out. *Of course* he understood out. Why, otherwise, would he be here at all?

Then along comes Earl Lovelock junior. With his old-money back-ground and his old-money quiff and his old-money smile. Swept her up in an unthinking whirl. Her idiot parents had loved the guy, of course, and that should have been a warning sign, but she was just nineteen, for Chris-sake, and he was twenty eight and already regional vice president, and what did she know? The sex had been good for a while, though. Gone to dust by the honeymoon, but pretty great before that, far as she could judge. And they can't take that away from you. Can they? Even though it's already long gone.

What else do you want to hear, Mister? What else is there? Can't you see it all around? And Hector, although he felt he had sensed and seen all he needed to already, looked around at this expensive kitchen once again. No kids here. Nor had there ever been. Miscarriages? Abortions? No, not even that. This customer was too lost, too dry, too empty, too cold. She was just in here with her cigarettes and her huge humming fridge, and Earl Lovelock junior away in some Pasadena hotel, and hating herself for the fact that, even though she knew exactly what he was doing, if not exactly with whom (there had been so many over the years, she'd given up keeping up), but somehow still hating herself and him even more for the fact that he wouldn't even phone.

"I sometimes think . . . " She waved her cigarette. Which was now dead at the tips of her fingers.

"Think what?" Hector prompted. He was close to a sale now he could taste it on the tip of his tongue.

"Think . . . " She gazed down at the table. Shook her psoriasis scalp. "If he came back and found me . . . " Then she looked up, and the look was so

ferocious, Hector almost blinked. "*That* would make the bastard think—
would make him realise."

"Well . . . " He shrugged. Genuinely noncommittal. Nearly added, *Have
you considered how you might . . . ?* But he didn't. Not yet, anyway. For
Hurry was the Enemy of Completion. And, at the end of the day, a good
customer always sold the product to themselves. " . . . You never know."

"You don't, do you?"

Then, at this most crucial of all moments, something went wrong. Even
before he could do anything to stop it from happening, the customer had
pushed herself up from her chair.

"You fancy a drink? The medication I'm on, I'm not supposed to touch
anything. But you've *listened* to me, mister, and it feels like you're the first
person to do so in years. So what the hell . . . "

What the hell, indeed. Here he was, so close to closing the sale he could
feel it tingling through him like it had felt back in the days he was still
demonstrating the Elation button on the Psiclean. And now things were
slipping out of his control.

A cupboard door open. A gloss of amber fluids, expensive labels.

"What's your poison? Believe me, we've got the lot."

She was almost selling the stuff to *him*. Which was awful, terrible. "I.
Er . . . "

Another cupboard. Two tumblers clashed together so hard Hector was
sure he saw chips of glass fly off. In this second cupboard, along with the
glasses, dozens of little brown bottles were lined like soldiers. The label
said *Nembutal* on every one.

"Jesus." She was almost playful now. Almost happy. Already, splashingly,
she was pouring out whisky. "Might as well *live* a little. Otherwise, hey,
what's the point? And what exactly have you got in that case of yours,
anyway, Mister, that you carry like it's nothing at all? Aren't you ever going
to show me? You're not just going to leave me here, are you? Oh, please!
Aren't you going to make me a sale?"

But Hector Douglas was already standing. Hector Douglas was already
picking up his boater and lifting his featherlight case and holding them
both tight to him and backing out through the kitchen door.

"Jesus. You can't do this! This is horrible. Please . . . ? You're just like—"

He was off down the hall and letting himself out into the night air even before the woman's shouts had faded. Not a sale, no. But nearly. So close that he could still smell the reek of whisky, cigarettes, hopelessness—and, yes, Nembutal, as well. But no cigar. The woman had already bought everything he could ever hope to sell. There was nothing he could offer, not Means or Despair or even the requisite Determination and Resolve, that she didn't already own. And, as ever, there was no point in arguing. For the Customer Was Always Right. He could, perhaps, have popped the catches on his case. Opened it up for her, as he sometimes did when a customer was wavering, just to display its lovely, empty depths in all their dark allure. But what would have been the point? For, in truth, you could never Sell To A Customer Who Has Already Been Sold.

But still . . .

Hector gave his case a another swing, yelped, and beamed up at the swarming stars. This particular suburb, his salesman's instincts told him, was stale and fished out. But there were always other places, fresh opportunities. He checked his watch under the nearest streetlight. If he was brisk about it, he would still be able to snag a bus downtown. It would be late, perhaps, already closing on midnight by the time he got there, but for many a potential customer—the hopeless hookers, the hungry hobos, the studio rejects, the failed businessmen living out of their cars—this was the very best time of all.

Hector skip-danced along the street, humming to himself.

He was still certain that, sometime tonight, he would make a sale.

AFTERWORD *A CUL-DE-SAC IN LOS ANGELES*

THIS STORY WAS ORIGINALLY SUPPOSED TO BE PART OF THE BEGINNING of my novel *Wake Up and Dream*. I often find that I have to explore many avenues which end up as cul-de-sacs when I try to get a big project going, and the idea of a sinister door-to-door salesman working in Los Angeles in the late 1930s turned out to be one of those.

I'd long fancied writing about a ludicrously over-committed salesman. Someone so committed, in fact, that their commitment goes beyond rationality and into homicide. So I sent Hector out into the Los Angeles suburbs, and I was very happy with the kind of character he seemed to want to become as I worked on the start of my novel. And inside his shiny black bag was . . . Well, it needed to be an invention which had some resonance with the whole amplified psychic aura technology of the feelies which I was developing for my alternate history novel. I could call it the "Psiclean", and it would be a kind of vacuum cleaner which removed any awkward psychological dirt from the home. The idea still sounds pretty cool to me as I write this now—maybe I should even give it another go— but the device somehow refused to fit properly into Hector's life and his black bag. So Hector stepped quietly back into the shadows and the novel began to take a different shape without him.

I still had fond memories of Hector and his wanderings through the new suburbs of Los Angeles when the novel was done, and when I returned to what was then a stub of an incomplete chapter some time after, I realised that the problem I'd been hitting against was a desire to be over-specific and over-technological, when all that Hector was really selling along those twilight streets was simply death itself. And the contents of his bag? Well, that could remain a mystery which need never be exposed. So it is that the twist which makes a story work is very often one of the last things the writer encounters, just as the reader does.

I once worked as a salesman myself back in my early years after leaving college. I sold life insurance, which I suppose isn't that far from selling death, although I used to have what are known as introductions and was given the specific names and addresses to toddle off to in my company car, rather than just wandering hopefully like Hector from door to door. But then, and much like Hector Douglas, and albeit in the English Potteries of the late 70s rather than mid-century Los Angeles, I'd still end up standing with my briefcase outside some house, and ringing the doorbell, and waiting to see who and what would loom up through the mottled glass from inside the hall. What I was selling was a form of mortgage repayment based on what turned out to be ludicrously over-cooked growth assumptions—one of those many financial scandals for which no one ever ends up taking the blame, seeing as those truly responsible are much too high up and well-connected to be allowed to fall. I didn't last very long at my job, for even then I didn't have much faith in the product, and wasn't very good at selling it. But I do remember one of my fellow salesmen telling me one of those small tricks of the trade that all professions have: that it's important to realise that the people you're selling to are, or should be, more afraid of you than you are of them.

FOREWORD *DIFFERENT WARTS AND ALL*

WHEN IT CAME TO PUTTING THIS BOOK TOGETHER, THE IDEA OF including some of the non-fiction pieces which I've produced over the years seemed a fairly obvious and straightforward one. At least, until I started reading them.

We all like to imagine that our opinions remain consistent and clear-cut. Sure, we might change some of them occasionally, but that in itself is a sign of our intellectual flexibility and a commendable willingness to adapt and evolve as the world turns and shows, all in all, what rounded people we are. But, reading what I'd written as my supposedly true thoughts over the last couple of decades made me realise that it's actually a lot more complicated than that. I certainly wouldn't call the me of about fifteen years ago, who wrote the piece about my childhood reading and desire to write which follows a liar. The books, the budgie seed, the early episodes of *Doctor Who*, discovering literature and SF's New Wave, are all present and correct, but the overall approach and attitude . . . Well, it doesn't feel quite like *me*. It's not even so much a difference in outlook or opinion as one of tone. Which, perhaps because the subject is so close to home, feels far more pronounced to me than any of the shifting of perceptions and approach I feel when I reread my earlier fiction.

Nick Gevers, a long-time supporter of my work who was involved in putting this book together, mentioned the piece which follows in his suggestions for inclusion, and I'm more than happy to give it an airing. He also suggested I might like to update it. And, when I was first rereading it and my other works of supposed non-fiction, I certainly did feel a strong desire to amend and re-phrase and re-edit what I'd done. Those slightly out-of-date references, the sideswipes at old targets such as Bush and Blair, the occasionally clumsy turns of phrase, not to mention the contradictions between what the me-of-now and the me-of-then seems to feel . . . All of these could surely be tweaked, or more elegantly expressed, or simply taken out. But in smoothing things over and trying to frame my thoughts more accurately, I'd be losing much more than I could possibly gain. So I've left these pieces as they are. Warts and all, even if I feel that some warts have vanished and different ones have appeared since.

A Truncated Life In Books

THERE were never many books at home when I was a child, and those were generally kept on the top shelf of a cabinet in the kitchen next to the budgie seed. There was a paperback about passing your driving test in four weeks, and an old Automobile Association *Book of the Road*, where the maps were separate cards that you could take out and put together like a jigsaw. There was a Superman annual, an old dictionary without its spine, a novel by Jeffery Farnol without any cover and half the last chapter missing, and a big blue-bound *Children's Encyclopaedia* which I imagined would tell me everything there was to know about the world if I could get past the pages on battleships and dinosaurs. A friend of mine at Junior School had actually read all of his *Children's Encyclopaedia*, and seemed to have access to every kind of secret knowledge as a result. He also had a thing about those lurid comics in which ladies were apparently kidnapped by green multi-armed creatures and placed in various kinds of magnifying glass coffins as more and more of their clothes were removed. I don't remember actually seeing one of those comics, but the image was vivid enough, and strangely fascinating, even if I didn't quite understand what the point of it all was.

Soon after, and as if sensing that something new was in the wind, a paperback copy the *Kama Sutra* made an inexplicable appearance beside the budgie seed on the cabinet's top shelf, and *Doctor Who* started on television. I loved *Doctor Who* from the first episode, and even wrote to *Junior Points of View* to tell the BBC. I loved the sense of strange places, the hidden worlds, and I loved the fear. I loved it most of all when the Doctor's woman companion—the very first woman, who was called Barbara—screamed when she was confronted by something terrible and alien just beyond the edge of the screen at the end of each episode. I didn't realise then that I was hooked on Science Fiction, but I had worked out that something dark and mysterious out there was just coming within range. Between plunging through the African adventures of Willard Price's Hal and David in the junior section of the local library, I made furtive forays around the counter into the adult side, where there was a book with a black and white cover that had something to do with caterpillars crawling down a window in the rain, and many other hidden and half-hinted delights.

Apart from stories of natural disasters involving volcanoes, I wasn't a particularly voracious reader of children's books, as I always thought they were second best to something else. The "something else" was, at first, serious and apparently factual books about the haunting of Borley Rectory which I found near the counter on the adult side and which nobody seemed to mind me taking out on my junior ticket, and of which I, desperate for strangeness in this seemingly mundane world, believed every word. Then there were collections of scary stories; the library was short on these, even in the adult side, and I never could quite find the book about the caterpillars, but my mates and I used to hang around in Woolworth's after school, and stuff one of the *Pan Books of Horror* under our blazers before charging down the Stratford Road to collapse breathless by the football pitches in the park. More than the reading, the possession of these books was the main part of the illicit thrill. Like the crumpled photos of naked women we were also passing around, we hid these books under the park bushes like dogs with bones. The first adult novels that I got around to actually buying and reading, in those days before teenage literature had taken hold, were by Alistair MacLean. I used to paint the covers with household varnish, or wrap them in clear stickyback, parting the pages gently to avoid putting the slightest crack in the spine as I urged the story on, while wishing at the same time that it would never end.

Books had already become a special commodity to me by then, something that was quite separate from knowledge and school and study and the apparently boringly real adult world that went on outside Woolworth's, and at home and in the newspapers. Books were something that were my own, to be shared sparingly, if at all, with one or two schoolfriends who had also discovered their mystery. I imagined that Alistair MacLean was quite esoteric. I also cultivated an interest in classical music, saving up to buy LPs by apparently obscure composers like Dvorak and Vivaldi despite a sneaking but unadmitted liking for pop music. I always liked to think that I was at least one step away from the crowd. Then my sister's new boyfriend suggested I might like to try reading John Wyndham, and took me to see *2001* at the local Odeon. *Doctor Who* by then was already getting into its knowingly funny phase, but this was something else again! Watching *2001*, reading *The Midwich Cuckoos*, I experienced the tingle that all lovers of Science Fiction must recognise at the time of their first discovery; I'd been hooked for a long time, but now at last I knew what I was hooked on.

Raiding the local library, I soon discovered Clarke and Asimov and all the other names who were big then and mostly still seem to be big now. I bought their books in paperback when I could actually afford them, and then find the damn things on the newsagent's carousels. SF writers themselves seemed to be an interesting breed; clever, capable men who talked about their adventurous lives in the smoothly laconic way of airline pilots. I found the short story collections particularly enlightening. The stories were thrilling in themselves, and the introductory bits in italics were full of details of how these men met up and gave each other awards, and appeared in oddly-named magazines in distant America. *Galaxy*, *If* and *The Magazine of Fantasy and Science Fiction* loomed big in my mind long before I ever set eyes on them. These SF men were disparaging about "mainstream fiction"—whatever that was—but reserved their special venom for something called Fantasy, which sounded like a sleazy version of the kind of stuff I hadn't enjoyed reading that much when I was younger, and which involved pixies and elves, for God's sake! I was equally disparaging about Fantasy in the italic bits I had started to write in my own head, until a friend suggested in passing that the greatest work of Science Fiction ever written was by this character called Tolkien. *The Lord of the Rings* had been there all along as a Novel of Note in the adult section of the library, which meant that, unlike all the cheaply enjoyable stuff, you could take it out on a non-fiction ticket. Discovering through Tolkien what Fantasy really meant was at least as thrilling an experience as the shock of my first exposure to SF. In many ways, it was more so, because I was moved by his work in a deeper way. At this stage, and despite the fact that I was lagging well behind most of my friends, I was getting farther into the physical changes of adolescence than I really wanted to go. For me, *The Lord of The Rings* expressed a glorious sense of sadness and beauty, of the loss of a world which might once have been but would never return, which fitted my mood perfectly. The fact that there were, essentially, no other works of Fantasy available at that time, made the whole non-genre even more appealing. When I found a proper bookshop in Birmingham where a small corner blossomed with the tentative first appearances of Lin Carter's Ballantine Adult Fantasy series with their lovely other-worldly covers, I felt sure that I had at last discovered the hidden glade, the lost world, the place that I alone could enter and be safe and free.

The world itself, meanwhile, was behaving increasingly strangely. Men—an exceedingly boring event for any true SF aficionado—had landed on the Moon. Skirts had gone short and then long again. The *Kama Sutra* disappeared from the shelf by the budgie seed just as I was beginning to fully appreciate its merits. But there were compensations. There was, it seemed, something called the New Wave in SF. The bits in italics that these writers put at the start of their stories were getting far wilder— these people sounded more like rock stars than airline pilots—and the stories were getting pretty strange, too. *Dangerous Visions*, in particular, made a big impact on me; it got the first A+ ever in the reading record book I was keeping, and seemed to embody everything that was new and daring in life and literature. Old Isaac Asimov himself wrote a kind of introduction about these precocious new writers with exotic names like Harlan and Zelazny who were springing up beneath his feet, and how SF must move with the times and take risks and generally set about changing the entire world. Even Judith Merril flipped a bit in the normally sober italic introductions of her yearly collections. Of course, all of this news was breaking pretty late on the shores of my particular world, but I reckoned I was, by now, far from the sight of anyone I knew, and that was what counted. SF was mine! Fantasy was mine! No one else I knew had even heard of the New Wave! I never read anything else, and that was just how I wanted it.

I transferred from a secondary to a grammar school when I was sixteen. I'd never really had much patience with "real" science and was useless anyway at maths, so I opted to do English Literature as one of my scraped A levels, along with History (which I enjoyed) and Geography (which I and any other reasonable person would have hated). For the first time, I was actually expected to read this stuff that SF writers—even the new ones with the fancy names—called "mainstream". I remember soberly telling my teacher that I'd read some Daphne Du Maurier and one Neville Shute, which was true, and then of course there was Alistair MacLean, with whose works I had a broad familiarity. I reckoned that that would probably stand me in pretty good stead. In fact, most of this mainstream stuff I was required to read was just as boring as I'd expected, but on the other hand, some of it was pretty neat. *The Waste Land*, for example, had just the kind of fancy, multi-layered complexity that I was planning to incorporate into *Lords of the Earth*, the novel I was working on set at the end of the Thousand Year Reich. *The Great Gatsby* wasn't bad either—at least short enough not to outstay its welcome—and, by about the third reading, I was falling in love with both Miriam and Clara in *Sons and Lovers*, and with the blazing reality of life that was conveyed in Lawrence's sensuous prose. The other thing was that one or two of the New Wave SF writers I was reading would occasionally toss in the names of writers who weren't SF as if their stuff was actually alright. Lin Carter, in his Adult Fantasy introductions, sometimes did the same. It was all both encouraging and confusing. I read, or tried to read, things like *Gravity's Rainbow* (searching that spineless dictionary in the cupboard to try to find out what a hardon was), and discovered John Fowles. Somewhere out there, it seemed, there was an even more dim and distant shore where all this good and sweet and scary stuff met up—the caterpillars and the hardons and Hal and the spaceships and the blazing reality and lovely infuriating Miriam and T S Eliot's fancy verbal jiggery-pokery. That, indeed, would be a place to be! Some modern writers, I reckoned—Silverberg and Le Guin and Keith Roberts in SF, and Fowles in "mainstream"—even got tolerably close to inhabiting it; and there was a feeling I got in the back of my throat when I felt the presence was there. I was sure, in fact, that it was the direction in which all modern literature was pointing, although no one else seemed to have the sense to realise it. Not that I was too bothered by that. By now, I was pretty sure that I'd be getting to write my own italic bits soon, and all the stories and novels that went with them. Neither rock star nor airline pilot, I'd end up as a Grand Old Man living somewhere bright and hot and expensive, occasionally visited by keen and pretty young journalists who would nudge me towards apotheosis, or some other fancy word. A bit like the hero in a John Fowles story, or Robert Graves or Picasso.

Too shy to insist on going away, I lived at home when I was at college, and studied law because I liked the books and the old libraries, and because I didn't want to admit to the careers officer that I was going to be a famous writer. For a few years, in fact, the whole famous-writerly business was almost forgotten. The world was, it seemed, really a pretty exciting place. I went to parties. I met girls. I tried playing the guitar. I still read books, and occasionally found variations of the words turning over in my head as if I was writing my own narrative, but generally they were just part of the background score. Rock music became important to me—lyrical singers like Joni Mitchell and Richard Thompson, and harder-edged stuff, especially Robert Fripp's King Crimson. A lot of people might have possessed a copy of *In the Wake of Poseidon,* but the darkly soaring free-form of the second side of *Starless and Bible Black* would always get just the right kind of uncomprehending reaction at a party. Films, too, and above all Nicholas Roeg's *Don't Look Now,* sometimes managed to combine the feelings that I had about love and horror and strangeness and beauty. They all spoke to me of something darker and brighter out there that I still might just manage to reach.

The world of work beckoned, and soon after, the world of books began to loom larger for me again. I'd had it with law, and was briefly assured by the branch manager of a life insurance company that I'd have a fine career in sales, just as long as I wasn't the kind of person who always had their head in a book, until I ended up comfortably marooned and slowly climbing my way along one of the more obscure branches of the Civil Service. Often bored in the long hot afternoons, I began to toy with writing again, and to read more avidly. I remade closer contact with SF, although by now it was just one part of my diet. It seemed to me, anyway, that SF itself had changed when I wasn't looking, but not in the way that I'd imagined. The Nebula Award winning novels that I always made a point of reading each year were disappointing after the earlier thrills of *The Left Hand of Darkness* and *Dune*. SF books were getting easier to find in the bookshops, but the books themselves were cosier, longer, less challenging. Fantasy was starting to spread across the shelves, too, as was horror. We were moving into the age of the multi-volume, the spin-off, the book written by one writer, but based on the idea of another who couldn't be bothered to actually write the thing.

I guess I was getting older, more twisted, more cynical; turning into the kind of person I sometimes am now, although I try hard not to be. The big readerly discoveries of your adult life rarely have the kind of impact of the books that you read when you're twelve or sixteen. The emphasis shifts, too, if you really want to be a writer. You're less tolerant of crap in case that crap infects your own work, and you're more envious of the successful and the brilliant. To list the books that have influenced me in the years leading up to now would be just that—a list. I plan ahead, I see things coming, I read around subjects that might or might not be worth a story or a novel. I know that there are people out there for whom books are still at least as precious as they were when they were young, but it isn't that way for me— although it's a sacrifice that I'm glad to make in exchange for the agonies and occasional glories of actually being a writer. But that's another story. Still, its a shame that writers aren't like airline pilots now, or rock stars, and that any ordinary word processor can print in italics. It's a pity that writers often seem like men and women on an odd career path, doing their best to help themselves or someone else with a more sensible job to meet the mortgage.

Me, when the mood still sometimes comes, I'm happier reaching out towards the caterpillars crawling on windows, and whatever else lies beyond.

The Cold Step Beyond

IN a clearing in an unnamed forest in a remote part of the great Island City of Ghezirah, there moved a figure. Sometimes, it moved silently as it swirled a sword in flashing arcs. Sometimes, it made terrible cries. It was high noon in midsummer, and the trees and the greensward shimmered. The figure shimmered as well; it was hard to get a proper sense of the method of its motion. Sometimes, it was here. Sometimes, there. It seemed to skip beyond the places which lay between. Then, when the figure finally stopped moving and let the sword thing fall to its side and hung its head, it became clear that it was scarcely human, and that it was tired and hot.

Bess of the Warrior Church sunk to a squat. The plates of her body armour—mottled greenish to blend with the landscape—were ribboned with sweat. Her limbs ached. Her head throbbed in its enclosing weight of chitin and metal. She swept her gaze around the encircling sweep of forest, willing something to come. She had been here many weeks now; long enough for grass to have grown back in the seared space beneath the caleche which had brought her here, and for its landing gear and rusty undersides to become hazed in bloodflowers.

She looked up across Ghezirah, arching away from her under Sabil's mirrored glare. There, off to the east and rising into the distance, hung the placid browns of the farm islands of Windfell. The other way flashed the greyblue seawall of the Floating Ocean. Somewhat closer, looming smudgy and indistinct over the forest, lay the fabled Isle of the Dead. But she knew she had no calling in any of those places. The intelligences of her

church had directed her to this clearing. Yet until her foe arrived in whatever shape or form it might take, until the killing moment came, all she
could do was practice. And wait.

Yet something told her that, today, she was no longer alone. Her fingers
re-tensed upon the hilt of her sword. She opened her mind and let her
senses flow. Something was moving, small and quick, at the shadow edge
of the forest. The movement was furtive, yet predatory. If Bess had still
possessed hairs along her spine, they would have crawled. She would also
had shivered, had she not learned in her novitiature that tension is part of
the energy of killing, and thus must be entirely reabsorbed.

Slowly, and seemingly more wearily than ever, Bess hauled her torso
upright in a gleam of sweating plates. She even allowed herself to sway
slightly. The weariness was genuine, and thus not difficult to fake. But she
was certain that she was being watched from the edge of the forest.

The blade of her sword seemed to flash in the hairsbreadth of an instant
before movement itself. It flashed again. Bess appeared to slide across
the placid meadow in cubes and sideways protrusions. She was there.
Then she wasn't. She was under the trees perhaps a full half second
after she had first levered herself up from a squat. Three severed leaves
were floating down in the wake of her sword's last arc, and the thing
crouched before her was small and bipedal. It also looked to be young,
and seemed most likely human, and probably female, although its
sole piece of clothing was a dirty swatch wrapped around its hips. Not
exactly the sort of foe Bess had been expecting to end her vigil; just
some feral forest-rat. But it hadn't scurried off into the green dark at her
arrival even now that the three leaves had settled to the ground. It was
holding out, in something which resembled a threatening gesture, a small
but antique lightgun. The gun was live. Bess could hear the battery's faint
hum.

"If you try to shoot that thing . . . " She said, putting all the power of
command into her voice. " . . . you will die." The sound boomed out.

"And if I don't?" The little creature had flinched, but it was still wafting
that lightgun. "I'll probably die anyway, won't I? You're a warrior—killing's
all you're good for."

Bess's expression, or the little of it which was discernible within her face's plated mask, flickered. Since first leaving the iron walls of her church and setting out across Ghezirah in her caleche three moulids ago, she had discovered that warriors were most often thought of by those who lived outside her calling as little more than heedless bringers of death. Scarcely better, in essence, than the monstrous things they were trained to kill. Stories passed in her wake of soured milk, broken mirrors and malformed births. Or the taunts, and the curses, and the things thrown . . .

"I'll put this gun down if you put down your sword," the little creature said. "You're quick—I've seen that. But I don't think you're quicker than light itself . . . "

Technically, of course, the runt was right—but was it worth explaining that the killing movement of any weapon was the last part of a process which could be detected long before it began by those trained in the art of death? Bess decided that it was not. It was apparent from the thing's stance that it was used to using this lightgun, but also that it had no intention of doing so within the next few moments.

Bess lowered her sword to her side.

The creature did the same with the lightgun.

"What's your name?" Bess asked.

"Why should I tell you that? And who are you?"

"Because . . . " If there were any particular reasons, she couldn't immediately think of them. "My name is Bess."

The creature smirked. "Shouldn't you be called something more terrible than that? But I'll call you Bess if you want . . . "

"Do you have a name?"

"I'm Elli." The smirk faded. "I think I am anyway."

"You only *think*? Don't you know who you are?"

"Well, I'm *me*, aren't I?" The creature—although Bess now felt that she could safely assume that she was merely female and human, and not some monstrous anomaly or djinn—glanced down at her grubby, near-naked self. "Names are just things other people give you, aren't they? Or just plain make up . . . ?"

The helm of Bess's head, which had now absorbed the forest's shades, gave a ponderous nod. She understood the Elli-thing's remark, for she, too, had no proper idea of how she had got her name.

"Been watching you . . . " Elli nodded across the clearing. "Dead clever, the way you flicker in and out as if you're there and then not there."

"So why in the name of all the intelligences didn't you back off when I approached?"

Elli shrugged. "I could tell you were just practising. That you didn't mean it . . . "

Not meaning it being about the worst insult that, in all Bess's long years of training within the walls of her church, had ever been flung her way.

"But it was still very impressive," Elli added. "If you could show me some more, I'd really like to watch."

The Dead Queen's Gambit. The Circle Unleashed. The Upwards Waterfall. The Welcoming Blade. The Twice-Backwards Turn. The Belly Becomes the Mouth. The Leap of Steel. Even *The Cold Step Beyond*, a manoeuvre of sword and space which Bess still found difficult to execute. She performed them all.

Before, she had felt tired and bored. But now that she had an audience, even one as lowly as this Elli-thing, she felt re-energised. Her blade sliced though the warm air and the fabric of local spacetime, drawing her sideways and backwards in intricate twists and turns. She remembered her dizzy exhilaration when she first managed this near-impossible trick in the practice yards. This was like that, but better.

"Bravo! Bravo!" Elli was clapping.

For want of anything else, and no longer feeling in the least goaded or stupid, Bess gave her sword a final flourish and made as much of a bow as her armoured midriff would permit.

It was late afternoon. The shade beneath the trees was spreading. As Beth straightened, she saw that the Elli-thing had already vanished into the wood-scented dark.

Bess felt different that night as she squatted inside the iron womb of her caleche. Laid before her at the central alter of the cabin's console, set around with the glow of the more ordinary controls, was the steel eye of the keyhole which admitted the will of her church's intelligences. Briefly, it had flashed the message which had borne her here, and all the time since it had remained blank and blind. The other instructions since her changing into warrior form and setting out on first quest had been plain—at least in their seeming purpose, if not in their execution and result . . .

That great seabeast which had supposedly been terrorising a community of fisherwomen who lived in a desolate village on the far side of the Floating Ocean. A task which had seemed worthy of her first killing—until she had faced the creature itself. A slobbering thing, true. Big and grey and, at least in appearance, monstrous. But it had been old and in pain and helpless. She had realised, as it sobbed and moaned on that rocky shore as she drove her sword into its quivering flesh, that she had been summoned to do this work not because the women of the village feared to kill the creature, but because they pitied it too much.

Then had come her duties in guarding a senior imam of the Church of the Arachnids, who was supposedly under threat from the incursion of an assassin djinn from an unspecified dimension. But her arrival and attendance upon this plump and near-regal personage had coincided with a summit meeting of all the churches of the animalcules in Eburnea regarding various issues of precedence and money. It soon became clear to Bess that her presence at the canny witch's brocaded shoulder through those interminable meetings was intended not as protection, but as an implied threat of force.

And so it had gone, and then her third instruction had come, and now she was set down here amid this nowhere forest, waiting to do battle with an unexplained *something*. Bess shuffled down into her night couch. There was little space inside this vessel for much else—after all, what else did a warrior need other than her will and her sword?—but she had been permitted to bring one small chest containing her personal belongings, although she would just as happily have gone without it. The lid gave a pleading scream as she lifted it. This, she thought, as she gazed inside in the caleche's dull glow and breathed a stale waft of air, reminds me why I don't bother to look.

Other new novitiates were brought to the great walls of the Warrior Church by a variety of means and accidents. Lesser daughters. Unwanted or unexpected products of the vats. Those cursed with malformations, either of the body or the mind, which other and more squeamish churches found themselves unable to accept. Girls who had performed some sacrilege or debasement which placed them *beyond the pale*, in the antique phase. Downright criminals. They were all admitted in an unholy gaggle through the iron gates of the Warrior Church, although almost as many were soon found to be lacking and cast back out.

Bess remembered the rusty towers, and the courtyards of trial and test and battle. She remembered the light from classroom windows which washed through drapes of platinum gauze as they were schooled in all the near-endless varieties of monstrosity, djinn, interjection, tulpa, dragon, quasi-dragon, behemoth and demon that they would be expected to destroy. Most of all, though, she remember the faces of her fellow novitiates, and night-silence in the dormitories, and the laughter which exploded as soon as the junior imams doused the lights.

Clubfoot Nika. Humble Talla of the auburn tresses. And Afya of the shadows. All now transformed into hulking warriors like her. Out fighting some terror in the great island city of Ghezirah or across one or other of the Ten Thousand and One Worlds. Or already dead. Bess gazed down at the few dry leavings of her past. A shrivelled starflower. A tress of auburn hair. A hand-written note about soon returning, casually left.

Just one other item lay in there. Bess's taloned fingers struggled to pinch the fine loop of chain.

Who are you, Bess . . . ?

Where do you come from . . . ?

What are you doing here . . . ?

Bess no-name—Bess who had barely belonged even in those dormitories of the dispossessed and deformed. From all the other novitiates, sitting along the dark lines of bunks, hands clasped around knees with eyes rapt and mouths agape, there was always some story to be heard. High schemes or low robberies. A birthmother knifed by a jealous bond mother. A hand let go in a market of slaves. Over the nights, the whispers echoed through the dormitory as the tales flowed on. And grew more elaborate, Bess began to notice, as well. So the suckling child came to remember the taste of her dying birthmother's blood, and the slave-sold

underling survived a jumpship's spectacular crash. But the essential seed
of truth of some lost life remained, and could thus be embroidered upon
much as a basic sword thrust can once—but only once—it is entirely
mastered.

But Bess was mute when the eyes turned to her . . .

What about you, Bess?

What do you remember about the time before you were chosen?

She couldn't answer such questions. She was Bess simply because that
was what some lesser manifestation of the church's intelligences had
deigned to call her. All there was, was this great iron-enclosed edifice, and
her friends, and dormitory nights such as these, and all the days of learning
and practice. Nothing else. She had no sense of who or what she had been
before. She might as well have come from nowhere, just as the chants and
the jibes insisted. But for this one object . . .

It was called a locket. Or so she supposed; the terminology for items of
jewellery was not a form of knowledge in which warriors were expected to
be versed. But the word seemed to come with possession of the item.
Which might mean something. Or might not.

She had rarely worn the thing, even when her head and neck would
have allowed such a vanity before she changed into full warrior form. But
she had kept it. The chain was as finely made as were the great chains which
anchored the islands against the spin of Ghezirah's vast sphere. From it,
flashing bright then dull in the glow globe's light, depended the silver
teardrop which was the locket itself, engraved with dizzying fractal
patterns and swirls.

Bess felt that she was being drawn into the pattern, and permitted
herself the wasted energy of a small shudder as her armoured fingers
unslipped the chain and re-closed the lid of her chest. Then she stretched
down to rest.

She was already awake when the caleche's interior brightened to signal the
onset of dawn. A fizzing buzz, a sense of some invisible liquid cleansing
her scales, and she was ready for yet another day of waiting. She raised the
hatch and reached for her sword. Outside, as the dawn-singers called in

the light from their mirrored minarets, her footsteps left a dark trail like the last of the night until, when she outdrew her sword and made her first leap, the trail vanished into misty air.

She was just re-practising *The Circle Unleashed* in its rarely attempted more elaborate form when she knew that once again she was being watched. She hadn't considered how well this particular sword-stroke was fitted to the brief and spectacular series of leaps across the bloodflower-strewn meadow which she then executed. But it was.

There was the Elli-thing, standing undaunted but admiring at the edge of the forest, where today Bess's arrival had stirred or severed not one single leaf.

"*Salaam*," Bess said, a little breathlessly.

"*Sabah il Noor*, Bess of the Warrior Church." Elli replied with surprising formality, and Bess wondered, as the creature then made a small bow, at her own flush of pleasure to be greeted thus. Then a thought struck her.

"You haven't been out here all night have you?"

"On no." Elli gave a quick shake of her head.

"Then where do you live?"

"Oh . . ." A quick shrug. A backwards point with a grubby thumb. " . . . just back there awhile. Would you like to come and look?"

A small, pale figure. A larger shape which was scarcely there at all. They both moved ever deeper into the nameless forest through dark avenues and spills of birdsong. This more resembled, Bess supposed, the kind of adventure which was sometimes associated in the popular mind with members of her church. Dragons to be slain. Monstrous shifts and anomalies in the fabric of spacetime to be annulled. Maidens, even, to be rescued. Bess should, she supposed, feel a deep unease to be deserting the precise spot where her church's intelligences had instructed her to stay. But warriors had to show bravery and initiative, didn't they? And how long could any human being, no matter how extensively changed and trained, be expected to wait?

They paused to take refreshment beside a tree hung with a kind of red fruit which Elli said were called pomegranate, and had existed as far back as the Gardens of Eden on the legendary first planet of Urrearth. They were also to be found, she added matter-of-factly, in Paradise itself. They were best cut apart with a sharp utensil. The trouble being with this thing, she patted the lightgun she had tucked into the tie around her waist, then glanced at Bess expectantly, that it cooks them as well.

Bess studied the fruit, an odd-looking thing with a crown-like eruption at one end, which Elli was holding out. Her hand went to the hilt of her sword, although she knew what the imams of the Warrior Church would have said about using her sacred blade for such a menial task. If they had happened to be here and watching her, that was.

"Tell you what, Bess—I could throw it up like this."

Quicker than an instant, Bess drew her blade, and, in executing the *Spatchcock Goose*, vanished and reappeared as the pomegranate, now separated into two halves, still span up.

"Wooh!"

Elli caught one half as it descended. Bess, the other.

"So . . . ? What do you think of pomegranate? Not bad, is it, if you can deal with the seeds."

Bess had to agree. All in all, pomegranates were delicious. But, at least when it came to eating, they were a frustrating fruit. Her huge hands soon grew sticky, and so did her plated face. It was just as enjoyable, they decided, simply to toss the things up for the joy of slicing them in half. Pith and fruit were soon flying, and Bess's armour acquired the mottled reds, whites and pinks of pomegranate flesh.

"So . . . ?" Elli asked eventually, after Bess had demonstrated so many ways of slicing the fruit that much of what was left lying around them seemed to exist in some sideways dimension. Or was perhaps, just a sticky mess. "This is what you do, is it? Cut things up in odd and interesting ways?"

Bess had been laughing too much to take offence. But she now explained how the origins of her church could be traced back to the time of the first jumpships, when gateways had been discovered where all time, space and matter turned back in a cosmic rent. It had been a great breakthrough for womankind and every other sentient species, but it had also brought an end to the simplicity of one reality and the linear progression of time. Now, other forms of existence which had previously been thought of as nothing but useful constructs in understanding the higher dimensions of physics rubbed close against our own. The true aliens, the real horrors and monstrosities, lay not in the far-flung reaches of galaxy, but sideways. And each passage of a jumpship disturbed enough of the fabric of this reality to allow in, like a breath of dark smoke from a crack beneath a door, a little more of the seepage of these other realities. Sometimes, they were comical or harmless. Often, they weren't noticeable at all. But sometimes they were the stuff of abject nightmare. Only through the use of creatures who were themselves close to nightmare could these monstrous interjections be fought.

Bess wiped her sword on a patch of grass and made to re-sheath it in her scabbard. But then Elli had laid her hand on a part of her forearm which still retained some sensitivity. It felt sticky and warm.

"That sword of yours—I suppose it does something similar? The way it seems to cut through the world."

"Well . . . You *could* say that I suppose. Although the principle is much more controlled."

"Can I have a go?"

The request was ridiculous. It was sacrilege. So why hadn't she yet sheathed her sword?

"You can try this, Bess." Elli held out her cheap lightgun. "It's quite deadly."

"No," Bess rumbled.

"Well, perhaps you could at least let me give the handle-thing a quick hold."

"It's called the hilt." Bess watched in something like horror or amazement as her own hand took the flat of the blade and held it out.

"Hilt, then."

Elli's fingers were so small they barely circled the banded metal. Yet Bess felt a small shiver—something akin to the sensation which she had experienced last night when she studied that locket—ran through her. The sword shivered, too. Sensing a new presence, it had responded with a blurring hint of the final darkness beyond all dark which was woven into the exquisite metal.

Elli's fingers retracted. She let out a shuddering breath. "It feels like . . . Everything and nothing at all."

It was getting colder and dimmer now when, by rights, even in a place as overshadowed as this forest had become, it should have been growing warmer and brighter. The trees were giant things, spewing mossy boughs over which they had to clamber.

Elli was quick and sure and sharp as she scampered over the deadfalls. Bess, meanwhile, felt clumsy and lost. Vulnerable, as well. She stole glances at this odd little creature. What exactly *was* she? And how did she survive in this confusing jungle? A giant beetle, a crimson thing more jagged and threatening than her own helmeted head, regarded Bess with its many eyes before raising some kind of stinging tail and finally, reluctantly, backing off. There were probably more fearsome things than that out here in this forest—perhaps even monstrosities fierce enough to merit the attentions of a member of the warrior church. What defence could this near-naked young thing with only a cheap toy of a lightgun possibly put up? Unless she was far more dangerous than she seemed . . .

The thought that all of this could be some kind of deathly trap niggled in Bess's mind. But, at the same time, it was good to explore and make new friends, and her caleche with all its duties lay only a few miles off, and she was enjoying herself too much to want to stop.

The forest's branches were now so crisscrossed as to give no sense of light or sky. It was more like a vast and twisty ceiling from which drapes of a livid moss now provided the only illumination.

Then Elli stopped.

"Where are we?" Bess asked.

"Just have to go up here . . . "

Here being a winding step of roots which then became branches, leading through a wanly glowing archway inside a rotting trunk. Was this where Elli lived? Oddly, though, this strange little hideaway had a another stairway within it, lit by strips of light which gleamed as they ascended over beautifully carved stretches of floor and roof. The fine-grained stairway swirled on and up. There were intricate settings of jewel and marquetry. And now, at last, there was sunlight ahead.

" . . . Nearly there . . . "

An ivy-embroidered gate screeched on a final rise of marble steps. Bess had expected to emerge at some eyrie close to Ghezirah's roof, but it was immediately apparent that they were on solid ground. This was a kind of garden—trees, buildings and strange eruptions of statuary tumbled all around them—yet it was oddly quiet; filled with a decrepit kind of peace.

"Where by Al'Toman *is* this?"

"Can't you tell?"

It wasn't so very hard. In fact, now that Bess was getting her bearings, it was obvious. Over there, seen at a slightly different angle from the view she was used to, lay the placid browns of the farm islands of Windfell. That way, churning with what was surely the beginnings of a storm, was the vast seawall of the Floating Ocean. And below them, yet curling upwards in ways which the air and Bess's own senses struggled to bridge, marched the green crowns of the nameless forest, and beyond that, flecked with the red hollows where the bloodflowers flourished, lay the small circle of her meadow.

"You can't *live* on the Isle of the Dead?"

"Why not? You live inside that iron carbuncle."

It was a given even in nursery books that the island city of Ghezirah was more than simply a smooth globe encircling Sabil's star in three plain dimensions. Yet it was dizzying, and more than a little disturbing, to think that they had contrived to reach this place of the dead by climbing through the forest's roof. Still, Bess followed Elli as they explored.

Most of the tombs were very old, but older ones still were said to be buried in their foundations. Indeed, the most fanciful version of the tale of the Isle of the Dead's origins told of how the entire island consisted of nothing but mulched flesh, bone and memorials. The place was certainly alarmingly uneven and ramshackle, and little frequented in modern times. The major churches now all had their own mausoleums, while many of the lesser ones favoured remote planets of rest. The Warrior Church, meanwhile, found no home for its servants other than in its memories, for its acolytes were always expected to die in battle.

Hayawans ambled around carved sandstone pillars. Spirit projections flickered and dissolved like marshghosts. The voices of ancient recordings called from stone mouths muffled by birds nests. But it was the fecund sense of *life* in this place which struck Bess most. The bumbling insects. The frantic birdsong. The heady scents and colours of the blooms. There were fruits, as well, which would have made the pomegranate seem homely, and Elli explained that this island was also a fine place for trapping foxes, for catching airhorses, for collecting honeyseed, and for digging up and broiling moles.

"So you live here alone?"

Elli gave a shrugging nod. That much was obvious, Bess supposed.

"So how did you—"

"Come here? Is *that* what you're wondering?" Elli's face was suddenly flushed. "You think I'm some kind of grave-robber or ghoul?"

Bess attended to removing a speck of grit from her scabbard. After all, she could hardly accuse someone else of being secretive about their origins when there was an empty space where her own should have been. Just that noisy dormitory, and no sense of anything before. As if, impossibly, she had been born into her novitiature fully-functioning and whole. Apart from that locket, which meant nothing at all. But no, there *was* something more than that, she thought, looking around at this pretty home of the long-dead. Some bleak moment of horror from which her mind recoiled. The most sense she could make of it was that her church had plucked her from something so terrible that the best way to keep hold of her sanity had been to empty the knowledge from her brain. And now, somehow, as the shivering thought trickled through her, something was pulling her back there.

Elli pointed. "You see that building, the one with the copper birch tree growing out of the middle?"

It was a dome which still partly retained its covering of mosaic glass. It looked to be on fire, the way the leaves flickered above it.

"Do you want to take a look?"

Bess's head gave its usual slow nod.

"There was a girl buried there. Oh . . . a long time ago," Elli explained as they clambered over the ruins. "Before the War of Lilies, when the seasons were unchanging, and even time itself was supposed to run more slow. Anyway, she was young when she died, and her birth mother and her bond mothers were stricken. So they made this fine mausoleum for her, and they filled it with everything about their daughter, every toy and footstep and giggle and memory. You see . . . "

They were standing beneath the dome. The tree shifted through its fractured lenses, giving the displays a dusty life. Animatronic toys seemed to jerk. Strewn teddy bears still had a residual glint of intelligence in their button eyes. But that, and the swishing leaves, only made the sense of age and loss more apparent.

"And they visited her here . . . And they prayed . . . And they cried . . . And, dead though their daughter was, they swore that her memory would never die. But of course—"

"What was this girl's name? Are *you*—?"

"—Shut up and listen will you, Bess! And her name was Dallah, and I'm called Elli if you haven't noticed. So no, I'm not Dallah. Although Dallah *was* my friend. My best friend, you might say. In fact, my only one. You see, Dallah was like most only children who've been longed for a bit too much by their mothers, and find themselves over-protected and alone. Of course, Dallah had all these toys . . . " Elli pinged a bike-bell. "And she could have anything else she ever wanted. She only had to ask. But what she really wanted, the one thing her mothers couldn't give her for all their kindness and wealth, was a friend. So . . . " Elli ran a finger over a cracked glass case which seemed to be filled with nothing but leaves and dust. " . . . she did what most girls have done since Eve first grew bored with Adam. She made one up. And her name *was* Elli. And that's me. That's who I am."

Bess had been gazing into a hologlass pillar which contained the floating faces of three women. They looked kindly, but impossibly sad.

"I was just intended as another part of the memorial," Elli said. "They extracted me from every breath and memory of their beloved daughter. Sweet little pretend-Elli, who always had to have a place laid for her at table, and did all the naughty and disruptive things to which Dallah herself would never confess. Elli who stole all the doughnuts, even though it was Dallah who fell sick. Elli who crayoned that picture of a clown's face on the haremlek wall. They'd come to me in the years after to reminisce. This whole mausoleum, they couldn't stop building and refining it. Nothing was ever enough. They kept Dallah herself within a glass coffin inside a suspension field so she didn't decay. Not, of course, that they could ever bring themselves to actually look at their dead daughter, but she was unchanging, perfectly there. They couldn't let her go. Even when they were old, the mothers came. But then there were only two of them. And then just the one, and she grew so confused she sometimes thought I was Dallah. Then she stopped coming as well, and the slow centuries passed, and the gardeners rusted and the maintenance contracts expired. And people no longer came to pay their respects to anyone on the Isle of the Dead. There were just these crumbling mausoleums and a few flickering intelligences. The thing is, Dallah's mothers had tried too hard, done too much. And the centuries are *long* when you're an imaginary friend and you have nobody to play with—and I mean body in every sense . . . "

Elli had been wandering the mausoleum as she talked, touching colour-faded stacks of studded brick and dolls with missing eyes. But now she was standing beside that long glass case again. Which, Bess now saw, was shattered along one side.

"So you took hold of Dallah's corpse?"

"What *else* was I do to? She had no use for it, and her mothers are long dead. If I looked in a mirror, if there *was* a mirror here that was clear enough, I suppose I might see a face which would remind me a bit of Dallah. But I'm not Dallah. Dallah's dead and mourned for and in Paradise or wherever with William Galileo and Albert Shakespeare and all the rest. I'm Elli. And I'm me. And I'm here." She stuck out her tongue. "So there!"

Bess had heard of the concept of body-robbing, and knew that most of the major churches forbade it. The punishments, she imagined, would be severe, especially if the robber happened to be something which couldn't properly call itself sentient. But Elli's tale, and that final pink protrusion of her tongue, made the deed hard to condemn. It was better, though, that she stayed eating berries and broiling moles on the Isle of the Dead. In any other part of Ghezirah, or any of the other Ten Thousand and One Worlds, life for her would be not so much difficult as impossible, and would most likely be brought to a rapid end.

"How long have things been like this?"

Elli now looked awkward. "I don't know. I . . . " she looked up at the hissing, dancing roof, " . . . can we leave this place?"

It was good to be back out in the warm afternoon, even if all the falling memorials were now a constant reminder to Bess that this was a place of the dead. But as for Elli, she thought, as she gazed at her friend sitting on a pile of rocks with her arms wrapped around her grubby knees, she's right in what she says. She isn't some ghoul or monster. She's truly alive. Then Bess's eyes trailed down to that lightgun. The reason it looked like a toy, she realised, was that it had probably once been one. But she didn't doubt that it was now deadly, or that Elli knew how to use it. In her own way, this little grave-runt was as much a warrior as she was.

It seemed a time for confidences, so Bess explained what little there was to explain about her own life. The long days of endless practice. The even longer dormitory nights. The laughing chants. That sense of not properly belonging even in a community of outcasts. And now—the way her entire church and all its intelligences seemed to have withdrawn from her, when she'd been expecting to face some kind of ultimate challenge through which she could prove her worth.

"You mean, like a dragon or something? A monster that needs killing?"

She nodded. A dragon, or even a quasi-dragon, would certainly have done. Anything, no matter how terrible, would have been better than this. It was as if she'd been thrown back into the empty nowhere from which she had come, but pointlessly trained in swordplay and changed into the thing she now was . . .

Something patted down Bess's scales, leaving blurry silver trails which her camouflage struggled to mimic. After a long moment's puzzlement, she realised it was tears.

"Don't you have any idea of your earlier life?" Elli asked. "I mean, some hint or memory?"

Bess gave an armour-plated shrug, and rumbled about a piece of jewellery which she happened to possess. A thing on a chain, oval-shaped.

"You mean a locket?"

"I think it's called a locket, yes. You've heard of them?"

"Of course I have. I've got one myself. So—what's inside yours?"

"What do you mean, inside?"

Elli laughed and leapt down from her perch.

"You really don't know much about anything other than killing things, do you, Bess?"

Then she explained how lockets came in two hinged halves—there were, after all, plenty of examples of this and every other kind of trinket to be found on this isle—although the main thing which Bess was conscious of as they talked was her friend's close presence, and the strange and peculiarly delicious sensation of a hand touching her own strange flesh.

It was getting late. The dawn-singers had already made their first preparatory cries, stirring up an evensong of birds. Contrary to the once-popular saying, it proved far easier to depart the Isle of the Dead than to get there, and Elli soon led Bess back toward the same marble steps through which they had entered, and down into the depths of the forest below. Moving through the pillared near-dark, Bess was conscious again of the danger of this place. Far more than the island above them, this was a landscape wherein monsters and wonders might abide. Yet Elli led on. The clearing lay ahead.

"You'll be here tomorrow?"

"Yes." Elli smiled. "I will."

Bess shambled across the meadowgrass, which, amid darker patches of bloodflower, already shone with dew. The caleche hissed open its door. She climbed in and laid down her sword. The keyhole eye at the centre of the cabin's altar, which would surely soon bear her a fresh instruction, and perhaps even apologies for this pointless waste of her time, remained unseeingly dark. The food tray hissed out for her, and she ate. Then, as she prepared to lie down, she remembered what Elli had said about lockets. Vaguely curious, but somehow still feeling no great sense of destiny, she opened her small chest and lifted the thing out. After a small moment of struggle, the two sides broke apart.

———

Another morning, and, although it was still too early for dawn, Bess was standing in the dim clearing outside her caleche with her sword. She, too, was a thing of dimness; her armour saw to that. But already the dawn-singers were calling. Light would soon be spilling from tower to tower. And there was Elli, standing out from the shadow trees, pale as stripped twig.

"Bess! You've come!" She was almost running. Almost laughing. Then she was doing both.

"I said I would, didn't I?" Bess's voice was as soft as it was capable of being. And as sad. It made Elli stop.

"What's happened?" They stood a few paces apart beside the rusty beetle of the caleche in the ungreying light. "You seem different."

"I haven't changed," Bess rumbled. "But I've brought you this. I want you to take it . . . " She held out the locket, glinting and swinging on its silver chain, from her hand's heavy claw.

"It's that thing you described . . . " Elli looked puzzled, hesitant. "The locket. But this is . . . " She took it in her own small fingers. Here, in the spot in which they were standing, the gaining light had a rosy flush. " . . . mine."

"Open it."

Elli nodded. Red flowers lay all around them. The silver of the locket was taking up their colour, and Bess now seemed a thing entirely made of blood. Swiftly, with fingers far more practised and easeful than Bess's, Elli broke open the locket's two sides. From out of which gleamed a projection, small but exquisite, of the faces of three women. They were the same faces which hung in the hologlass pillar of Dallah's mausoleum. But in this image they looked as happy as in the other they had been sad.

"Dallah's mothers." Elli breathed. "This thing is yours, Bess. But it's also mine . . . "

"That's right."

Elli snapped it shut. Dawn light was flowing around them now, and the bloodflowers made Elli beautiful, and yet they also made her pale and dangerous and sharp. "This doesn't really have to happen, does it?" she whispered.

"I think it does."

"Don't tell me, Bess." She almost smiled. "You remember already . . . ?"

"I didn't—not at all. But I'm beginning to now. I'm sorry, Elli."

"And I'm sorry as well. Isn't there some way we can both just go our separate ways and live our own lives—you as a warrior and me just as me? Do I really have to do this to you?"

"We both do. Nothing is possible otherwise. We're joined together, Elli. We're a monstrosity, a twist in spacetime. Our togetherness is an affront to reality. It must be destroyed, otherwise even worse things will break through. There are no separate ways."

The killing moment was close. Bess could already hear the lightgun's poisonous hum. She knew Elli was quick, but she also knew that the use of any weapon, be it blade or laser, was the last part of a process which any trained warrior should be able to detect long before the final instant came. But how by all the intelligences was she supposed to do such a thing, when Elli was her own younger herself?

Then it happened. All those hours of practice and training, all the imam's praises and curses, seemed to collide in a moment beyond time, and emerged into something deadly, precise and perfect. For the first time in her fractured life, Bess executed *The Cold Step Beyond* with absolute perfection, and she and her blade were nowhere and in several places at once. Elli was almost as quick. And could easily have been quicker.

Yet she wasn't.

Or almost.

And that was enough.

Bess swung back, a blur of metal and vengeance, into the ordinary dimensions of the spreading dawn. Around her, still spraying and toppling, spewed the remains of Elli of the Isle of the Dead. Nothing but hunks of raw meat now, nothing you could call alive, even before the bits had thunked across the ground.

Bess stood there for a moment, her breathing unquickening. Then she wiped and sheathed her sword. She knew now why the bloodflowers bloomed so well across this meadow. Without them, the strew of flesh which surrounded her would have been to horrible to bear. But something glinted there, perfect and unsullied. She picked it up. Her blade had cut through everything else—time, life, probability, perhaps even love—but not the chain and locket. It was the one strand which held together everything else.

She remembered it all now. Remembered as if it had never been gone. Playing with Dallah—who had called her Elizabeth, or sometimes Elli, or occasionally Bess—all those aeons ago when she'd been little more than a hopeful ghost. Then pain and emptiness for the longest time until some kind of residual persistence took hold. It was, Bess supposed, the same kind of persistence that drives all life to strive to *become*, even if the body of someone once loved must be stolen in the process. Long seasons followed. There was little sense of growth or change. The once-sacred island around her slid further toward decay and neglect. But now she was Elli, and she had Dallah's discarded body and she was alive, and she learned that living meant knowing how to feed, which in turn meant knowing how to kill.

Elli had always been alone apart from a few of the other mausoleum's residual intelligences. But it wasn't until one warm summer's morning when the light seemed to hang especially pure that she looked down at the other great islands, and saw something moving in a clearing with jagged yet elegant unpredictability, and realised she felt lonely. So she found a way down through the twisty forests which lay below the catacombs, and came at last to a space of open grass, and watched admiringly until she was finally noticed, and the monstrous thing came over to her in blurring flashes, and turned out to be not quite so monstrous at all.

But that locket. Which had once been Dallah's. Even as the Bess-thing held it out, Elli had understood that there was only one way that Bess could own it as well. That time, like the locket's chain, had looped around itself and joined them together in a terrible bond. And Elli then knew that only one of them could survive, because she was the monstrosity which this creature had been sent to kill.

The killing moment, when grace, power and relentlessness are everything. But in the memory Bess now had of holding Elli's lightgun, the warrior-thing had hesitated, and her own laser had fired a jagged spray.

Even as Bess gazed down at the remains of Elli's butchered body lying amid the bloodflowers, the memory of the burning stench of her own wrecked chitin and armour came back to her. She had died not once this dawn, but twice. And yet she was still living.

It was fully day now. The clearing dazzled with dew. Looking back toward her caleche, Bess saw that its door had opened, and that, even in this morning blaze, the light of her altar shone out. More questing, perhaps. More things to kill. Or an instruction for her to return and recuperate within her church's iron walls.

The intelligences of the Warrior Church were harsh and brutal, but they also welcomed the creature which no other church would ever think to accept. And now they had given Bess her memory back, and made her whole. She realised now why her earlier quests had seemed so pointless, and why she still hadn't yet felt like a true warrior at all. But she was truly a warrior, for she had that taken that final step into the cold beyond, and been found not to be wanting.

Bess gazed at the open door of her caleche, and its eerie, beckoning glow. She had climbed in there once clutching that locket, been borne away in a long moment of forgetting to begin the life which had eventually brought her back here. But now her gaze turned toward the encircling forest, and she remembered that sense she had had of different dangers and mysteries lurking there. Wonders, perhaps, too.

The caleche awaited.

The light from its doorway blared.

Its engine began to hum.

Bess of the Warrior Church stood bloodied and head-bowed in a clearing in a nameless forest, wondering which way she should go.

AFTERWORD *THE FUTURE ISN'T REAL*

I'M NOT VERY GOOD AT WRITING ABOUT THE FAR FUTURE. MAINLY, I think, because I find it hard to imagine that we humans will still be around. Or, if we are, we'll be so changed as to make the lives of future humans impossible for any writer or reader of the twenty first century to understand.

I'm also fully aware that these kind of objections are, in terms of writing fiction, absolute nonsense. Every story that's ever been written is essentially about now, be it set in the Neolithic age, a Birmingham council estate, or the remote ice-fastnesses of the planet Zarg. In any case, there's great fun and insight to be had in imagining people much like ourselves continuing to jostle for status and discover new things and fall in and out of love across vast new swathes of time and space. So why not write about such things? I honestly can't say. Other than that, as a writer rather than a reader, I find describing a future which lies much more than a century or so ahead of the world I'm in astonishingly hard. Or maybe I just take realism too seriously, or lack the right kind of imagination. At least, most of the time.

The trick, when I do manage to reach toward the far future, is to look back as much as forward, and to think in terms of the myths from which story-telling and the human experience first emerged, and then to try to create my own vision. The particular myth which I've developed and reused a few times over the decades being that of something I call the Ten Thousand and One Worlds; a universe populated almost exclusively by women, yet with a strong Arab influence. I suppose that, as a white European male, I was probably looking for various opposites of myself which I could cast into the future.

I can't give you a rationale for this supposed universe, or anything resembling a history. My mind seems to veer away from such things in much the same way as it veers from understanding mathematical equations or reading musical notation. Too reductive, maybe. That, or perhaps I just don't want to address the difficult, vision-destroying feeling that the kind of future Warrior Bess inhabits, where science becomes magic and magic is everyday, and the space between the stars has been crossed and the universe is alive with terror and wonder, is just a hopeless, hopeful dream.

"A Concise and Ready Guide"

IN the latter part of the 19th century, books on etiquette became enormously popular. One of the many areas of everyday—and less than everyday—life which they addressed was what was then most often described in polite society as *a dietary indisposition*. Many volumes, such as Mrs Beeton's famous *Book of Household Management*, were hastily reissued with new chapters on the subject, but the small pamphlet abstracted below is of particular interest in that it represents one of the first attempts to provide much-needed social and practical advice to those who have already succumbed to the condition then more commonly known as *Vampirism*.

A Concise and Ready Guide For
Ladies and Gentlemen Of
Good Birth and Bearing
Recently Afflicted by
An Uncommon Malady
In All Matters
And Formalities
of *Decency*
Decorum
and the Full
Social Graces

By
"A Cheltenham Lady"

Comprising Information on Manners, Dress and Conversation in Society, in Public, at Home and at Worship with Special Reference to Dining Out, Good Health and the care of the Complexion.

"Agreeableness of Person Should Never Succumb to the Inconvenience of Death"

LONDON
1890

ON BECOMING INDISPOSED

In recent decades, the spread *via* a few Noble Families of the Eastern Portion of the Continent of Europe of a condition which requires certain dietary arrangements is no longer a matter of public ignorance. Banished to the sorry pages of history are the prejudicial attitudes which saw many a promising eternity cut brutally short merely because the subject had become what the ill-educated might call — and we will use this term only once — "a vampire". Nowadays, the possession of such a condition, at least amid those of otherwise good character, can be better regarded as a charming and essentially innocent attribute, comparable perhaps with the possession of red hair or left-handedness. Indeed, these comparisons are particularly apt in that, as long as such differences from the supposed norm are displayed with appropriate modesty, they can add much to the character and interest of a well-mannered lady or gentleman. In essence, the question which those readers who have already passed to the far side of life must ask themselves whenever faced with a situation which gives them pause for concern is agreeably simple. It is thus:

How would I most properly have deported myself while I was still living?

Or, if this does not suffice:

1

How would my Dear Mother (or Father) (and assuming they are not undead themselves) have deported themselves?

If this is borne in mind, there is little else which will not become clear and straightforward, as these few following short pages shall demonstrate.

SOCIAL INTERCOURSE

The question by far most commonly posed in the writer's experience is *"When should I let people know I am become undead"*? The answer is, most emphatically, As Soon as Possible. Any other course of action, for all that it may seem superficially convenient, leads, almost inevitably, to embarrassment and confusion. It is to be hoped that the posting of a notice in an appropriate column in *The Times*, and also in a suitable local periodical might one day serve the same purpose it does for the announcement of other changes of circumstance. It is also to be hoped that the stationers might show the imagination to provide a suitably discreet form of card which could be easily consigned to the postal service. But in the writer's experience, the actual requirements of good society can sometimes lag behind the needs of its individual members and meanwhile we must all make use of the existing courtesies.

2

The watchword is openness and frankness. If this approach is clearly understood and rigorously adhered to, the undead reader may be assured that the knowledge of their change will soon pass freely and easily amongst family, social and, indeed, business circles. Conversely, if one is seen to be shamefaced in conveying this particular item of "news" one is most likely giving others the excuse to make inappropriate judgements, or to keep secret that which one wishes to be freely but discreetly broadcast. So, in social circumstances, a breezy, "of course, I find myself indisposed in the daytime" will often suffice. Do not underestimate, either, the rapidity with which word from "below stairs" migrates upwards to reach the ears of employers. While ill-advised gossip and rumour-mongering should always be condemned, a comment from a much-trusted maid that she has heard that a certain personage has been notably changed in recent times is often to be welcomed.

When meeting new acquaintances, much the same rules apply. A gentleman may shake hands with his fellows as briskly and openly as normal, should bow lightly and raise his hat to ladies, and should no more initiate a discussion with an unfamiliar female personage than he would have before becoming undead. A lady should similarly maintain her characteristic feminine reserve. Excessive smiling, which some find to be a symptom of social embarrassment,

3

and the consequent showing of one's teeth, is to be avoided. It goes without saying that one need hardly accost the strangers one passes in the street with one's "news". Similarly, shop assistants, cab drivers and other members of the working classes have no need to become privy to matters concerning one's private life. If it becomes apparent that you do need to tell them of your condition, you should do so as freely and frankly as you might ask a waiter for a fresh napkin. A short, simple statement such as, for example, "I live at so-and-so, although in point of fact I am no longer alive," when asked for your address is these days commonly recognised amid those employed in the service industries. You should treat any lack of understanding beyond this point as a failure on their part rather than your own.

There is, as this writer is aware, a current fad for communication by small signs amongst those of the undead who move in certain "smart sets". The reader, however, should be warned against such signals. It is all very well to expect a close friend of one's own age and outlook to knowledgably interpret the wearing of a red neckerchief, certain arrangements of rubies on a lady's bosom, and the use of fans at dances, but what, the reader must ask themselves, would an elderly maiden aunt, or a much-admired member of the priesthood, make of such fripperies? It is out of respect for these and many other less "up-to-date" members of good society that all supposed cleverness with regard to this condition should be avoided.

The reader may imagine that much needs to be said about the more intimate forms of acquaintance which can spring up between parties of the opposite sex. This is not the case. The good-mannered will have made their condition apparent to all within their circle. From there, with suitable precautions, matters may proceed almost in their normal way. The only matter to be emphasised — and this cannot be stressed more strongly — is that any lady or gentleman of proper breeding must be as absolutely clear in this particular matter as they would in all other questions such as breeding, religious persuasion and family background. Nor should the reader ever consider entertaining a member of the opposite sex without a chaperone being present. One need hardly speculate about the misunderstandings which might otherwise arise.

DINING AND VISITING

First of all, it is clear that no personage of good breeding would ever cross the threshold of a house without being invited. Thus, this supposed "old chestnut" can easily be consigned to the fires of ill-advised speculation.

When it comes to entering the dining room, however,

the undead reader may find the situation more taxing. It is, one would have thought, the most commonly understood fact about our condition that we do not obtain our sustenance in the manner of the living. On that basis, one would have thought that ill-advised attempts to serve rare beef, ruby wine or (heaven forbid!) blood pudding would have long ceased. Sadly, the writer must report that this is not the case. One can imagine (at least at a stretch) a circumstance wherein a society hostess might invite a Hebrew or Mooslem to her table. Surely, they would then ensure that roast pork was not served? Is there not, then, a precise parallel with the current fad for serving foreign dishes doused in garlic at the English table?

It is to this writer's considerable frustration that the situation at the dinner table is still not as clear-cut as it might be. The situation can only improve, but to be clear to those living readers who still appear to need the matter explained, the whiff of blood at the dining table is as disturbing to those of our disposition as might the scent of a gazelle be to a lion on the plains of Africa. I would recommend that the considerate hostess provides well-cooked fish, and possibly new-baked bread and fresh fruit when the undead are at table, all of which will be enjoyed by the living, while we who cannot partake can admire the fare much as one would admire a still-life Dutch painting.

It is to be fervently hoped that none of the above should

cause our gentle reader any excess of difficulty. If one does find oneself faced, perhaps, by an ill-considered slice of liver served in a pool of its own blood upon a silver salver, one can only remind oneself that the hunger which this spectacle engenders cannot be satisfied by it. At least, not unless the liver is human. Which, at polite tables, is unlikely. If these thoughts are not enough, one should politely excuse oneself for a few moments. No hostess worthy of merit will ever question a guest's need for a moment's contemplation in a darkened room.

Finally, it is unlikely that any reader "at visit" will have to contend with unwonted shows of religious impedimenta such as the display of crucifixes, or carelessly disposed troughs of holy water, as we English do not practise the excesses of the Latin races. Again, though, should such a situation occur, a swift withdrawal rather than an excessive and unnecessary display is all that is required. Explanations, should they still be necessary, can be given later when the moment of horror has fully subsided.

AT WORSHIP

Churches and consecrated ground of all kinds are best avoided. Should invitations arrive pertaining to occasions such as weddings, funerals or christenings, they must be refused briefly and politely. Over-elaborate excuses are attention-seeking and invite unnecessary further specula-tion. In most cases, the reader may be assured that the invitation has been sent merely with the kind intention of ensuring than an undead friend or relative does not feel "left out", rather than because of an ignorant wish to insist on their attendance.

ONE'S PERSON

It has oft been remarked that the undead lady is more greatly blessed than the gentleman with regard to her complexion. Even to the most critical eye, a fine pallor combined with ruby-red lips and flashing eyes can only be regarded as appealing. Many a so-called "English Rose" would happily die to acquire such an appearance. Indeed, many have. There is no need to make any change to one's previous wardrobe. The wearing of cape-like apparel, along with an over-reliance on reds and blacks, or excessive displays of flesh, are all to be considered showy and tasteless.

It may be a small sadness to the reader that they can no longer confirm their appearance by reference to a mirror. This can be easily mitigated, however, by the knowledge that the undead are likely to find themselves more complimented on their looks than in their lifetime. Should any small disarrangement of a lady's toilette occur in a social situation, the reader may be assured that the same signals which any considerate companion might give to the living will still be forthcoming. A few moments retirement to rectify the problem with your attending maid is all that is required.

For the gentleman, the situation is admittedly more complex. With regard to the absence of any reflection, the writer has heard male personages lament how they miss the opportunity to shave themselves, although most will have few problems delegating such chores to their valet. The greater issue concerns the pallor of complexion. What appears "charming" and "delicate" upon one sex may easily become "sinister" and "threatening" upon the other. To return to the question of shaving, however, the simplest solution on offer to masculine readers is to sport a set of side-whiskers, a moustache (which, if generous, may also help disguise any unwanted displays of "toothiness") or even a full beard.

ON OBTAINING SUSTENANCE

It is to be feared that some ill-educated and sensation-seeking readers will have skipped directly to this section.

They will, however, most certainly find themselves disappointed.

It goes without saying that the well-bred undead gentleman or lady would never consider making an unwanted advance to any of the living who are of similar or higher social standing to themselves, no matter how enticing that idea might occasionally seem. Even a direct invitation should be treated with extreme circumspection. It is as well to enquire, for example, whether the person has fully consulted their elders and superiors, and what their reaction to this suggestion might be. Might this writer even humbly suggest that any approach regarding this subject be responded to with a suggestion that the interested party first purchase and peruse a copy of this very Pamphlet?

It is becoming increasingly common for undead personages of good standing to advertise in publications in the provinces for what are usually referred to a "Caministas" or "Red-Nurses". These creatures, who are invariably drawn from unfortunate backgrounds, thus have the privilege of spending a few delightful months living in a well-established household, enjoying a good bed, plentiful rest and food, and the frequent companionship of their (dare one say?) generally considerate and charming Sponsor, until they are eventually sucked dry. Many a happy short-term relationship has thus ensued. This writer can only recommend this arrangement, and merely suggests that a

10

little prior training in the arts of conversation, hygiene and home-dwelling can make the experience even more enjoyable for both sides. Of course, such creatures should never be exposed to the glare of good society.

Another alternative, at least if one is "caught short", are the various "night cafes" which have sprung up in many of this nation's great cities. Currently these establishments can often leave much to be desired, but it can only be hoped that a system of registration and inspection will soon be introduced by the Authorities, to bring this arrangement fully into the modern age.

Need it be said, finally, that "informal dining" is by its nature informal, and can be scarcely expected to involve the niceties of fine society occasions? For the undead, such areas as the East End parishes of London, Little London in Leeds, or Digbeth in Birmingham, can be seen much as the Cook of a great house might see a lower cellar. She would certainly not wish to invite her master and mistress to come with her on her visits there, but nevertheless she knows that this is where much useful sustenance can be stored.

Further discussion on this subject lies outside the scope of this pamphlet.

ON EXPOSURE TO SUNLIGHT

Shutters are easily installed, and heavy blinds and curtains are available in all good drapers. Servants should have no more cause to disturb their undead employer during daytime than they would the living in the depths of night, while consultation of a watch and a sound knowledge of lighting-up times soon becomes a habit. After all, punctuality and regular time-keeping lie at the root of all the social graces. Should, however, a stray beam at sunset glance down from a high widow to strike our reader as they rush between house and carriage to catch the early performance of a play, there will inevitably be some withering of any exposed flesh. A brief retreat to a dark, well-confined space will normally ensure a return to full vigour, but meanwhile it is best to try to deflect the concerns of any well-intentioned onlookers with a small show of rueful good humour, much as one might with a spillage of tea. Above all, the undead reader confronted by sunlight should avoid, at all costs, excessive teeth baring, or any tendency to hiss.

AT THE BALL

The reader may be assured that ostentatious displays

Sadly, the pamphlet's last pages have been torn away. Most of the usual social situations seem to have been covered already however, so it is unlikely that much of significance has been lost. The tone, along with the depth of the writer's knowledge, is clearly primitive, but the pamphlet conveys a strong sense of the types of prejudice which were then common, along with providing a charming glimpse into the social mores of a lost age. For contrast, more modern works as *Debrett's Correct Form* and *Good Manners After Sunset* are both recommended.

It is entirely possible that the semi-anonymous writer is still extant. If that is the case, the current editor would very much like to hear from her *via* the front piece address of this magazine. It would be fascinating to learn of a journey from those distant times to the present, and to find out whether further editions of the pamphlet were ever issued, especially following the so-called "dietary indisposition" which was soon after visited upon our very own dear—and still very much unliving—Queen.

AFTERWORD *BLOODY DRAGONS*

I'M A GREAT ONE FOR DRAWING UP LISTS.

Tasks around the house. Reminders about the car insurance. Things to do with writing. Names, places, ideas for projects, bits of information to jog my mind. That, and questions, and lists of things I don't know about whatever I'm currently working on.

This particular piece—story, if you can call it a story—arose in part from a list I'd made of approaches to writing I didn't feel I'd tried. I was about to write that the list included a wish to "write non-narrative fiction", but having just found the right page in the right notebook (no small feat in itself), I see that, on that list, beginning with the heading "I don't" are things which include "writing drunk", "using a typewriter" and "keeping ragged hours". That, and "writing stuff with no beginning, middle or end", which, at least with the false clarity of hindsight, is the impetus from which this piece came about.

"A Concise and Ready Guide" also expresses a personal interest in vampires which seemed to start with reading Alan Hollinghurst's *The Swimming Pool Library*, a beautifully written novel which isn't remotely supernatural in its themes and certainly doesn't feature any vampires. But the delicious physicality of Hollinghurst's writing, the intensity and intimacy he brings to his descriptions of humans and especially sex, while somehow remaining totally detached, triggered a desire, as is almost always the way with me, to do something which is both vaguely similar, but also totally different.

I can't say the piece you've just read owes anything else to Hollinghurst, although it does revisit my liking for Victoriana and guides of the "Miss

Manners" sort which have shown up in quite a few of my works. What was being prompted by *The Swimming Pool Library* was the first conscious surfacing of a desire to write about a fictional creature that was and is very much in the cultural forefront, and which I'd never attempted to tackle. As I write this, I'm still wrestling with vampires in a big novel spanning a great deal of time and many settings and characters of which the novella *The Reparateur of Strasbourg*, also published by PS, is but a glimpse.

The truth is, though, that I absolutely hate vampires. Sure, I've greatly enjoyed some of Ann Rice's vampire fiction, along with Jon Courtenay Grimwood's *The Fallen Blade*, I'd recommend Kim Newman's *Anno Dracula* series to anyone, and I have fond memories of reading Sheridan Le Fanu, but—I mean, well, come *on*. The things make no sense. Not only that, but they've been lazily gutted and over-done in so much recent adult and teenage fiction, not to mention on TV and in the movies, that there must surely be very few fresh angles left to explore. I'm basically a logical person, as well, and try to seek out the logical heart of whatever story I'm trying to tell. Which is also why, although you'd have to press me pretty hard to admit it, I'm more of an SF writer, or even a frustratedly naturalistic one, than a writer of fantasy or horror fiction.

To my mind, vampires stand for a great deal of the same sort of lazy wish-fulfilment thinking which brings people to all kinds of illusory beliefs, assumptions and acceptances, from holistic therapy to tarot-reading to accepting the musty premises of organised religion to imagining that Aston Villa will ever be anything more than a makeweight in the Premiere League. And there are just too *many* of the bloody things. There are vampire perfumes. There's Count Chocula, a vampire-themed break-fast cereal. There's even a vampire in Sesame Street, for Chrissake. That's how scary and other-worldly vampires have become.

So, all in all, my writerly instinct, maintained over many years, has been to give the things a wide berth. And, it has to be said, "A Concise and Ready Guide" only dips a cautious toe into the subject's cooling, pooling blood and plays with its essential ridiculousness, up to and including the unfortunate truth that, if they were anything like as common as they now seem to be on Victorian streets, we'd all be vampires today.

Still, annoyance with a subject is something I've long learned to look out for as a writer. Friction, even—or especially—of a negative kind, can be a strong source of ideas. And as Shakespeare put it, I probably do protest too much. Vampires might be nonsense, but they're powerful nonsense. Like dragons, they're an archetype, and pop (or rise) up in the stories and myths of many cultures in one form or another, which clearly means they have a resonance which any self-respecting writer who enjoys tinkering with the edges of reality would be foolish to ignore.

As for dragons, I did include one near the start of my novel *The Light Ages*, but it was a sad, puny thing, stuffed into a rabbit hutch in the corner of a fairground to be either pitied or ignored. So it seems as if my first reaction to these big, mythical stereotypes is to use their supposed power to achieve a reverse effect.

As for the second . . . Well, in some Jungian corner of my brain I really don't want to acknowledge, maybe a much bigger dragon also lurks.

AN EMPTY GREY CELL OF ONE'S OWN

BEFORE I write anything about this room where I work, I should say how privileged I am to have such an arrangement. Virginia Woolf once famously announced that a woman needs two things if she wants to write: a room of one's own (with a lock and a key), and some money to be independent. Woolf's world-view was elaborate, but dated and limited. Forget about women and writers; few people in this world of ours are lucky enough to have either of these things, let alone both of them at the same time.

But here it is—this is the place where I do most of my writing, and I'm very lucky to have it. Not that I don't spend a lot of my time thinking things through as I walk the dogs, or talk to myself in the car or the kitchen, or sit working at writing or researching in other rooms, be they in our house or in public places such as bars, cafes and libraries, or doing all the other things which are necessary to lead a writer's life, and also to help generate that other necessity which Woolf mentioned. But at the end of the day, for me and I suspect for most other writers, it usually comes back to one desk, and one seat, in one particular room. There are some things you can escape as a writer, such as the normal restrictions of reality and moral responsibility. But the place where you do your work isn't one of them.

The view I have from my window is actually rather a pretty one, even if it is just of a lawn and some trees and a garden gate. People even comment that it must be helpful, for "inspiration", to look out on such a charmingly rustic scene. I don't usually bother to explain that I normally write with the blinds at least half down, and that I often miss the arrangements of all

my previous "writing rooms", where my desk generally faced a wall and
the views were less attractive. The main objective of writing fiction is to
shut yourself off from the world you're in, not open yourself up to it.

Some writers need silence to help with this shutting off process, but I
generally work with music playing in the background. Most often it's
Radio 3, the BBC's classical station. Not that I don't enjoy music with a
beat or recognisable lyrics, but I find that's distracting when I'm writing.
Sometimes, when I'm really pumped up, I can write to the jagged heavy
metal of King Crimson. Most of the time, though, the timeless master-
pieces that the great composers sacrificed their lives and health to produce
simply drift by my ears. Like those half-drawn blinds, the music is just
another way of blocking things out and keeping the part of my mind that
might otherwise notice something else occupied.

Obviously, there are many bits and bobs on display in this room of
mine. Reference books, stationery. A Klimt reproduction that always
reminds me when I look at it of Nick Roeg's "Bad Timing". That, and an
out-of-date "Sexy Priests" calendar I got in Rome, which makes me smile,
and a Cthulhu cuddly toy I was given a few years back by the people at
Clarion West, which makes me smile as well. Along with pictures my
daughter has done for me over the years, and photos of my nearest and
dearest. But although I'm noticing these things now—they're really not
there when I'm deeply involved in writing. In fact, I sometimes think that
the ideal writer's room would be an empty grey cell with nothing in it but
the most basic tools needed for writing. A scary place, certainly, and difficult to enter of a morning or evening. But then, stripped of all its comforts
and illusions, writing itself is a scary business. At least, it should be.

On a TV programme many years ago, Gore Vidal was touring the rooms
of a Venetian palace. There, he was shown the desk where Henry James
had supposedly sat to write one of his later novels. The desk faced one of
those huge gilt mirrors you get in such places, and Vidal pointed out that
the thing must have been moved since James spun out his interminable
sentences. No writer with the sole exception of Ernest Hemingway, he
pronounced, could possibly sit writing at a desk facing a mirror. He's right,
of course. I can't imagine anything worse, or less productive.

One of the main tricks of writing fiction is to somehow try to train yourself not to think too hard about what you're doing as you're doing it. This includes being conscious of yourself, your writing materials, and the room in which you happen to be sitting. Not that the walls are likely to dissolve, or your characters emerge from a bookcase and start talking to you. But it does mean that, at least when things are going well, an amount of forgetting about yourself is going on as you are writing.

Like a mechanic deeply involved in working out a problem with a piece of machinery or an actor in character in a play, it's a trick that most writers develop simply through hard work and repetition. Thoughts about whether you've put out the bins or what to have for dinner may still intrude, just as I'm sure they do for an actor on the stage or a musician in mid-performance, but you try to push those things aside. The great advantage and disadvantage with writing being that, unlike a musician in full flow or a salesman in mid-sale, you have nothing other than your own willpower to stop you from being distracted and starting to do something else.

The fridge, the next cup of tea, jobs around the house and other far more urgent real-world tasks, not to mention that latest episode of Top Gear, always beckon. Worse still, or better, especially in these days of the internet, there often arises the genuine need to check up on a fact, or invent a name for a minor character. Next thing you know, you're sorting through the spam in your e-mails, setting up pointless macros on Word, using cotton buds to clean your keyboard, reading the cooking pages of last week's Observer, or looking at Facebook. But there should and most likely will be a voice at the back of your head telling you that this isn't what you're supposed to be here for, that this isn't getting the job done, that this isn't writing.

So, back to the page, or the computer screen, and a quick check of those notes you scrawled out before you started to remind yourself of what is supposed to be happening, even if it isn't . . .

People meet and fall in love. Empires clash. Hopes are raised and destroyed. Time passes. Seasons fade. Snow sparkles. Rain hisses. Galaxies wither. All at the click of a key or the flick of a pen. Writing *is* a pretty magical business, when you think about it. I've had my moments of laughing out loud in admiration at my own cleverness in this room of mine. I've punched the air and whooped like a sports fan. I've been close to tears. I've felt hot when I've been writing about hot places, and have shivered as my characters shivered. I've had moments of delight, and at least as many of absolute emptiness. But I think you could probably say many similar things about most rooms where people do their work, at least if they care as much about it as they could and should.

For most of the time, and when things are going well, what I'm really hoping for as I sit in this room of my own (which doesn't have a lock and a key, although I have to keep it properly shut to stop the dogs from barging in) is nothing more than that same steady sense of progress I hope to get when any job is going okay and the wind's in the right direction and my mind isn't distracted. A sense of forgetful involvement, in other words, inside a space which I'm not really noticing.

RE-CROSSING THE STYX

WELCOME aboard the *Glorious Nomad*, all nuclear-powered 450,000 tons of her. She is, literally, a small country in her own right, with her own armed services, laws and currency. But, for all her modernity, life afloat remains old-fashioned.

There are the traditional fast food outlets, themed restaurants, coloured fountains, street entertainers and even a barber's shop staffed by a charmingly impromptu quartet. There are trained armies of chefs, litter collectors, pooper-scoopers and maintenance engineers. Firework displays are held each evening on the main deck above the Happy Trillionaire Casino, weather permitting. It's easy to understand why those who can afford her tariffs carry on cruising until—and then long after—death.

Wandering the decks in his lilac-stripe crew blazer, resident tour host Frank Onions never paid much attention to the news reports he saw in magazines left glowing over the arms of sun loungers. Still, he knew that dying was no longer the big deal it had once been. Death, it had turned out, was the answer to many of the problems of old age. With your weakening heart stopped, with your failing body eviscerated and your memory uploaded and your organs renewed, you were free to shuffle around on your titanium hips for another few decades. And, after that, you could book in for the same procedure again. And again. There were, admittedly, some quibbles about whether the post-living were still technically the same people they had once been. But, working as Frank did in an industry which relied so heavily on the post-centenarian trade, it would have been churlish to complain.

It seemed like there were more corpses than ever as he led the morning excursion to the ruins of Knossos in Crete, with the *Glorious Nomad* anchored off what remained of the city of Heraklion. At least fourteen out of the forty two heads he counted on the tour bus belong to the dead. Make that double, if you include their minders. The easiest way to tell the dead from the living was by a quick glance at their wigs and toupees. Not that the living oldies didn't favour such things as well, but the dead were uniformly bald—hair, like skin, seemed to be something the scientists hadn't fully got the knack of replacing—and had a particularly bilious taste in rugware. The lines of bus seats Frank faced sprouted Elvis coxcombs, dyed punky tufts and Motown beehives. The dead loved to wear big sunglasses, as well. They shunned the light, like the vampires they somewhat resembled, and favoured loose-fitting clothes in unlikely combinations of manmade fabrics. Even the men wore too much makeup to disguise their pasty skins. As the tour bus climbed towards the day's cultural destination and Frank took the mike and kicked into his spiel about Perseus and the Minotaur, a mixed smell of corrupted flesh, facecream and something like formaldehyde wafted over him.

The September sun wasn't particularly harsh as Frank, *Glorious Nomad* lollipop in raised right hand, guided his shuffling bunch from sight to stair-lift to moving walkway. Here is the priest-king fresco and here is the throne room and here is the world's first flush toilet. The only other tour group were from the *Happy Minstrel*, another big cruise vessel berthed at the old American naval base at Souda Bay. As the two slow streams shuffled and mingled in their frail efforts to be first to the souvenir shop, Frank couldn't help but worry that he was going to end up with some of the wrong guests. Then, as he watched them—so frail, so goddamn *pointless* in their eager-ness to spend the money they'd earned back in their discarded lives as accountants from Idaho or lawyers from Stockholm or plant hire salesmen from Wolverhampton—he wondered if it would matter.

He corralled what seemed like the right specimens back on the bus without further incident, and they headed on toward what today's itinerary described as *A Typical Cretan Fishing Village*. The whole place looked convincing enough if you ignored the concrete berms erected as protection against the rising seas, and the local villagers did local villager as well as anyone who had to put on the same act day after day reasonably could.

Afterwards, Frank sat under an olive tree in what passed for the harbourfront taverna, took a screen out from his back pocket and pretended to read. The waiter brought him stuffed olives, decent black decaf and a plate of warm pita bread. It was hard, sometimes, to complain.

"Mind if we join you?"

Frank suppressed a scowl and put away his screen. Then, as he looked up, his contractual smile became genuine.

"Sure, sure. It would be a pleasure."

She was wearing a strappy sundress made of some kind of fabric that twinkled and changed in the same dappling light that animated her golden hair and shoulders.

"I'm Frank Onions."

"Yes . . . " There was a curious intensity to her gaze, which was also golden. " . . . We know." She raked back a chair. Then another. And beckoned.

Shit. Not just her. Although Frank supposed that was to be expected; apart from crew, the only young people you found on board ships like the *Glorious Nomad* were minders. The dead man who shuffled up was a sorry case indeed. His toupee was a kind of silver James Dean duck's arse, but it was wildly askew—so were the sunglasses. The tongue which emerged from between ridiculously rouged lips in concentration at the act of sitting looked like a hunk of spoiled liver.

"Oh, I'm Dottie Hastings, by the way. This is Warren."

As this Dottie-vision leant to re-straighten the rug and sunglasses, the dead man slurred something which Frank took to be hello.

"Well . . . " She returned her gaze to Frank. "We really enjoyed your tour and talk this morning. What can we get you? A carafe of retsina? Some ouzo?"

Much though he'd have loved to agree with anything Dottie suggested, Frank shook his head. "I really don't drink that kind of stuff . . . Not that I have a problem with it . . . " He felt compelled to add. "I just like to take care of myself."

"Oh yes." Frank could feel—literally fucking *feel*—Dottie's gaze as it travelled over him. "I can see. You work out?"

"Well. A bit. There's not much else to do in time off when you're crew."

She made a wry smile. "So. About that drink. Maybe some more coffee? I'm guessing decaf, right?"

Dottie, he noticed, settled for a small ouzo, although the Warren-thing restricted himself to orange juice, a considerable amount of which she then had to mop up from around his wizened neck. There was a strange and unminderly tenderness about her gestures that was almost touching. Lovely though she was, Frank found it hard to watch.

"You do realise," she said, balling up paper napkins, "that most of the stories you told us about Knossos are pure myth?"

Frank spluttered into his coffee. But Dottie was smiling at him in a mischievous way, and her mouth had gone slightly crooked. Then the knowing smile became a chuckle, and he had to join in. After all, so much of what they'd just been religiously inspecting—the pillars, the frescos, the bull's horns—had been erected by Arthur Evans a couple of hundred years before in a misguided attempt to recreate how he thought Knossos should have been. But Evans got most of it wrong. He was even wrong about the actual name. Frank never normally bothered to spoil his tales of myths and Minotaurs with anything resembling the truth, but, as Warren drooled and he and Dottie chatted, vague memories of the enthusiasm which had once driven him to study ancient history returned.

Dottie wasn't just impossibly beautiful. She was impossibly smart. She even knew about Wunderlich, whose theory that the whole of Knossos was in fact a vast mausoleum was a particular favourite of his. By the time they needed to return to the tour bus to view the famous statue of the bare breasted woman holding those snakes—now also known to be a modern fake—Frank was already close to something resembling love. Or at least, serious attachment. There was something about Dottie. Something, especially, about that golden gaze. There was both a playful darkness and a serene innocence somewhere in there which he just couldn't fathom. It was like looking down at two coins flashing up at you from some cool, deep river. Dottie wasn't just clever and beautiful. She was unique.

"Well ... " He stood up, as dizzy as if he was the one who'd been knocking back the ouzo. "Those treasures won't get looked at on their own."

"No. Of course." A poem of golden flesh and shifting sundress, she, too, arose. Then she leaned to help the Warren-thing, and for all his disgust at what she was doing, Frank couldn't help but admire the way the tips of her breasts shifted against the fabric of her dress. "I'm really looking forward to this afternoon. I mean . . . " After a little effort, Warren was also standing, or at least leaning against her. His mouth lolled. His toupee had gone topsy-turvy again, and the skin revealed beneath looked like a grey, half-deflated balloon. "We *both* are." Dottie smiled that lovely lopsided grin again. "Me and my husband Warren."

Minders were always an odd sort, even if they did make up the majority of Frank's shipboard conquests. But Dottie was different. Dottie was something else. Dottie was alive in ways that those poor sods who simply got paid for doing what they did never were. But *married*? You sometimes encountered couples, it was true, who'd crossed the so-called bereavement barrier together. Then there were the gold-diggers; pneumatic blondes bearing not particularly enigmatic smiles as they pushed around some relic in a gold-plated wheelchair. But nowadays your typical oil billionaire simply accepted the inevitable, died, and got himself resurrected. Then he just carried on pretty much as before. That was the whole point.

Frank Onions lay down in his accommodation tube that night with a prickly sense of dislocation. Just exactly where was he going with his life— living on these crew decks, deep, deep below the *Glorious Nomad's* waterline where the only space you could call your own was so small you could barely move? It might not seem so up along the parks and shopping malls, but down here there was never any doubt that you were at sea. Heavy smells of oil and bilge competed with the pervasively human auras of spoiled food, old socks and vomit. It was funny, really, although not in any particularly ha-ha way, how all the progress of modern technology should have come to this; a hive-like construct where you shut yourself in as if you were a pupae preparing to hatch. No wonder he wasted his time in the crew gym working his body into some approximation of tiredness, or occupied what little time was left hunting the next easy fuck. No wonder none of the ship's many attractions held the slightest interest for him. No wonder he couldn't sleep.

All he could think of was Dottie. Dottie standing. Dottie seated. Dottie smiling her lopsided smile. The sway of her breasts against that prismatic fabric. Then Frank thought, even though he desperately didn't want to, of what Dottie might be doing right now with that zombie husband of hers. Mere sex between them didn't seem very likely, but mopping up food and levering withered limbs in and out of stairlifts was merely the tip of the iceberg of the tasks minders were required to perform. The thing about being dead was that blood, nerve cells and tissue, even when newly cloned, were susceptible to fresh corruption, and thus needed constant renewal and replacement. To earn their salaries, minders didn't just give up a few years of their lives. After being pumped full of immune-suppressants, they were expected to donate their body fluids and tissue to their hosts on a regular basis. Many even sprouted the goitre-like growths of new replacement organs.

Frank tossed. Frank turned. Frank saw throbbing tubes, half flesh, half rubber, emerging from unimaginable orifices. Then he felt the rush of the sea beneath the *Glorious Nomad's* great hull as she ploughed on across the Mediterranean. And he saw Dottie rising shining and complete from its waters like some new maritime goddess.

As the *Glorious Nomad* zigzagged across the Aegean from the medieval citadel of Rhodes to the holy island of Patmos, Frank Onions kept seeing Dottie Hastings even when she wasn't there. A glint of her hair amid the trinkets in the backstreets of Skyros. A flash of her shadowed thighs across the golden dunes of Evvoia. He felt like a cat on heat, like an angel on drugs. He felt like he was back in the old times which had never existed.

Warren Hastings wasn't hard to find out about when Frank ransacked the *Glorious Nomad's* records. He'd made his first fortune out of those little hoops used to hang shower curtains. His second came from owning the copyright on part of the DNA chain of some industrial biochemical. Warren Hastings was seriously, seriously rich. The sort of rich you got to be not by managing some virtual pop band or inventing a cure for melancholy, but by doing stuff so ordinary no one really knew or cared what it was about. For all the money a top-of-the-range Ultra-Deluxe Red Emperor Suite must be costing him, he and Dottie should by rights have been plying the oceans on their own cruiser, living on a private island, or floating in a spacepod. Perhaps they enjoyed the company of lesser immortals. Or perhaps they simply liked slumming it.

The more Frank thought about it, the more the questions kept piling up in his head. And the biggest question of all was Dottie herself. It was an odd shock, despite all the times he'd now seen her and Warren exhibiting every sign of tenderness, to discover that she'd married him ten years earlier—before he'd even died—in a small, private ceremony in New Bali. There she was, dressed in virginal white beneath a floral arch, with Warren standing beside her and looking in a whole lot better shape than he did now. The records were confused and contradictory about exactly when he'd chosen to die, but he must have started seriously decaying before he finally made the leap. Dottie herself seemed to have emerged, beautiful and smiling and entirely unchanged, into the more discreet and upmarket corners of the society pages, and into what you could no longer describe as Warren's life.

It all felt like a mystery, but for once Frank was grateful for the contract clause which insisted he spend a designated number of hours in the company of paying passengers. He mingled at the cocktail hour of the Waikiki Bar, and feigned an interest in a whole variety of passenger activities about which he couldn't have given the minutest fuck, until he worked out what kind of social routine the Hastings were following, and then began to follow a similar routine himself.

Onward to the island of Chios with its Byzantine monastery and fine mosaics, and the autumn waves were growing choppier as Frank Onions ingratiated himself with what he supposed you might call the Hastings crowd. Sitting amid the spittle rain of their conversations as Warren gazed devotedly in Dottie's direction with his insect sunglasses perched on his ruined Michael Jackson nose, Frank could only wonder again at the continuing surprise of her beauty, and then about why on earth she'd consented to become what she was now. Most minders, in Frank's experience, were almost as dead as the zombies they were paid to look after. They'd put their lives on hold for the duration. Apart from the money, they hated everything they were required to do. Even in the heights of passion, you always felt as if their bodies belonged to someone else.

But Dottie didn't seem to hate her life, Frank decided once again as he watched her wipe the drool from her husband's chin with all her usual tenderness and Warren mooed equally tenderly back. The thought that they made the perfect couple even trickled across his mind. But he still didn't buy it. There was something *else* about Dottie as she turned to gaze in proud and lovely profile through the panoramic projectaglass window at the wide blue Mediterranean. It was like some kind of despair. If her golden eyes hadn't been fixed so steadily on the horizon, he might almost have thought she was crying.

He finally got his chance with her after a day excursion on the tiny island of Delos. The Hastingses had opted to join this particular tour party, although they hung back as Frank delivered his usual spiel about the Ionians and their phallic monuments as if Dottie was trying to avoid him. Then there was a kerfuffle involving her and Warren just as the launch arrived for the return to the *Glorious Nomad*. A lover's tiff, Frank hoped, but it turned out there had been some kind of malfunction which required immediate action as soon as they got on board ship.

Dottie still had on the same white top she'd worn all day when she finally emerged on her own at the Waikiki Bar later that evening, but it now bore what looked to be—but probably wasn't—a small food stain on the left breast. Her hair was no longer its usual marvel of spun gold, either, and the left corner of her mouth bore a small downward crease. She looked tired and worried. No one else, though—all those dead real estate agents and software consultants—noticed as she sat down. They didn't even bother to ask if Warren was okay. The dead regarded organ failure in much the same way that flat tyres were thought of by the petrol car drivers of old; a bit of a nuisance, but nothing to get too excited about just as long as you made sure you'd packed a spare. The spluttering talk about annuity rates continued uninterrupted, and the tension lines deepened around Dottie's eyes as her fingers wove and unwove in her lap. Even when she stood up and pushed her way out through the corral of matchstick limbs toward the deck, Frank was the only person to notice.

He followed her out. It was a dark, fine night and the stars seemed to float around her like fireflies. A flick of hair brushed Frank's face as he leaned close to her on the ship's rail.

"Is Warren alright?"

"I'm looking after him. Of course he's alright."

"What about you?"

"Me? I'm fine. It wasn't me who—"

"I didn't mean that, Dottie. I meant—"

"I know what you meant." She shrugged and sighed. "People, when they see us both, they can see Frank's devoted to me . . . "

"But they wonder about you?"

"I suppose so." She shrugged again. "I was just this girl who wanted a better life. I was good at sports—a good swimmer—and I had these dreams that I'd go to the Olympics and win a medal. But by the time I'd grown up, Olympic competitors no longer used their own limbs or had anything resembling normal human blood flowing in their veins. So I eventually found out that the best way to get steady work was on ships like this. I did high dives. I watched pools in a lifevest. I taught the dead and the living how to swim—how to paddle about without drowning, anyway. You know what it's like, Frank. It's not such a terrible life just as long as you can put up with the tiny sleeping tubes, and all those drinks served with paper umbrellas."

"What ships were you on?"

"Oh . . . " She gazed down into the racing water. "I worked on the *Able May* for most of this time."

"Wasn't that the one where half the crew got killed in the reactor fire?"

"That was her sister ship. And then one day, Warren comes along. He looked much better then. They always say the technologies are going to improve, but death hasn't been particularly kind to him."

"You mean, you really did find him attractive?"

"Not exactly, no. I was more—" She stopped. A small device on her wrist had started beeping. "I have to go to him. Have you seen a suite like ours Frank? Do you want to come down with me?"

"Wow! This is nice . . . "

Gold. Glass. Velvet. Everything either glittery hard or falling-through soft. Frank had seen it all before, but this wasn't the time to say. The only jarring note was a large white structure squatting and humming beside the cushion-festooned bed.

" . . . I just need to check . . . "

It looked as if Dottie was inspecting the contents of some giant, walk-in fridge as she opened a chrome and enamel door and leaned inside. The waft of air had that familiar tang; a chill sense of spoiling meat. There was even that same bland aquarium light, along with glimpses of what might have been trays of beef and cartons of coloured juice, although by far the biggest item on the racks was Warren himself. He lay prone and naked in such a way that Frank had a fine view of his scrawny grey feet, his hairless blue-mottled legs, his scarred and pitted belly, the winter-withered fruit of his balls and prick. He looked not so much dead as sucked dry. Far more alarming, though, was the empty space on the rack beside him, which was plainly designed to accommodate another body.

"He's fine," Dottie murmured with that weird tenderness in her voice again. She touched one or two things, drips and feeds by the look of them. There were flashes and bleeps. Then came a sort of glooping sound which, even though he couldn't see exactly what was causing it, forced Frank to look away. He heard the door smack shut.

"He'll be right as rain by morning."

"You don't get in there *with* him, do you?"

"I'm his wife."

"But . . . Jesus, Dottie. You're *lovely*." Now or never time; he moved toward her. "You can't waste your life like this . . . Not when you can . . . " It seemed for a moment that this oh-so direct ploy was actually working. She didn't step back from him, and the look in her golden eyes was far from unwelcoming. Then, as he reached out to her cheek, she gave a small shriek and cowered across the deep-pile, rubbing at where his fingers hadn't even touched. It was if she's been stung by a bee.

"I'm sorry, Dottie. I didn't mean—"

"No, no. It isn't you Frank. It's me. I like you. I want you. I *more* than like you. But . . . Have you heard of imprinting?"

"We're all—"

"I mean the word literally. Imprinting is what happens to the brain of a chick when it first sees its mother after it hatches. It's an instinct—it's built in—and it's been known about for centuries. It's the same to some or other degree even with the more advanced species. That's how you can get a duckling to follow around the first thing it sees, even if it happens to be a pair of galoshes."

Frank nodded. He thought he understood what she meant, although he hadn't the faintest idea where this was leading.

"We humans have the same instinct, although it's not quite as strong or simple. At least, not unless something's done to enhance it."

"What are you saying? Humans can be imprinted and attached to other humans? That can't be legal."

"When does whether something's legal matter these days? There's always somewhere in the world where you can do whatever you want, and Warren already knew he was dying when I met him. And he was charming. And he was impossibly rich. He said he could offer me the kind of life I'd never achieve otherwise no matter how long I lived or how hard I worked. And he was right. All of this . . . " She gestured at the suite. "Is nothing, Frank. It's *ordinary*. This ship's a prison with themed restaurants and a virtual golf range. With Warren, I realised I had my chance to escape places like this. It didn't seem so difficult back then, the deal I made . . . "

"You mean, you agreed to be imprinted by him?"

She nodded. There really did look to be tears in her eyes. "It was a small device he had made. You could say it was a kind of wedding gift. It looked like a silver insect. It was actually rather beautiful. He laid it here on my neck, and it crawled . . . " She touched her ear. "In here. It hurt a little, but not so very much. And he made me stare at him as it bored in to find the right sector of my brain." She shrugged. "It was that simple."

"My God! Dottie . . . " Again, but this time more impulsively, he moved toward her. Once more, she stumbled back.

"No. I can't!" She wailed. "Don't you see? *This* is what imprinting means." The stain on her left breast was rising and falling. "I'd love to escape this thing and be with you, Frank. But I'm trapped. At the time, it seemed like a small enough price to pay. And it's true that I've been to incredible places, experienced the most amazing things. Living on a cruise ship like this, looking at the ruins of the ancient world because we can't bear to look at the mess we've made of ours . . . It's meaningless. There's a different kind of life out there, Frank, in the high mountains, or up in the skies, or deep beneath the oceans. For those few who can afford it, anyway. And Warren could. *We* could. It's like some curse in a fairy tale. I'm like that king, the one who wanted a world of made of gold, and then found out that he was killing everything that was important to him in the process. I wish I could be with you, Frank, but Warren will carry on and on as he is and I can't give myself to anyone else, or even bear to have them touch me. I just wish there was some escape. I wish I could unwrite what happened, but I'm forever tied." Her hand reached towards him. Even in tears, she looked impossibly lovely. Then her whole body seemed to freeze. It was as if a glass wall lay between them. "I sometimes wish we were dead."

"You can't say that, Dottie. What you and I have—what we *might* have. We've only just—"

"No. I don't mean I wish *you* were dead, Frank. Or even myself. I mean things as they are . . . " She raised her golden eyes and blinked more slowly. " . . . and Warren."

The tides were turning as the *Glorious Nomad* beat against the deepening autumnal waves. Frank found himself giving talks about the Grecian concept of the transmigration of souls, and how the dead were assigned to one of three realms. Elysium, for the blessed. Tartarus for the damned. Asphodel—a land of boredom and neutrality—for the rest. To reach these realms you first had to cross the River Styx and pay Charon the ferryman a small golden coin or *obolus*, which grieving relatives placed on the tongues of the dead.

"To attain your desires," he concluded, gazing at the papier mache masks of ruined, once-human faces arrayed before him in the Starbucks' Lecture Suite, "you must be prepared to pay."

Poison? The idea had its appeal, and there were plenty of noxious substances on board which Frank might be able to wangle access to, but neither he nor Dottie were experts in biochemistry, and there was no guarantee that Warren couldn't still be re-resurrected. Some kind of catastrophic accident, then—especially in these storms? Something as simple as disabling the magneto on one of those big bulkhead doors as Warren went tottering through . . . ? But getting the timing exactly right would be difficult, and there was still a faint but frustrating chance Warren would make some kind of recovery, and then where would they be?

The options that Frank and Dottie explored as they met on the spray-wet deck over the next few days seemed endless, and confusing. Even if one of them worked flawlessly, other problems remained. There was an opportunity coming for them both to leave the ship together, when the *Glorious Nomad* dropped anchor by the shores of the old Holy Land, for an optional tour in radiation suits, but Dottie would be expected to act the role of the grieving widow, and suspicions would be aroused if Frank were to resign his post and then be spotted with her. No matter how many jurisdictions they skipped though, they'd still be vulnerable to prosecution, and also blackmail. But one of the things which Frank was coming to admire as well as love about Dottie was her quickness of mind.

"What if *you* were to appear to die, Frank?" she shout-whispered to him as they clung to the ship's rail. "You could . . . I don't know . . . You could pretend to kill yourself—stage your suicide. Then . . . " She gazed off into the tumbling light with those wise, golden eyes. " . . . we could get rid of Warren instead."

It was as perfect and beautiful as she was, and Frank longed to kiss and hold her and do all the other things they'd been promising each other right here and now on this slippery deck. Disguising himself as Warren for a few months, hiding under that toupee and behind those sunglasses and all that make-up, wouldn't be so difficult. Give it a little time and he could start to look better of his own accord. After all, the technology was continually improving. They could simply say that he'd died again, and been even more comprehensively re-resurrected. All it would take was a little patience—which was surely a small enough price to pay when you considered the rewards which awaited them: Dottie freed of her curse, and she and Frank rich forever.

Drowning had always been the most obvious option. They'd toyed with it several times already, but now it made absolute sense. Toss Warren overboard, he'd sink like a stone with all the prosthetic metal he had in him. And if they did it close to the stern—threw him down into the wildly boiling phosphorescent wake of the *Glorious Nomad's* eighteen azimuth propellers—he'd be torn into sharkmeat; there'd be no body left worth finding. Sure, alarms would go off and one of the hull's cameras might catch him falling, but even the most sophisticated technology would struggle to make sense of whatever was going through the forecast force eight gale. Especially if they waited until dark, and Warren's body had on one of the transmitting dogtags all crew were required to carry and was wearing a lilac-stripe blazer.

By next day, the kind of storm which had shipwrecked Odysseus was brewing, and the *Glorious Nomad's* public places soon fell empty as her passengers retreated to their suites. The barber's shop closed early. The several swimming pools were covered over. The ornamental lake in the Pleasure Park franchise was drained. The air filled with the sounds of heaving and creaking, curious distant booms and bangings, and a pervasive aroma of vomit.

Heading along the swaying passageways to their pre-arranged meeting point, Frank already felt curiously convinced by the details of his own suicide. His last talk on board the *Glorious Nomad* was of how Orpheus tried to rescue his dead wife, Euridice, from the Underworld, and it had taken no effort at all, staring at those white-faced zombies, to put aside his usual catch-all smile and appear surly and depressed. Ditto his few last exchanges with colleagues. Fact is, he realised, he'd been this way with them for years. Everything, even the ferocity of this storm, had that same sense of inevitability. Back down in his sleeping tube, he even found that it was far easier than he'd expected to compose a final message. He'd been able to speak with surprising passion about the emptiness of his life: the sheer monotony of the talks and the tours and the berthings and the embarkations—the long sessions in the gym, too, and the ritual seductions with their overcoming of fake resistance, and the inevitable fuckings and even more inevitable break-ups which followed, with their equally fake expressions of regret. Just what the hell, he'd found himself wondering, *had* he been living for before he met Dottie? Looked at dispassionately, the prospect of his own imminent death made every kind of sense.

He arrived at the junction of corridors between Challengers Bowling Arcade and the smallest of the five burger franchises just two minutes early, and was relieved to find the whole area empty and unobserved. Dottie was as punctual as he'd have expected, and somehow still looked beautiful even dressed in a grey sou'wester and half-hauling her dead husband up the sideways-tilting floor. Warren was in his usual brushed velour top, crumpled nylon slacks and velcro trainers, although his sunglasses and toupee were all over the place.

"Hi there Frank," Dottie said, grabbing a handhold and supporting Warren by a bunched ruff behind his neck. "I know it's a terrible night, but I persuaded Warren that we might feel fresher if we took a walk." Frank nodded. His mouth was dry. "Maybe you could help me with him?" she added, shoving Warren into Frank's half-surprised embrace.

"There you go, fella," Frank heard himself mutter as he propped the withered creature against the bulkhead. "Why don't we take this off . . . ?" Quickly, he removed Warren's black top, which slipped worn and warm and slightly greasy between his fingers, although it was the feel and sight of Warren beneath that really set his teeth on edge. The dead man muttered something and looked back toward Dottie with his usual puppy-dog longing, but made no discernible attempt to resist.

"Maybe this as well . . . "

The toupee felt ever warmer and greasier.

"And this . . . "

Here came the sunglasses, hooked off from what passed for ears and a nose. Frank had to judge every movement against the rising, falling waves. But, Jesus, the man was a mess.

"Looking a bit cold now, Mister Hastings . . . "

Frank shucked off his own blazer.

"So why don't you put this on?"

A few more manoeuvres and Warren was wearing Frank's crew blazer. Frank almost forgot the crew dogtag until Dottie reminded him in a quick whisper. Even then, Warren, in this new attire, looked like nothing more than a particularly bald and anaemic scarecrow, and Frank was wondering how the switch would convince anyone until he swung the weighted hatch open and was confronted by the sheer size and scale of the storm.

The deck was awash. Dottie hung back. Salt spray ignited the air. It was a miracle, really, that she'd been able to do as much as she had to help when you considered the deal this dead husk had forced on her. Now all she had to do was keep hold of his nylon top, toupee and sunglasses. The sky shattered in greys and purples. For all his slips and struggles as he manoeuvred Warren Hastings toward the *Glorious Nomad's* stern, Frank Onions felt like he was Odysseus sailing from Circe's island, or Jason with his Argonauts in search of the Golden Fleece. Soon, he would reach those warmly welcoming shores that Dottie had been promising him.

A few last staggers and he was clinging to the final rail, and still just about keeping hold of Warren, although they were both equally drenched, and it was hard to distinguish between sea and sky out here. Then he felt the steel clifface of the *Glorious Nomad's* stern rising and straining until her screws were swirling above the waves, and it seemed for a long moment that the whole ship would simply carry on climbing until the ocean dragged her down. Frank skidded and nearly fell as he grabbed Warren's arms and tried to haul him over the rail.

"Stop squirming you bastard!" Frank screamed into the wind even though Warren wasn't squirming at all. As the ship teetered and began to fall back he tried to lift him again, and this time got some better kind of purchase. This, Frank thought, as he and Warren swayed like dancers over the stern's drop, was far closer to a dead man than he'd ever wanted to get, but for all the wet grey skin, cavernous cheeks and birdcage chest, there was something about Warren Hastings in this stuttering light that didn't seem entirely dead. Something in the eyes, perhaps, now they were stripped of their goggle sunglasses, or in the set of that mouth now that the powder and rouge had run. The guy had to have worked out what was happening, but there was still no sign of any resistance, nor any sense of fear. If anything, Frank thought as he finally managed to hook one hand under Warren's wet and empty armpit and the other under his even emptier crotch and gave the final quick heave which tipped him over the rail, that last look conveyed something like relief—perhaps even a sense of pity . . .

"Did it work? Are you okay?"

Already, Dottie had managed to clamber up the deck. Already, the curse of her imprinting was broken, and her arms are quickly around him. Roughly and wetly, they kissed.

"I love you, Frank," she said, and her arms were strong and the ship's searchlights and alarms were blazing as she drew him behind a lifeboat into the lee of the storm and took out something silver from her sou'wester pocket that squirmed and uncurled like a living jewel.

"I love you."

She said it again, and kissed him harder as he felt a sharpness crawl across his neck.

"I love you."

She held him tighter than ever as pain flared inside his ear.

"I love you."

She said it again and again and again and again.

Where has he not been? What has he not seen? He's looked down on an Earth so small that he could blot it out with his thumb, he's skysailed to the peak of Mount Everest. If there was a price to pay for all this glory, Frank Onions would willingly have paid it. Most glorious of all to him, though, eclipsing every moonrise and sunset, is his continuing joy at sharing Dottie's company. The money—even the incredible things that it can buy; the glass terraces, the submarine gardens, the refurbished Burmese palaces—is just the river, the coin, the *obolus*. To be with her, and to share his flesh and blood with her, is an experience which pales even the farthest heights of sexual ecstasy.

Days change. The living die and the dead live, but Frank's love for Dottie is unchanging. He has, once or twice, much as one might gaze in awe at bare footprints left across an ancient floor, looked back along the path which brought them together. He knows now that the real Warren Hastings married his beautiful sixth wife just a few months before he died, or perhaps simply disappeared, in circumstances that other times and cultures might have regarded as mysterious. Since then, and as before, Dottie has remained just as stunningly, agelessly, beautiful. And she always has a companion whom she likes to term her husband. Sometimes, when the circumstances suit, she even calls him Warren. Frank has no need to ask Dottie why she chose death above life. He already understands perfectly. After all, why would anyone who had the money and the choice wait for old age and decrepitude before being resurrected? And what sacrifices and demands wouldn't they then make, to ensure that they remained eternally beautiful?

Dottie is Frank's world, his lodestone. He lives with and within her, and would sacrifice any organ or appendage or bodily fluid joyously. As for himself, he knows that he's no longer the well-kept specimen of a man who was first enraptured by her. Only last week on the glassy plains outside Paris, he gave up a good portion of his bone marrow to her, and a third re-grown kidney. The effects of these and other donations, along with all the immune-suppressants he must continually take, leave him thin and weak and dizzy. His hair has long gone, he must wear sunglasses to protect his bleary eyes, and he shuffles hunched and crabways. He realises that he's already starting to look like the creature he tossed over the stern of the *Glorious Nomad*, and that the wonders of the life he's now living cannot last forever.

In the circles in which they move, far removed from the *Glorious Nomad's* ruin-inspecting tribes of meekly departed middle executives, Frank and Dottie's relationship is seen as nothing unusual. As she once said to him in what now seems like a different existence, who now knows or cares about what is legal? Sometimes, when the weakened husks like himself who accompany Dottie and her companions grow close to failing, they head off to live some lesser life for a few weeks, and enjoy the thrill of finding a fresh and willing replacement. They call it *re-crossing the Styx*. It's a new kind of symbiosis, this imprinting, and it strikes Frank as a near-perfect relationship. It's only when the pain and weakness in his thinning bones sometimes get the worst of him, and he gazes around at the golden creatures who surround him, that he wonders who is really dead now, and who is living.

AFTERWORD *ON BEING DARK*

NO WRITER CAN EVER REALLY UNDERSTAND THE EFFECT THEIR WORDS have in the minds of their readers, but it has often been said over the years that the general tone of my writing is "dark".

This assessment surprised me when I first began to come across it, back in the times when I made an effort to read rather than avoid my reviews. After all, I don't think many of us devote much thought to wondering how the tones and moods in which we view the world differ from those of others; we simply see and interpret things as we believe they truly are. Neither do I think of myself as a particularly gloomy person. Quiet, sure. Thoughtful, maybe. But pessimistic, or miserable, or prone, even, to depression? No. Not that I don't love the strange and the gothic, and I am at least as inclined to watch a horror film as a rom-com. But I love Father Ted and the Simpsons, and revere P G Wodehouse, and I am, as my patient family will attest, a ready source of many stupid jokes. Still, I do accept that we all carry a kind of weather with us, be it sunny or rainy in the world outside, just as in that Crowded House song. And perhaps, although I'd like to think of it as a willingness to deal with the wide range of human experience, my personal weather is a little dark.

When you're writing a story, there's generally—or at least there should be—far too much else going on to worry about the overall mood or world view. Not that the mood and attitude isn't there, of course. And, at least if you have any variety in you as a writer (which, let's face it, some very successful writers don't) it should vary from scene to scene and story to story, as well. But this tone thing, this mood business, is one of those areas that I'd certainly advise anyone who wanted to write fiction to try to ignore, or at least not to dwell on. If a story works, it works.

The best insight I've been able to give myself into the moods and atmospheres which are to be found in my fiction, came from considering the works of other artists in a variety of fields for which, over the years, I've felt the strongest response. Here, again, I'd never really thought of them as being of any particular mood at all, but simply thrilling, liberating, memorable and moving in all their very different ways. My favourite music, for example, runs from Mahler to King Crimson with Richard Thompson and Joni Mitchell and Keith Jarrett along the way. I had to take a few steps back from my normal reaction for me to realise that, just possibly, one of Mahler's death marches, or the slow-rolling mellotrons and dark sunsets of King Crimson's "Starless," could be considered "dark". That, or Donald Sutherland lying juddering to his death in a ruined palazzo in *Don't Look Now*, or Robert de Niro's rictus smile as he lies lost in an opium daze at the end of *Once Upon a Time In America*. Or, come to think of it, the fate of the two lovers in Keith Robert's *Weihnachtsabend*. For me, they all just feel *right*.

Then there's death, which has also always felt pretty right to me as an artistic subject to explore, from Elgar's *Dream of Gerontius* to Led Zeppelin's "In My Time of Dying," with Richard Thompson's "When I Get To the Border," Richard Strauss' *Death and Transfiguration* and Brahms' *German Requiem* thrown in. We all die, of course, and we all grow old. In fact, along with love, and life itself, it's surely the greatest subject of the shared human experience, so to me it's hardly surprising that it should crop up a great deal in my work, or the work of anyone else with any serious pretensions of being a writer. In fact, it's likely that one of the great subconscious appeals of SF to me has always been the way it allows death and all its attendant woes, glories and mysteries to be examined and interrogated from angles which more naturalistic fiction cannot hope to achieve. Robert Silverberg, in his brilliant patch of *Dying Inside* and *Born with the Dead,* which meant and mean so much to me, did little else.

To the extent that I can ever judge these things, I don't imagine, that "Re-Crossing the Styx" is a particularly dark story by my standards. But it clearly is about death, and, even more, about growing old. Which, and as the story probably illustrates, I find the more alarming prospect. I've never been on a cruise, and I'm sure I'm being hard on the people, especially the elderly, who take such holidays. But, with a writer's usual callousness, as the idea of this story seemed to work pretty well with the zombie dead afloat on the *Glorious Nomad*, I was more than happy to ditch any moral qualms and push on.

The trigger for "Re-Crossing the Styx" came from reading the entertaining and beautifully written *Narrow Dog to Indian River* by Terry Darlington, which describes a gloriously foolhardy attempt to navigate the rivers and canals of America's deep south's in an English narrowboat. Something about the evident disgust with which Darlington, a retiree himself, describes the elderly communities he, his wife and his dog encountered in Florida struck a deep chord. That, and I'd been reading a fair amount of classic American crime fiction, and really wanted to try out something resembling a *The Postman Only Rings Twice* scenario where a hapless man gets led by stupid passion into an even stupider crime.

As I was writing, I thought that the story I was telling was twisty and bitter and funny. Although I now suspect that, despite the sunny locales, its hues are also slightly dark.

Sad Songs, With Lots of Drumming

You have to be of a certain age to remember *The White Heather Club*. Back in the times when the TV was still in just one room in the house and you had to wait for it to warm up, vague grey shapes sword-dancing to tiddildy-dee music or singing about speeding bonny boats was what passed for light entertainment. Not that there was any choice, but it was a favourite in our family, my father being a typically nostalgic expat Scotsman. The first record that was bought for me (rather than that supposed landmark; the first you buy yourself) was a single of Andy Stewart's "A Scottish Soldier," which I remember enjoying a great deal. I also liked the theme tune to *The Lone Ranger*, which I didn't then know was Rossini's *William Tell Overture*. That, and Perry Como singing his way through the states of the USA (although I didn't realise that either) in "Oh, What Did Delaware, Boys?"

It's easy to try to shut the doors on the embarrassing things we thought we liked before we really knew about music. The novelty records and one hit wonders. But they're there—they're part of all our heritage—and their influence remains. My coordination is poor to this day, but apparently one of my favourite toddler pursuits was to go into the lounge and bang the poker against the coal scuttle and the fire grate; I've always been a frustrated drummer. I think I can still just about remember the noisy pleasure of those sessions, and perhaps that rat-a-tat martial drumming was the appeal of Andy Stewart's song. That, and the solider dying.

Music was played each day on some big old gramophone as we marched into assembly at infants' school, and again as we stomped around pretending to be dinosaurs or curled up like the seeds of flowers in something called "Music and Movement". I have no clear recollection of what the music was, but it was "improving" and classical, and I reckon it may well have included some of Prokofiev's *Peter and the Wolf*, and the much more jagged *Romeo and Juliet*. He's still a favourite composer. There always did seem to be something about classical music that I found interesting. My next "bought for me" single, actually an EP, came from my elder brother after I'd been to see Disney's *Sleeping Beauty*, which takes its music from Tchaikovsky's ballet. I remember being a bit disappointed as we sat waiting for "the tune" . . . but I also remember how much I liked the nice lady ballet dancer photographed on the cover. One of my pleasures was to dress up in my sister's old ballet costume, and pretend to be a fairy. I even went to school dressed that way once or twice when the occasion seemed to demand it. In those days no one seemed to worry about such behaviour.

After that, up through infants' and on into secondary school, music, and dressing up, took a back seat. I had no great interest in what was becoming the "Top Ten", but listened as most kids then did to *Junior Choice* on the BBC Radio's Light Programme. I enjoyed songs such as "Little White Bull" and "The Ugly Bug Ball" because they told a story, and particularly liked "Puff the Magic Dragon," because it ended so sadly—"dragons live forever, but not so little boys . . . " But my two biggest favourites were "Feed the Birds" from *Mary Poppins*, and "Somewhere Over the Rainbow." Great songs by any standard, and both filled with sad yearning. I suspect that this was the first music to make me cry, and to realise what an oddly glorious feeling that was.

My elder sister, meanwhile, had noticed this group called the Beatles, and I was very happy to dance along with her to the singles she bought and played on our new radiogram that sat in the lounge on the far side of the fireplace from the telly. Jolly, melodic stuff, and Mum and Dad liked the Beatles as well. In fact, everyone seemed to like the Beatles. But that very likeability made me wary. That, or perhaps their songs simply weren't sad enough, and lacked the right kind of drumming. But I played "Rain" on the B side of "Paperback Writer" often, fascinated by the hypnotic way it drawled and jangled. My elder brother's tastes went in the direction of Harry Secombe and Andy Williams, but there was one track on an LP of his that I also played and played. It was from an "original cast" (i.e.—not the people from the movie) recording of *West Side Story*, and was called "The Rumble"—a modern ballet piece, all jagged angles and misshaped chords. Then, and now, it struck me as fresh and sharp and brilliant.

School, being school, still involved random bits of exposure to music. We even used to get so-called "music lessons" each week, for no reason any of us could understand, least of all the teacher. Still, one day he set about demonstrating the capabilities of his nice new stereo by playing us a surprisingly lengthy piece of classical music. To his credit, he explained how this symphony started sadly because the composer had travelled to America without his family, and how it might help if we imagined him arriving on a big steamer into New York harbour, and to try to feel his spirits lifting as he sees the city skyline. I thought this was fabulous stuff, a story told in sound. And there was this churning sadness, those slow drums rolling . . .

A week or so later, I bought my first record with my own money, an LP of Dvorak's *New World Symphony*, and the music was even more fabulous than I remembered. In those carefree days, and I and most of my mates used to go home for lunch from our secondary school. As everyone else was out, I'd take my white bread and mashed banana on a tray into the lounge, turn on the radiogram, and let this music flow around me. This is *it*, I thought. This is something that I love. The sixties had moved on, and my mates were also buying records of their own. Not classical LPs, but singles from the charts by the likes of Herman's Hermits and Sonny and Cher. I didn't have any problem with much of this—I watched *Top of the Pops* just like everyone else—but at the same time I was happy to tell them that it was all a bit . . . well, simple.

So there I was, my head in the clouds and following on Dvorak with Holst's *Planet Suite* and a compilation called *Classical Fireworks* which wasn't quite on the same level. No easy decisions, seeing as LPs cost a lot. I liked being different—I liked liking stuff that other people didn't know or understand or care about. As the radiogram had to remain in its sacred place in the lounge, I was also regularly inflicting my music on the rest of my family, or being told to turn it down, or evicted so they could watch telly. The Beatles, meanwhile, had gone a bit odd, and my sister seemed to have lost interest in them. Another of my random musical experiences at school was when our geography teacher took it upon himself to play their new LP called *Sergeant Pepper's Lonely Hearts Club Band* instead of telling us about towns of the Potteries. I can remember hearing Lennon singing "For the Benefit of Mister Kite," and thinking it was strange and wonderful, and like nothing I'd ever heard, least of all "She Loves You" and those other sugary hits. Not that I bought the record, of course. After all, I only bought classical stuff, didn't I?

I had the radiogram in the lounge mostly to myself now, as my bother had left to get married and my sister was off at university, and my Dad only had a *Black and White Minstrels* LP and some Scottish pipes and drums stuff he played at New Year or when he got sentimental. When my sister returned with a boyfriend in tow, they were gracious enough to take me with them to see a film called *2001: A Space Odyssey*, and my world was changed. Partly, of course, because of the look of the film, and the mystery of whatever story it was telling, but at least as much because of the music. Not just the iconic stuff by the two Strausses, brilliant though that was, but the other, weirder, pieces. When I played one of my mates some Ligeti from the *2001* soundtrack, I remember him commenting that he would, genuinely, rather listen to Mrs Mills on the piano. Which was great as far as I was concerned. More of this strange and wonderful music left just for me.

But, alarmingly, I found that I now rather liked some of the singles from what was now called the "Top Twenty". Between buying Richard Strauss tone poems and exploring Karl Nielsen's symphonies, my secret shame was that I thought some of Deep Purple's stuff, and Alice Cooper's, not to mention Cream and the Stones, was actually pretty good. I liked the drumming, and the riffs, and the sense of risk, and the jangling, twisting melodies. And then there was David Bowie. Not because of the way he dressed—my own dressing-up days were behind me—but because of the music. I particularly loved "Life on Mars," with its soaring wistfulness, and "Space Oddity," because of Major Tom dying.

Maybe this pop and rock thing had something going for it after all. Not the stuff you heard all the time on daytime Radio One, of course, but by now I was listening to John Peel as I played with my Airfix soldiers on

Sunday afternoons, and enjoying a new, different, sense of exclusivity. I never bought singles, but the first rock LP I bought was Emerson Lake and Palmer's *Pictures at an Exhibition*. The classical link was obvious, but at least as important was that it came in Island's cheaper Help series instead of at full price. That, and the cool gatefold cover. But it was great, and I absorbed it with the same edge-of-the-seat enthusiasm I'd had for Dvorak, Richard Strauss and Ligeti. I loved the shrieking, atonal bits where Keith Emerson attacked his keyboard. And then there was the drumming . . .

Ah! Drumming. It wasn't something you got much of in classical music. Even Holst's *Mars* doesn't have the same propulsion as Karl Palmer at full tilt. My next LP, and the first live act I saw, was the Mahavishnu Orchestra. Drumming aplenty there, and brilliant solo playing. One of my favourite live musical memories is of John McLaughlin and Jean-Luc Ponty trading fours (although I didn't then know what it was called) on the stage of the Birmingham Odeon. That, and Michael Walden's thirty minute drum solo. For a long while after that, by now a sixth-former, then a college student, I bought complex jazz-edged rock music, often with very little singing. This was the era of prog rock, and there was plenty of this stuff to go around, although to my mind, as ever a musical snob, a lot of it was still a bit simple-minded. The Floyd, for example, who I liked for a while, at least until the *NME* laid into them for being lazily commercial. Not to mention Genesis. And as for Supertramp . . . Actually, I secretly loved my tape of a friend's *Crime of the Century* because it was such a sad album.

From here on in, it probably all gets much more predictable. Step forward Henry Cow. Step forward Keith Jarrett and pretty much anything on the ECM label. That, and Steely Dan, and Joni Mitchell, along with a slow return to the classical stuff I'd always loved, especially the great, sad, romantic composers, combined with all the folk, ambient and *avant-garde* music I began listening to. Thanks in major part to Richard and Linda Thompson's brilliantly pessimistic *I Want to See the Bright Lights Tonight*, which starts with a song about suicide and ends with the fabulously bleak "The Great Valerio," I finally realised that there was elegance and profundity in seemingly simple music. But probably the last great *aha* moment in my musical life came when I purchased, for no exact reason I can now remember, a copy of King Crimson's *Red*. I already had *In the Court of the*

Crimson King, but, if you discount the great cover and "Twenty First Century Schizoid Man," that's a surprisingly quiet album. I took *Red* from its sleeve, opened up the record player, which still sat in my parents' lounge opposite the telly, and played it, and played it, and played, and played it. Again. And again. I could play it now. In fact, I will . . .

The prowling thunder of the title track. The jagged, free-form of "Providence." Above all, the churning mellotron chords which begin "Starless," with that yearning guitar theme and those bleak lyrics about grey hope and sunsets that quietens to a riff which builds over clashing drums until the main theme returns in a howl of saxophones. Complex, intelligent music, played with a ferocious mixture of joy, anger and passion. Maybe it helped that Fripp and his band were imploding. Who knows? To me this is still, and always will be, earth-shatteringly brilliant. I could cry. I *am* crying. It all seems a very long way from Andy Stewart's "A Scottish Soldier." But then, I always did like sad songs, with lots of drumming.

THE TRAVELLER AND THE BOOK

L OST, thirsty and exhausted, the traveller crawled across the desert. When the sun was at its highest, he came across a book half-buried in the sand. He thought at first that it was an illusion, then almost laughed to see that its pages were empty, although they became smeared with the blood of his scabbed fingers as they crackled in the wind. In his delirium, he shaped the smears into letters which formed the word *WATER*. Then, still clutching the book, he crawled on.

Somehow, evening came. Somehow, the traveller remained alive. Although he was certain that the shape he saw ahead was nothing but a trick of the fading light, he dragged himself toward it, and his hands encountered what seemed to be the curved stones of a low wall. Impossible. But still, the traveller hauled himself to the wall's lip, and found himself looking down into the cool waters of a well.

In a fever of thirst, he lowered his head and drank. He knew he should only sip at first. But that was impossible. He drenched himself. And drank. And drank. The pains which came to the traveller that night were incredible. So was the cold. He did not expect to see another morning. But it came, and the well was still there. And so—fluttering a little way off in the sand—was the book.

He drank more cautiously this time. Tried to use what shade the well offered to protect himself from the heat. But the sun was rising and the shadow was shrinking. If he was to survive, he knew he would have to move on. He picked up the book. Turned to the next blank page and nibbled at a fingertip until it began to bleed. Again he shaped the word

WATER. Then he added *FOOD.* Nothing changed. The well remained, his belly ached, and now there was no shelter from the sun. Clutching the book, the traveller stumbled on.

Another hopeless day. Nothing but the deepening pains of hunger to go with his returning thirst. By the time the sun began to set, he was certain that the well had been nothing but a dream. Even when he saw a shape on the horizon, he knew that he had done nothing but complete an aimless circle. The well certainly looked the same, even if the arrangement of its stones seemed slightly different. In the reddening light beside it—and surely this was the fruit of his delirium—lay a loaf of bread. His senses swooned at its scent, but this time, he tried to be cautious. Even then, he almost choked. Then, shivering, exhausted, and clutching his book, the traveller fell asleep.

Another freezing night. When morning finally came the traveller decided he must make better plans. It was hard to write with the blood of a bitten finger, but he managed to shape the word *SHELTER* to follow *WATER* and *FOOD.* After he had picked the last breadcrumbs from the sand, he took his book and headed on. The day proved hot and long and as difficult as any he'd experienced. In many ways, it was worse, for now he was tormented by hope. But once again as evening came, he saw a shape on the horizon. There was a well, but this time a scrap of grey canvas fluttered beside the loaf of bread. As night settled, he wrapped himself in it against the cold.

Next morning the process of writing proved even more difficult as, after inscribing the same painful words as before, he added *INK* and *PEN.* Using the canvas as a kind of cloak and clutching his book, he headed on across the desert. That evening, exhausted though he was, he scanned the horizon with something like anticipation, and his cracked lips broke to form a smile when he saw the shape of a well. Laid beside the bread and the fluttering canvas, he found a brass-nibbed pen, and a small pot of ink. After he'd drank from the well, and chewed at his bread, in a few quick sentences and a shaking hand, he described a cottage.

Another dawn. The pen and the ink, he took with him, although the second canvas was too heavy to carry and he left it beside the latest well. The hours, his legs, dragged and ached intolerably. He even considered simply sitting down where he was. But how was he then to reach his cottage, if it lay a full day's journey ahead? He carried on walking until he saw a larger shape against the evening horizon. Then he broke into a run. The cottage was a rough place. Its roof sagged. Its boards creaked. But there was food—again, it was merely bread—and a proper pump and a bucket which he could use to wash himself, and a hard old bed. Such was the traveller's exhaustion that he fell asleep without thinking of his book. Even when morning came, he toyed with the idea of staying here for a day or two. But everything about the place was rudimentary, and he was sick of dry bread and water, and he was sure he could write of something better than this.

That day's journey across the desert was made easier by anticipation, and the place he came to at evening was a proper house, with a vegetable garden, and good boots and decent clothes laid beside a soft bed, a larder well-provisioned with wine and food, and the traveller was grateful for what he'd created, even if he ate and drank too much and made himself ill. When morning came, he was slow to rise. After all, he was sick of journeying, and he had more than enough here to satisfy his needs. There were even seeds which he could plant a vegetable the garden . . . but no. Sat at his rough table, the traveller flicked through his book to the next blank page and began to write. He described a much grander house, with warm lights that would glow out to welcome him, and a pretty garden filled with the scents of flowers, and a bath foaming with hot water.

That day, the traveller strode briskly across the desert. And there it was—the glowing lights, the many tall chimneys, the garden, all just as he'd written. That night, drowsed by wine as he lay in his bath, the traveller decided that he would stay here for a few days. But he felt dissatisfaction begin to arise and was thinking of his book even as he pulled on his bathrobe.

So, for many days of travelling, it went. Soon, the traveller was sleeping in palaces, lulled to sleep by the hiss of fountains and the coo of doves. Each night, especially in the first flush of his delight at the new glories he'd created, he told himself that here, finally, was a place he could rest. But there were always small disappointments, and better—or at least newer—

ideas formed. Each morning, as he looked across the vistas he had created, he knew that he would have to head on.

For a while, the desert he crossed remained as pitiless as ever. But why, he began to wonder, should he not describe the features of his journey as well as his destination? Soon, the traveller was able to stride along smooth pathways amid the shadowed green of hills. But why was he walking at all? At least until this restlessness ceased and he had finally created what he was looking for, what other than his own stupidity was stopping him from describing a wagon, and two good horses to pull it along? It was as he journeyed in this way, more easily and at a greater speed, but often stopping to admire the pretty scenes he'd created along the way, that the traveller realised that he of all people should not have to go to the trouble of driving a wagon when he could surely create a someone to do it for him.

The task was easily accomplished, although the traveller thought the man to be a sullen and dull sort, and nothing like his best work. He left him behind the following morning and set out through the gates of his latest creation alone. Next day, he described a fine carriage, and a much less surly driver, and two liveried footmen to go with him, whose wit was far more to the traveller's taste, even if he'd heard almost all their jokes before. Still, the traveller found he grew to like their companionship, even if their ribald talk stirred other needs he'd not felt since he first began to cross the desert alone.

There followed a time of which the traveller was not proud. He grew dissolute and fat as he sated every conceivable appetite, and many others of which he'd never previously thought. He was entertained, fed and pleasured by willing legions of all sexes, constructions and hues. He dwelled within the catacombs of crystal mountains far vaster than the desert he'd once struggled to cross. He rode upon the backs of beautiful harpies, and coupled with them in midair. Many times, such was the feasting and carousing, that he no longer moved on each morning to some new and even grander creation, but this was mainly due to the effects of over-indulgence rather than any lasting satisfaction with where he was. For he was still a traveller, and he still yearned to improve on his creations, and he knew, if only because of a creeping but increasing sense of disgust, that he must move on. The methods of his journey were now more complex. He found, for example, that it was both possible to stay in one place, and to travel as well. If you created a great sea filled with many islands, for example, you could sail in the grandest of all possible ships surrounded by courtiers, courtesans and sycophants. He made ships of the air, as well, and continents of cloud, and looked down upon the vast and splendid patchworks of his creation, and wondered why it still wasn't enough.

Finally, the traveller reached a conclusion. He'd had enough of travelling. In fact, it was the very act of travelling that was making him into the perennially dissatisfied creature he still was. He was running out of space in his book. It was time for him to make proper use of all that he'd learned, and employ his powers of description to create one place, and to learn to live there, even if not every single aspect of it was entirely perfect.

The traveller thought.

The traveller planned.

With a diamond pen, using exquisite ink, seated at a fine table in a beautiful room surrounded by fabulous views, the traveller used up his book's last precious pages to describe a city which represented the apotheosis of all he had learned. It was glorious, of course. Filled with marble thoroughfares and glass-spired buildings, threaded with rivers and islanded with gardens of infinite delight. But he knew that pomp and beauty alone could never be enough. So he created slums and industrial districts, and surrounded his city with forests to its north, mountains to its east, and a limitless expanse of desert to its south and west. Then, he set about the most difficult task of all.

First, the traveller created a whole variety of advisors, merchants, craftsmen, bankers, engineers and businessmen. To this he added actors, artists—even writers. Not to mention, although he did, whores and cutthroats and hermits and beggars and every other kind of street flotsam. He created composers of genius, dancers of supernatural agility and politicians of incredible deceit. Some people he made brilliant, and others he made stupid. Some were handsome and many were ugly. Finally, the traveller set about creating a family for himself. Children, of course, of varied but complementary appearance, sex, ability and temperament to keep him interested and entertained. Last came his wife, helpmate, confidante and companion—the woman of his dreams made flesh. In this last labour, the traveller worked especially hard. He had long known how hard it was to settle on one thing when you could have many, but it had never been this difficult before. The colour of an eye, the set of a cheekbone, the curve of a breast, the lilt of a voice ... But finally the traveller was almost content, and, although he felt he had written neatly and economically, there was only half a page of his book left. The traveller stared at this last blank space for some time. Then, he smiled and raised his pen.

The traveller set out next morning for what he was certain was the last time. For all its beauty and grandeur, the place he was leaving now seemed homely, and was almost sorry to see it go, and perhaps would have lingered, had he not known what lay ahead. In this nostalgic mood, he elected to set out on foot rather than use any of the other more elaborate means of transport he'd devised, and it was past midday by the time he'd left the last of his old creations behind. Then came dark forests, which were just as he'd described them. Clutching his book, almost fearful, the traveller quickened his pace. Then, just as evening thickened, there came a glint on the horizon, and the trees bowed back and a widening path showed the way.

Now, the traveller thought, my new life finally begins. But he did not run, for it was important that he maintain every kind of dignity. He heard the blare of trumpets, and saw the great, glittering walls of a fabulous city with open gates set to welcome him. The citizens began cheering as rumour of his arrival swept along the thoroughfares, and the air shimmered as he entered to pealing bells. The traveller strode on though showers of cast petals and impromptu songs, nodding occasionally towards the faces of those he recognised in the crowds. But he'd been a king before in many other cities, and much of this was almost wearingly familiar. Here, soon, he would become something more ...

There, at the far end of the greatest of imaginable avenues, reared a vast and empty temple to a mysterious god these people did not yet know. Still, the traveller was already their king, and here was his wife, the very image of grace with all their children clustered around her in pleasing variety, and for now that would be enough. After all, these things could not be rushed, and he had been careful to give his subjects free will.

The traveller fell into his family's embrace, and soon established himself in what was undoubtedly the finest palace he'd ever described. He hid away his book. He began living his new life. There were many happy days. He found the ebb and flow of things, the challenges, triumphs, vicissitudes and disappointments, almost entirely to his taste. There were moments, certainly, when he was troubled by the self-serving deviousness of his advisors, and even the unpredictable feistiness of his wife. But that was to be expected, and the traveller was prepared to be patient—at least, for a while. He also thought his children to be charming and entertaining. But—and here was something he'd stupidly failed to consider—he was astonished by the rapidity with which they grew. That, and how much they argued. Once, in a particularly vexed mood, he even went to the secret chamber where he kept his book and studied its crowded pages, wondering whether, even if there was no room left for him to add anything, he might make a few small deletions. But he closed the book firmly, for in that direction lay only madness and destruction. What was important was that he lived his life as regally as possibly as he waited for the even greater elevation which was certain to come. Sometimes, dressed in hooded rags, he went to stand on the steps outside the great, empty temple around which the city's life thrummed. The people hardly seemed to notice the place—or him, for that matter. They took him for granted even when he strode amongst them in his finest pomp. And as for his wife, who looked at one of his most handsome and devious courtiers with suspicious regard, and his bickering children—he sometimes wanted to stop everything and explain the true nature of what he was. But would they believe him? He doubted it. At least, not without some kind of sign.

The traveller's family and advisors were puzzled when he announced his intention of going on a journey. Not that they seemed to disapprove of the idea. In fact, he suspected that some—his wife included—relished the prospect of his absence. But he would show them. Without him, they were nothing, an empty page, lost and ungoverned. With such thoughts still swirling in his head, the traveller set out through the very gates that had once welcomed him.

He thought he might visit those great mountains—the idea of the infinite desert he'd created to the south and west still made him shudder—but instead he followed the path that led back through the forest. If he kept this way for a day or so, he would reach the place he'd left previously, of which he had many fond memories. But the forest was deep and dark, and the path soon dwindled, and the traveller found that he was lost, and huddled amid dry leaves beneath an oak as evening fell. Next morning, although he was no longer sure of his direction, the traveller headed on. The corridors of the forest loomed, but at least there were nuts and berries on the bushes, and a stream to quench his thirst, and shelter from the sun. By that evening, though, hearing distant howls, the traveller would have settled for any kind of habitation. Instead, there was only cold and dark. Still, next morning dawned prettily with mist and birdsong. Studying the fallen boughs, and ropes of vine, and the nearby brook with its glinting stones, the traveller set to work as he realised that here was everything he needed to make a shelter.

Through several seasons, the traveller lived in this way. He liked the simple peace of this place, and was almost happy. Always something in need of doing—fires to be lit, seeds to be planted in the clearing he'd created—and he often whistled as he went about his work. Once, he was attacked by a bear, but by now he had fashioned himself a staff, and was able to fend the beast off. In a dream that night, as he lay in his rough cottage, the traveller saw his city and his temple, and knew it was time for his return.

He had become skilled in the ways of the forest. By heading against the flow of the stream and noting the lie of the moss, he knew his way was true. He cut a very different figure, certainly, to the grand-seeming man who had arrived in his city before. Now, he was long-bearded, and wore homespun clothes, and carried a whittled staff. He had been though much, and felt that he had acquired great wisdom, which he would soon impart to the people of his city, who would doubtless then worship him for what he truly was. After all, wasn't that the way these things worked, even in books other than the one he'd written himself?

It was all as he'd hoped. The city gates were open. The streets were filled with merry-making and cheers. His temple was no longer ignored, but seemed to be the centre of everything. Had he overdone things with all this grandeur? the traveller wondered as he limped toward it up the great thoroughfare. No, he decided, he had not. Odd, though, how he was ignored as he climbed the steps. But his appearance was very different and—wonder of wonders—the temple's walls were covered with vast friezes depicting his many creations. The ships, the seas, the castles, the clouds . . . Even the traveller felt awed as he gazed up at them. At the far, high altar, many clerics awaited. Serenaded by hymns, the traveller shuffled toward them. And here, at the highest point, a last few marble steps led up to a kind of dais, where the traveller was certain he would now be worshipped. But why was there some kind of display case up there instead of a throne, and why were these priests holding him back?

The Book . . . Book . . . Book . . . The murmured echo passed down through the temple, and the traveller shook his head when he saw what lay upon the dais. This was absurd. "That book!" he shouted. "It's just words on the pages of something I once found. I wrote—" His staff was wrenched from him and jabbed into his belly as cries of horror at this blasphemy rose up. Then he was dragged from the dais, out of the temple and down into the streets where many kicks and curses were aimed in his direction until someone intervened.

"Why are they so angry?" he muttered, wiping blood from his mouth as the crowd around them jeered.

His wife crouched down, looking almost as beautiful as she'd always been, even if her eyes were cornered with something close to disgust.

"That book," he said, but more quietly, "it's nothing but *words*. Without me—"

"But that's *why*," she said, gripping his arms. "I found the Book in a hidden room in our palace and discovered how we, all of us in this city, are written of within it, along with many other things beside. I discovered that the Book is the source all life, truth and wisdom. It's true that you were once king of this city in our Times of Transgression, but now we see clearly, and know that the Book is everything. The reason these people hate you so terribly, my old ex-husband, is that the only thing that's lacking from the Book is you . . . "

For once, the traveller was lost of words. Now, she was dragging him up, hauling him into one of the city's grimmest back streets where a surly-looking driver was seated on a wagon.

" . . . if you go quickly," she said as she helped him climb onto its back, "and cover yourself with this old sack, you may yet escape with your life."

He did as she bid and curled himself up as a whip was cracked and the wagon rumbled off. Although his aches were many and the journey deeply uncomfortable, he found himself drifting in and out of dreams of great buildings, humble cottages, high mountains, vast forests, limpid wells . . . He had no idea where he was being taken, nor how long his journey took. All the traveller knew when he was finally abandoned was that the ground he lay upon was sandy, and that the sun that blazed down upon him was very hot.

I CAN'T RECALL EXACTLY WHICH FICTION MAGAZINE EDITOR IT WAS WHO told me that they regularly received the most God-awful stuff from a variety of greatly respected writers, but I remember finding it deeply encouraging. Not just because it meant there was still hope for me, if even so-and-so can write tedious nonsense, but because I strongly believe that the ability, or at least a willingness, to write rubbish is a talent that all writers need to develop.

Of course, and as we all know to our cost, some of this rubbish ends up getting published, especially if the work of the writer concerned will sell by the skipload irrespective of quality, and even more so if they happen to be dead. Poor J. R. R. Tolkien and Jane Austen have no say in how their juvenilia and shopping lists are now being foisted on us, but living authors also suffer, if suffer is the word, from the malady of being very prolific but lacking proper editorial—and self—control. Step forward, and it hurts me to say this, because I'm also a huge admirer, Stephen King. And, dare I also say it, Joyce Carol Oates.

Not that I'm suggesting that all writers—especially those with less talent than King or Oates, which is pretty much all of us—should ditch any efforts at quality control, or look merely to others to filter what they produce, but I do think that the self-censorship which discourages risk is a far greater enemy for most writers than the problem of inflicting literary diarrhoea on a an unsuspecting public. I, certainly, have learned that it's important to try things out without any great cares or expectations, and continually remind myself not to worry about quality in an early draft.

In other words, you have to try to train yourself to just give it a bash and push on—to remember that the cautious draughtsman, the one who draws a line and then rubs it out and tries to draw a better version of the same line, will be left with nothing but a smudged and dirtied sheet of paper. It's all too easy for a writer, bogged down by issues of quality and merit and, worse still, perfection, to spend whole days, and possibly entire decades, seeming to work on something but ending up with nothing but a worn-out and empty page. Word processing, with its easy deletions and changes, is particularly dangerous when it comes to this. Which is why I most often strive to write my rubbishy first drafts by hand, just as I've done with most of these afterwords.

I have, I admit, often written stuff which felt okay as it came out but, for one reason or another, was simply tedious, or awful, or just didn't work. As to submitting this rubbish for publication, and then even getting it published . . . Perhaps you, reader, are the best judge of that, at least when it comes to what you find in this book. But one of the other skills writers need to cultivate is the ability to assess their own work with something resembling critical detachment. You should never attempt to do this, of course, as you're writing, but some time after when your recollection of what you actually wrote has started to fade. Which could take days, weeks or years.

This self judgement and detachment is obviously partial and flawed. My own writing can still catch me on a good or a bad day, and there's no real way, as I say in my afterword to "Re-Crossing the Styx," that I or any writer can ever really tell what the effect of what we've written will be on other readers. But, at least in this respect, I'll admit that I find it helpful to have had at least some success as a writer.

Knowing, or at least kidding myself, that I've written some reasonably good stuff in the past, means that the question I can ask as I look at a draft isn't, *Is this any good?* but, *Is this, in its own rough and different way, anywhere close to what I was aiming for?* I can well remember, though, the many years when I simply had no sense of whether what I was capable of writing was any good, and longed to somehow *know*. Or, better still, be told. Of course, there is no empirical answer to the question of quality, and I'm sure we can all think of writers who clearly can't write at all, yet still seem to do pretty well. I guess the thing that I and other writers strive to develop is a critical facility that's cut with a mixture of bitter experience and fragile self-confidence. That, and the essential arrogance which anyone who wants to foist the fruits of their imagination on others needs to possess.

The "Traveller and the Book" started out with a rough idea, which goes back decades, of a perfect tourist guidebook which actually created the places it described. I don't think I even started to try to write that out—it felt too flimsy—but the idea slowly evolved into something in which a stranger visits a town and finds that their offhand descriptions of the place in their travel diary are mirrored by what they then find. This one, I did try out for a few paragraphs. There was someone on a road and there was a town ahead, with the whole thing being perhaps situated in one of those imaginary central European countries which have been used for centuries by writers who know very little about central Europe. But, again, it seemed too slight. There was no sense of conflict or drive, and I felt that if I tried to inject some by introducing other characters or incidents, the whole concept would probably start to lose focus.

More recently, though, some very slowly circling sub-routine in my subconscious must have picked up the idea again, and identified a Borgesian, fairy tale element (as by then I'd probably read Borges). Not a great insight, really, but enough that when, one day, I just sat down and decided to make myself write something for the hell of it, the idea of a traveller and a book came together in a way that broadly seemed to work. Or at least, didn't immediately fall apart. I wrote the thing out in longhand over the next two or three days in, it has to be admitted, no great fever of inspiration. More, so I reckoned, to finally knock the whole stupid thing finally on the head than to create a workable story. Then I left it, ignored and unread, for about a year, and came back to it more out of the feeling of duty you might get when revisiting a not-particularly beloved aunt than with any great anticipation.

But, although the story lacked focus or any clear ending, I was enthused encouraged by what I found. The dramatic tension, of course, lay not so much in the feelings of the main character, or even what he does, but in the increasingly extravagant development of the idea of the whole world equalling the book itself. It was, or could be, the kind of story I recognised, but had rarely ever managed to write. Once I'd worked that out, the route toward a circular ending, with the traveller back in the desert, suddenly seemed as obvious to me as the realisation that Hector Douglas' bag was empty, Not a surprise at all, in fact, but simply an acknowledgement of the seeming inevitability of how a story of this particular kind should work.

It now occurs to me that "The Traveller and the Book" is, in its way, a purer, better example of what might usually be termed SF than almost anything else found in this collection, for all its determinedly fairy-tale tone. It's certainly more openly about concepts and ideas than, say, "Re-Crossing the Styx," which, despite all its various technologies is really about death, aging, and arrogance undone. Maybe (and a little unusually; see my essay "I've Got this Idea for a Story . . .") there's just one main idea in "The Traveller and the Book," but I'd like to think that I've managed to wring as many variations out of it as I possibly could. A kind of high-wire act, in other words, which I certainly wouldn't have achieved if I'd paused as I was writing out the piece in longhand to look down and wonder if it was any good.

I'VE GOT THIS IDEA FOR A STORY ...

MOST writers get approached now and then by non-writers who say they have an idea for a story—or, more likely, a best-selling novel. The idea itself is often so excitingly new and valuable that it can barely be hinted at, for which small mercy the writer is quietly grateful. I suppose it's just possible that someone who's never previously written fiction might have hit upon something which will surprise and delight the world, just as it's possible that, through some theoretical quantum fluctuation of matter, you and I may now both find ourselves instantly transported to Venice. But the truth is that "ideas for stories" are rarely that surprising or original, and that most great, or even mediocre, fiction is a clever rehash of things which have been done before.

I don't mean to say that writers aren't continually and often obsessively on the look out for new ideas, and treasure and nurture the ones they find. But (and seeing as you and I probably aren't currently stranding in the shadow of Saint Mark's) it's necessary to accept as a writer that you're turning over stones which have been looked under before, and gathering up treasures which will probably seem trite or at least unexceptional in the cold light of another day.

The real trick isn't to discover something new to the world of literature, but to find something which feels fresh and interesting to you. If you try to find out whether something similar has been done before, the chances are that, one way or another, it probably has. Frankenstein wasn't the first man-made automaton, there were vampires long before Dracula, stories of love and loss go back to antiquity, as do those of hidden identity ... and don't even get me started on Harry Potter. But, if the idea interests and intrigues you, that's what matters. And rather like the old joke about being able to fake sincerity, if you can convince yourself that you're onto something, you are.

This isn't a recipe for rehashes and unoriginality. Nor is it a counsel for cynicism and doom. Neither, I have to add, are "ideas" anything like the be-all and end-all of writing fiction, as some non-writers seem to assume. Many other skills, which need practice and determination, along with some innate ability, are required. But without the germs of ideas, most of these other skills are of little use.

So how, at least from the viewpoint of this particular writer, does the whole ideas business work?

ONE IDEA IS RARELY ENOUGH

After the initial enthusiasm for an idea has died down (and it will) the next thing you need to do is to look around for others. I plan to avoid any detailed discussion of what an "idea for a story" is. It can be a person, a setting, a particular scene, a picture, a painting, a piece of music, an odd feeling, an atmosphere, an item on the news, something overheard, a nugget of experience, or the eternal SF trope of "What if . . . ". The key thing, most likely, is that it triggers the urge to write.

Simply by listing these things, it becomes apparent that quite a few of them are necessary to almost any piece of fiction, and will then need to be developed and expanded and added to if they're going to work. That wet camping holiday in France, some character in a book you're reading and an on-off interest in medieval churches may create what feels like the interesting beginnings of a story, but in itself they probably won't be enough. Neither are the twists and surprises that often resolve a story usually the crucial element when it comes to ideas; as the way many of the stories in this collection evolved demonstrate, such things often only make themselves known to the writer much later on.

Are these things all ideas, anyway, or mere ingredients? And are ideas "things", or mere abstract concepts? I really don't know. What I do know is that you need a great many of them to make up the fabric of even the shortest story, let alone a novel, and that fiction sucks up ideas the way blotting paper sucks up ink, or watching *The Jeremy Kyle Show* consumes all optimism for humanity and any sense of self-worth.

SF AND IDEAS

SF is commonly thought of as being a fiction of ideas. It certainly helps those of us who sometimes try to write it that there's a lot more new stuff going on and being discovered (or refuted) in science and technology than in the areas of knowledge a writer of, say, exclusively historical fiction might expect to encounter. But clearly a theory, concept or gadget, real or invented, can't be dramatised entirely on its own. Nor should a writer aim to take too obvious a route. Setting a story about cold fusion in a power station, putting a new weapon in the middle of a battlefield, or setting meditation-assisted levitation in an ashram, all make for a pretty thin soup. Sure, there was a time in the genre when pipe-smoking professors worked with the help of their glamorous assistants on experiments which went interestingly wrong, but those days, at least if you exclude parody, are long gone. At the very least, a writer needs to accept that taking a straight route into the laboratory, the observatory or the high-tech factory complex to dramatise some interesting twist of science or technology is setting the bar for originality either very high—or, more probably, extremely low.

As for the many books in the SF genre which are said to be "brimming with ideas", I do think that the genre's approach (and the sort of reviewers who come up with that kind of cliché) often gets tangled up in a misguidedly narrow sense of how ideas, in all their potential breadth and confusion and complexity, are viewed and can be used. To take a writer I love, Douglas Adams, whose work certainly brims with ideas, it's part of his brilliance that he manages to channel them through such a sharp and narrow focus, and often leaps from one to the next so quickly we scarcely have time to wonder what the last one really meant or how it would really work. There's a lot to be gained from this sort of scattergun approach, but there's a lot to be lost as well.

Some ideas simply wouldn't stand up to more than a brief mention without collapsing, whereas others might gain power and resonance through being expanded and explored. Adams' trick is to repeatedly leave us wondering which is true, but many lesser writers in the SF genre throw ideas around far more thoughtlessly, or resort to the sort of technobabble which even I, as a scientifically literate layman, find hard to follow, and then generally end up wondering why on earth I should. Is this really a literature of ideas? It can certainly work as a means of expressing how strange our universe is, but for me it's depth and interesting tangents rather than shallow breadth that really counts.

The real trick for me, the real *aha*, comes from managing to combine something I've read about genetic crop engineering in *New Scientist* with, say, the plot of *The Man in the Iron Mask*. And even that won't be enough.

ODD COMBINATIONS

Genuine freshness and excitement in writing comes not from one idea, but intriguing combinations of many of them taken from a wide variety of surprising sources. Apart from anything else, you're considerably lengthening the odds on someone else having done the thing you're planning to do before—or at least only a few of them, and perhaps not in quite the same way. Then, of course, you have to decide how many ideas you really want to throw in, and how you use them. "Literary" fiction tends to combine ideas and themes in a more complex way. "Popular" fiction, on the other hand, tends to use ideas more straightforwardly, and to take those ideas from a narrower range. John Updike's *Rabbit* novels, for example, or Shakespeare's plays, somehow manage to wrestle with a great deal of the human condition, whereas Ian Fleming's James Bond novels, for all their many glossy locations, are much more one-note. I should add that I love all these writers almost equally, and that this isn't a judgement of quality or worth. In fact, doing something very similar over and over again and yet somehow keeping it interesting is at least as brilliant an achievement as continually exploring something different.

FINDING IDEAS—AND RUNNING OUT OF THEM

Having established that ideas are many things, and that you need lots of them, and that they need to be combined in fresh, contrasting ways, and that different writers handle them very differently, doesn't get us very much closer to dealing with how they arise in the first place.

Most of us who nurture hopes of being a writer have a few ideas for stories which have sprung up in our heads and which we feel we'd like, one day, to try out. At this point the actual process of how they came about is generally of much less concern than how to turn them into readable fiction. Many of them will have been with us for years, have perhaps come with us from childhood or favourite books and films, and it's part of the rite of passage of becoming a writer to discover how hard it is to actually get the bloody things to work.

But, if you're determined enough, you may eventually tip beyond the level of aptitude which allows you to express what you want to say on the page. You may even find yourself writing, and even selling, on a regular basis. Meanwhile, though, this store of ideas, impressions, feelings which you've been tapping into will have been running down. It's my theory that most writers who do well for a while and then falter or stop entirely have found themselves running short of ideas and don't know how to deal with the problem. That, or they've finally realised how poorly most writers get paid.

As someone who's been writing and selling for getting on for thirty years, I long ago had to accept that the storehouse of ideas I grew up with or just happen to be struck by isn't enough, and needs regular topping up, maintenance and encouragement. So, what are you supposed to do as a writer to keep the things popping up? First of all, and pretty obviously, you need to expose yourself to the ideas of others. Films, TV, blogs, plays, song lyrics, conversations, work and travel are all important sources. Events that directly affect you and the changes and challenges of life are important as well, although real experience, the person I've met or whatever I've been through in life, rarely works for me as a direct source of ideas for my fiction. Reality's un-malleable. It's already what it is. Writers do, of course, endlessly write about themselves and their lives, but most of it is given a sideways slant and is heavily disguised, even from themselves.

Another thing to say about my impromptu and incomplete list of obvious sources is that you need to keep trying to widen your tastes and interests, and should never stop doing so. Reading the same author, watching the same kind of film, visiting the same places, listening to the same kind of music, talking to the same friends, are all recipes for stagnation, no matter how enjoyable all those experiences might be. Sure, we all have our guilty pleasures, be it rereading Sherlock Holmes stories or watching reruns of *Friends*, but new voices, new ways of saying and seeing things, are crucial, especially when it comes to reading. Even if the author you're enjoying and returning to is as indubitably brilliant as, say, Ann Tyler or Stephen Jay Gould, you still need to move on. Above all, you need to keep exposing yourself to plenty of fresh voices in fiction which, far more than non-fiction books and articles on science, history and travel, will always tell you much more about the world.

THE NURTURING INSTINCT

I'm conscious that the sort of attitude I've described so far, this desire for new experience, is hardly the exclusive territory of writers. Any person of intellectual ambition would surely feel much the same. But this is an area in which I think writers train themselves to deal with things a little differently.

Most of us are struck with odd, stupid or clever, thoughts as we bumble through our days. What would it be like to actually be that poor sod at the other end of your broadband help line, for example. Or what would happen if the big information companies like Sky and Virgin really took over the world. And then we tend to throw those thoughts into our mental rubbish bin, and they're forever lost. Writers, on the other hand, train themselves to pay more attention to these passing thoughts, and to seek them out, and nurture them, and encourage them to hang around.

When I say that writers train themselves to do this, I'm using more than a turn of phrase. Modern research on brain development and function has proved beyond question that repeating the same or similar mental processes will encourage the part of the mind which is being used to grow stronger and more proficient. This is also intuitively correct—otherwise, how do we learn to drive, or play the piano? The process also works with stroke victims who are able to persuade a different part of their brain to take over a function which has been degraded in another part.

This process is called neuroplasticity, and, when it comes to recognising and developing ideas, it's a really useful mental trait. But neuroplasticity also has a downside. In much the same way that fresh thought pathways can be strengthened in positive new ways, redundant and over-used processes can also leave you stuck in a rut. So, if you want to write, and find fresh ideas, and continue writing, you need to keep testing and challenging yourself with new ways of writing and thinking. Otherwise, the very things which worked so well a year or two back will become ingrained and repetitive. If the idea of neuroplasticity sounds interesting, by he way, I'd strongly recommend *The Brain That Changes Itself* by Norman Doidge.

KEEP A RECORD

Most writers maintain some kind of notebook—although I managed to get through to my forties without really making much use of the ones I occasionally bought. Some writers have whiteboards, or index cards. These days others use apps and programs. For all I know, there may be some who have each new idea that strikes them tattooed on some part of their body. One way or another, what with expensive Moleskine notebooks and multi-coloured highlighters and different kinds of indexing systems, this aspect of ideas-generation can easily acquire a fetishistic mystique.

To be honest, I used to feel guilty about not keeping a notebook, and less the "real writer" as a result. Although I do have a notebook now, or rather a whole mess of them, and also have a whiteboard on the wall in my study, and am continually compiling lists of questions, I've come to realise that all this organisation, or disorganisation, is only a means to an end, and is exactly as useful as I, the writer, find it to be. I'm also wary of anything that seems over-reductive or neat. Writing is an art as well as a craft, and the messy stuff of true creation always goes on inside your head.

All this record-keeping, or non-record keeping, has two functions. First of all, and most obviously, it's to stop ideas from being lost. But, more importantly, recording something in some way, and then coming back to it, is a way of giving your mind a nudge. No surprise, I suppose that the desire to keep some kind of written record, rather than spasmodically reviewing the contents of my head, arose in my forties when I'd already been writing for some time and was probably losing both my fund of ideas and my youthful acuity of memory.

Looking back through my notebooks, there's inevitably a great deal of dross, and the ideas I can make out as having eventually made it into stories are only half-recognisable from whatever I wrote down, if they're there at all. Things transmute and change as they develop, and gather up and shed other things, and none of this is going to happen merely by putting something down in a notebook, or even by having it inked into your skin.

DECISIONS, DECISIONS

Writing fiction involves endless, endless decisions, most of which don't feel particularly inspired. Is my character wearing a coat when they enter the café? Do they take if off? Is it cold anyway? What kind of drink do they order when they sit down? Is the cafe busy or quiet? And is a café an appropriate place for this scene in the first place? Maybe it should happen on a bench in a park? But perhaps the park's outside the café window, so my characters can walk through it on their way and feed the ducks . . . And so on, and on, a drift of possibilities, and most of the time there's no great sense as you go through them of what will or won't work.

I've worked more often with kids than with adults when it comes to teaching fiction writing, and it's noticeable how the brightest, ablest teenagers find this process of making simple decisions about the small, stupid stuff of writing incredibly hard. Finding a name for a character. Deciding whether it's going to be cloudy or sunny in the scene they want to create. It's something they've simply not been encouraged to train their minds to do.

Adults do tend to be somewhat better at decision making in my experience, no doubt because it's a skill we're all required to use in many areas of our lives. But, when it comes to writing fiction, they often rely too heavily on the details of what they think they know, and then over-focus on that. So, for example, they'll give the café in the scene they're writing some over-fancy name and start wondering too much about what kind of coffee their character would order. In other words, they get bogged down in knowledge and detail, whereas the real trick is to realise that the seeming quality of all these small decision is less vital than simply making them, and moving on.

This mixture of hell-for-leather going for it, combined with some judicious planning, are another thing which writers train their brains to get better at, and are continually adjusting day to day and line to line and story to story. Some of these small decisions, whether my character takes off their hat as they enter the café, or spills their coffee, may lead to the kinds of surprises and insights which will shape the story into whatever it becomes. Others may turn out, with hindsight, to be wrong. It's certainly true that no story can be complete until it's written, and that the many decisions you have to make as you proceed on the narrative's journey will generate fresh ideas and influence where you finally end up.

If this all sounds a bit confused and contradictory and mysterious, that's because it is. Not just to non-writers, but to writers as well. But there is a reason for this, and it's tied up, once again, with how our brains work.

NUDGE, NUDGE

So I'm making lots of decisions as I plan and even more as I write, some of which will generate major new ideas and some of which will lead to dead ends, but most of which will simply help push the story on in a variety of smaller or bigger ways, and all of which will contribute to the overall sense of pace, theme and mood.

When it comes to the broader range of planning and ideas generation, I now have notebooks, and put things up on a whiteboard, and scribble on Post-its, and keep old drafts and try to return to them now and then. I also have a regular habit of writing down lists of questions and things I don't know. That, and I keep a kind of word-processed journal in which I type out and discuss problems and issues on an almost daily basis. I also take long walks, and worry about stuff, and probably talk to myself a great deal more than I should. But all of this is on a conscious level, and doesn't lie at the heart of how the human mind deals with this kind of stuff.

We all know that the answer to some small but intractable problem— why a printer won't work or where the spare car keys went—tends to pop up when we've ceased concentrating on it. The sudden realisation in the shower or while walking the dog is a common experience for all of us. This is, intuitively, how our brains seem to work. But there's a great deal more to it than that. The conscious mind is far from the be-all and end-all it thinks itself to be—in fact, consciousness itself is largely an illusion—and research has shown that most decisions and opinions which we think we're forming for logical, worked-through reasons have in fact been made by our subconscious before we've even realised what's going on.

Freud, with all his talk or penis envy and the Oedipus complex, was seen to have portrayed the subconscious as a dark, animalistic place; the source of base hungers and destructive desires which we then try to act out or overcome. But that isn't how it works. The subconscious, the true subconscious, is doubtless many things, but it is our main problem-solver and ideas generator, and without it we humans wouldn't be the complex and clever creatures we are.

Sure, we can work out consciously (or we think we can) where next to put the x in a game of noughts and crosses, or which brand of detergent to buy at the supermarket (although package designers and advertisers might quietly disagree), but when it comes to the sort of complex, varied, multi-level decisions which life throws at us all the time, our conscious mind alone is not at its best. After all, we instinctively want to "sleep on some-thing" if the decision seems important or difficult enough. We also know that, when we've wasted an hour trying to get the printer to print, or find the car keys, the best thing we can do is forget about it for a while and get on with something else. We also know that when we're struggling to recall a fact or a name, the answer which first pops into our heads stands a much better chance of being right than the one we spend the next few minutes struggling over.

Stories, let alone novels, are incredibly complex things, demanding endless decisions, assessments and revisions, different varieties of judgement and planning, and sucking in all sorts of impressions and ideas along the way. When they're going well, the process of writing them can, indeed, seem almost magical. The scenes, the ideas, the characters, all just fall into place. For which every writer should thank their subconscious. And when they're not going well, it's our subconscious we need to turn to again. The trick all successful writers learn in their own way—and it never becomes an easy one—is to nudge their ideas along, to plan and analyse, sometimes to push hard at an idea to try to force it to work, but at other times to leave things the time and space they need to develop. A process which, as we're not consciously aware of it, often seems to happen almost magically, and on its own.

If you're interested in finding out more about the subconscious mind and its vital role in problem-solving and creativity, I'd recommend you read *Hare Brain, Tortoise Mind: Why Intelligence Increases When You Think Less* by Guy Claxton. That, and try to bring the power of your subconscious to bear next time your printer's on the fritz.

PROBLEMS ARE IDEAS IN DISGUISE

Clearly, writing fiction, and coming up with big or small ideas, is about making things up. You start with the dreaded blank page, but the more decisions you make, the more you narrow things down as your character enters that café and hangs up their hat and orders a latte , the more real it starts to become. Instead of dealing with ideas, abstract notions and weird desires, you're dealing with proper *things*. I think of this process, this narrowing down from ideas to clear specifics, as a kind of keyhole. The smaller you can make the keyhole, the clearer and more wonderful and challenging will be the world which awaits on the far side of it.

The writing process I'm describing, the seeking out of ideas, nurturing and coming back to them, shoving things together in odd ways, making endless small decisions, allowing your subconscious the freedom to do its work, will often go swimmingly for a while, then refuse to swim at all, at least for me. I'll hit issues and practicalities I hadn't thought through, or the ideas which had seemed so exciting in prospect seem lifeless and pointless on the page.

You hit problems, in other words. The poltergeist which won't polter. The couple who dawdle in the park resolutely refuse to even meet each other, let alone fall in love. That idea for cold fusion which they're supposed to discuss in that café, which, in a sudden insight of the wrong kind of *aha*, you realise simply doesn't make any proper sense. All deeply frustrating, and seemingly a long way away from the business of ideas, which now seem to be the very things which have you down. For me, and for anyone who's serious about being a writer, these times hurt. You've put in the time, you've put in the effort, and all for what . . . ?

I've certainly got plenty of half-done pieces which have come to this point and stayed that way—it's another rite of passage which all writers have to undergo and repeat now and again—and probably the most important thing to say about these problem pieces to any striving writer is that you will, genuinely, learn a great deal more about your craft from the things which fail than from those which succeed. Maybe you can't write about love in the straightforward way you'd planned, for instance—but why *is* that, and what kind of love, or not-love do you really want to write about? Or maybe you just decide you've got a thing about nonsensical science such as cold fusion, or hackneyed scenes set in cafés. Whatever it is, that knowledge has added to your understanding of yourself as a writer, and is something you can use as you move on.

But perhaps it's a tad too early to dismiss a whole project as a failure and the ideas which generated it as worthless simply because it hasn't yet worked. The trite truth I've had to learn and re-learn about dealing with problems is that they're often opportunities in disguise. That brick wall, the thing which simply won't work, is really crying out for a spot of lateral thinking, a fresh twist—a new idea, in other words. To take my story "Tumbling Nancy," which appears later on in this collection, as an example, I first tried to write about a second-rate writer of grim children's stories about a decade ago. It seemed like something creepy and fun, but simply wouldn't work. Somehow, there was no surprise or edge. I returned to it a couple of years back, and encountered the same problem. I had the main character down as someone decent and passive. Then, aha, the dreadful Ros Godby leapt into view as an acidic counterpoint to the story's other half, and it took off.

GIVE IT TIME

The long timescale that's sometimes involved in getting problems to work out and ideas to cohere is something I've long had to resign myself to. The title story in this collection, "Frost on Glass," to take an extreme example, is based on an idea of writers on a dystopian commune island which I can well remember trying out a first scene for in my bedroom in my parents' old house when I was about 19. I came back to it again, oh, fifteen years ago, and for a while I seemed to be on to something, and then again I was stalled. Then, about ten years back, I looked at what I'd written five years earlier, and reckoned there really was something there. But I still couldn't get it to work. Until, finally, when I returned to it again as I was thinking about a "new" story for this collection, I managed to wrestle the thing to the ground in ways I'll say more about in the story's afterword. Other stories, thank God, do come to me quicker and more easily. Both "Letter to Will" and "A Concise and Ready Guide," to take two examples in this book, were essentially both done over a few days, and were based on ideas which had only recently occurred to me, and stood up pretty well at first draft.

ANNOY YOURSELF

If there's one common illusion I've noticed that many people who want to write, or try to write and even do so competently, yet find results somehow lacking, tend to foster, it's that writing is somehow a "safe" activity. Writing could and should be difficult and dangerous and uncomfortable and annoying and edgy. Above all, it needs to be deeply personal. If it isn't, you're writing something that someone who cares more could write better.

There are times when you need to feel angry about what you're writing, or seriously worried about what it's saying about you, and what others will think if and when they read it. Of course, some people who want to write—and they're generally men—hear this kind of advice to "open up" and then immediately start filling their stories with violence and sex. Most of the time, of course, it's just another shield, a showy way of deflecting attention from their true vulnerabilities. As are those writers—and I have to say they're generally women—who create pieces where serious issues are raised but everything gets resolved too easily, and everyone's basically just too nice.

Catherine Cookson was the illegitimate child of an alcoholic, grew up thinking her unmarried mother was her sister, and suffered a severe mental and physical breakdown in her thirties before she went on to write about the struggles of other dispossessed and under-privileged women. Anne Rice wrote her novel *Interview with a Vampire* soon after her daughter had died from leukaemia.

You may think your own life lacks that kind of harsh experience, but I promise you that not facing up to the things which really bother you, or at least finding a vein of embarrassing honesty, will seriously hold you back from ever being the writer you could become. Of course, this process of mining our deeper feelings is rarely totally deliberate. Nor should it be. The first story I ever sold, about a boy trying to make things better in a fractured family, had strong autobiographical elements which I only noticed long afterwards. But I certainly knew when I was writing the piece that it mattered to me.

Those no-go areas we all have in life are well worth exploring. Why exactly *is* it that you find erotic fiction sordid, heroic fantasy stupid, super-heroes ridiculous, whodunits trite or Jane Austen boring? What is that problem you have with people who let their dogs sleep with them in their beds, or drivers who don't indicate, or shellfish served whole? The things that you actively dislike are telling you at least as much about yourself as the things that you love. You may or may not want to know what it is, but trying to find out will either open fresh doors or, at the very least, confirm your prejudices with a deeper knowledge.

DON'T GIVE UP

Writing successful fiction requires an element of talent—a facility with language and a way of seeing things—which is probably at least in part down to early upbringing, or simply genetic. But this level of talent is fairly common. At a rough guess, I'd say that about 10% of the population possess it, and of course the majority of the people who strive to write will fall into that group. Then there's "luck" and "opportunity" which, at least when it comes to being successful, doubtless play their part, just as they do in every other field of human endeavour. It does no harm having a charismatic personality either, or knowing the right people, or looking good in snug trousers or a tight skirt. But most of these things—at least, the non-physical ones—can be faked or worked on, and they don't lie at the heart of what's needed to develop ideas and write. What writing is really about is hard work and an overpowering drive that's difficult to explain, especially when it persists in the face of a great deal of failure, rejection and personal defeat. I've talked to other professional writers, and most of them see this in the same way.

I honestly don't have a recipe for developing this incredibly persistent trait, and I'm not even sure it's desirable in a balanced human being, but I guess I must have it. I write about rejection later on in this collection, but I remember how, when I was first trying to sell, my response to one of those dreaded *pro-forma* notes arriving in the post was to want to immediately write something else. I still love writing, and I trawl my head and the world beyond for ideas, and I still push on through rejection, and hate it when my stories flounder, even though I know I have to tell myself that "problems are opportunities" and "ideas take time to develop" and "failures are more useful than successes". I'm far from being so focussed and persistent in any other area of my life, but for some reason writing fiction makes me that way.

When it's going badly and the ideas won't fit, it can feel like struggling to get a jumble of unmatched sticks to lean together into some kind of structure, with no idea of how the finished object is supposed to look, or even what it's for or why you're doing it. In my more optimistic and mystic moments, it can feel like releasing a statue from within a stone. Both, at the end of the day, are part of the same deal, and I somehow know I have to try to push on.

WRITING FICTION IS A SKILL

I began this piece by describing one of those times when someone who doesn't write talks to a writer about their amazing ideas for a story or novel. Because the ability to write, at least in the sense of putting words together into a sentence, is something almost everyone in the first world possesses, the art and craft of writing fiction seems to attract both a peculiar mystique and a contrary sense that almost anyone can do it. You rarely hear people who aren't musicians talking about the songs they might write, or telling composers what chord sequences they should employ, or explaining to actors how to deliver a line—although, come to think of it, I'm sure that does happen—but this, again, is something that all writers have to put up with now and then.

I hope I've deflated the illusion that one idea, or even several of them, will be all that's necessary to get anyone who wants to write fiction very far, and I also hope I've explained how the creative process and the development of ideas doesn't exist in some magical haze, but is a skill that can be developed like any other. In my occasional work in the classroom, I've found "story ideas" are actually pretty easy things to generate, at least if you think of them simply as surprising combinations of things. An elephant in a zoo, or one in the jungle, isn't much of a thing to write home about, but an elephant wandering down the local high street . . . ? A dead body in a freezer in a morgue similarly sounds sort-of interesting, but somehow not interesting enough. But how about a dead body in the meat freezer at Sainsburys?

All that's going on as we think about these odd images is that we're

forcing elements that seemingly don't belong together to somehow fit.
Which is, essentially, a way of forming the beginnings of story ideas. I'm
continually counselling young writers to avoid the kind of obvious links
that first come into their heads and try to drag in something more left-
field. Of course, go too far that way and you end up with a chaos of
mismatched settings, characters and themes, a kind of wild circus with
elephants trumpeting down the high street while police cars rush by to
deal with all the bodies in the supermarket, but even that may boil down
to something genuinely interesting if you work on it, and give it enough
space and time.

By now, I feel as if I've said most of what could be said to that poor,
notional person who's wandered up to me at some party to innocently
share their views and ideas about writing. They'll have headed off long
before now, anyway. After all, writing is hard work, and ideas, for all the
reasons I've tried to explain, might be complex and slippery things, but
they don't exist on their own, or simply pop up as if by magic.

THE CRANE METHOD

DESPITE the elegiac tone of his many portrayals in the popular and academic press, few people who knew Professor Crane actually liked him. He had, it was true, advanced the study of Anglo-Saxon history farther than anyone in the modern age. He had, it was also true, overseen the expansion and development of Welbeck College until it could hold its head—and indeed, raise its new brick tower—high over the more antique and established seats of learning in Cambridge. His personal manner and appearance were also impeccable. It was often said that there was something of the medical man about him—a tang of formaldehyde, perhaps—and that he studied people through those heavy glasses much in the way a physician might study a patient. Because of his extreme slimness and height and the furled umbrella he often affected to carry with him he also, it was frequently muttered, although rarely within his earshot, possessed a remarkable resemblance to the bird with which he shared his name, right down to that patient yet predatory stoop.

Professor Matthias Crane was intent upon nothing other than the advancement of his college and his field of learning, and both of those objectives coincided conveniently with the advancement of Professor Crane himself. Students and post-graduates whose avenue of research looked particularly promising were invited up for tea and seed cake in his large and comfortable study, and then perhaps a little more Amontillado than they were used to drinking, although he himself always abstained. They would find themselves quizzed and encouraged and given tips and suggestions to advance their chosen project. Most often, these tips proved extraordinarily useful, or happened to link in with the work which another fellow was pursuing, which had also been discussed on some afternoon seated beside the crackling applewood of Professor Crane's ever-convivial hearth. There would then be a subsequent period of dazzled excitement and discovery, which was always followed by dazed disbelief, and then a more permanent sense of betrayal. Professor Crane's output of books, lectures, essays and pamphlets was legendary. It was often said that they issued forth with a profligacy which could scarcely be the work of just one man. In this, there was an element of truth.

The sponsors of Welbeck College's new halls and exhibits found themselves similarly used and then discarded, although in ways about which it was impossible to complain. There was always that occasion when the professor had perhaps bent a rule, studiously ignored a small personal infraction or performed some other act of vaguely underhand generosity which at the time had seemed purely altruistic, but which was nevertheless mentioned once or twice afterwards with what came to be seen as chilling casualness. Many a night's sleep—indeed, many a promising career and marriage—had been wrecked on the remembered cold appraisal of Professor Crane's gaze.

No one was at all surprised when the professor disappeared for a few months during the summer of 1900. It had always been his habit to head off alone on his researches with little if any word about where he was going, and usually to return burdened with some literal or figurative treasure. The Saltfleetby Codex which had brought a new understanding of the Christianisation of the Anglo-Saxon kingdoms, and the reattribution of the previously ignored carvings in the Suffolk church of Beck, both owed their origins to such excursions. So did many of the finest items in the small but exquisite college museum. All, of course, came with full and detailed provenance. But there was always a sense with each new wonder of a conjurer producing a fresh rabbit out of a hat. Those who knew Professor Crane better than they probably wished, speculated that he had some secret horde from which all of these discoveries somehow originated.

At any rate, his delayed return in the autumn of 1900 was taken as nothing more than the prelude to the announcement of a particularly dramatic breakthrough in Anglo-Saxon studies. There was certainly no sense of any concern for the much esteemed professor. He was one of those people who were thought to be inextinguishable.

Richard Talbot, BA and MA hons, recently appointed Junior Assistant Tutor and Keeper of the Keys of the Welbeck Museum, was at least as unconcerned by Professor Crane's absence as anyone. He had grown up with a love of history, and especially that vague yet glittering era between the fall of Classical Rome and the Norman Conquest, which bordered on obsession. It was a love which had absorbed his childhood and concerned his stolid parents back in Penge, and which had been fuelled in no small part by the works of Matthias Crane. To become an undergraduate at the great professor's college and then to attend his famous lectures was the fulfilment of a dream. To be invited into the professor's private confidence on the new method of indexing and cataloguing on which he was working for his master's thesis was beyond his wildest imaginings. Also beyond imagining was how Professor Crane could then describe the same method to his fellow academics at a symposium held shortly after as if it was something entirely of his own invention.

Richard was livid. Richard was desolate. Richard felt totally betrayed. But who could he complain to, and where could he go? Specialists in the cataloguing of Anglo-Saxon artefacts were hardly in great demand. The only other obvious refuge lay in Oxford, where Professor Freethly-Chillmorn had long been reduced to academic impotence and chronic alcoholism by his shambling attempts to compete with Professor Crane. So the long and damning letter to *The Journal of Early English Studies*, with copies to as many fellow academics as he could think of, and another to *The Times*, remained undrafted, and he found that he attracted many a sympathetic smile in the college library or the snug of the Eagle and Child. He had been—well, there was no real word for it because no one had ever spoken up . . . But whatever had been done to him by Professor Crane had been done before and would be done again. Meanwhile, he would have to swallow his pride and quietly put aside his stolen thesis and scrabble around for another less promising subject.

So it was that Richard Talbot gained his MA through wearily reworking the existing evidence regarding Anglo-Saxon agricultural practice. He was then offered a junior tutorship for his pains. He of course had no choice but to accept, and—and this was the final insult—was granted a new role in reorganising the records, displays and artefacts at the college museum on the basis of a fabulous new system which was universally described as the Crane Method.

It was now almost three weeks into term, Cambridge was basking in the warmth of an Indian summer, and Professor Crane had still not returned. Welbeck College, it had to be admitted, was a somewhat happier, if rather more aimless, place without him. Meanwhile, Professor Meecham fulfilled the role of Acting Temporary Head of Department, although the man was far too good-natured to be anything more than a makeweight.

To Richard, this was all a matter of some frustration. What the college needed to apply itself to, he decided, was the careful grooming of a proper successor. After all, Professor Crane couldn't carry on forever, even when he did make his inevitable and irritatingly discovery-laden return from wherever he had been hiding this long summer. The college should be looking for a younger man capable of publishing ground-breaking works of great technical brilliance, but also with a popular touch which could reach the best-seller lists. The sort of man who could be equally at home supervising a summer dig in some windy field in East Anglia (although not actually doing any digging) as dining in the finest clubs in London amongst the great and famous. The sort of man whose face would fit well in the national papers and whom the undergraduates would look up to as a paragon of erudition, elegance and self-effacing charm. The sort of man, indeed, whom Richard Talbot believed he saw gazing back at him as he shaved each morning. Still youthful by outward appearance, of course. But with those high cheekbones and darkly solemn eyes. A fine physique, as well; he was especially proud of his long-fingered hands, with nails which he kept well-manicured and pared despite the occasional demands of his curating work. A voice which was made for compelling command. He was even known to possess a fine light tenor which he occasionally employed for the singing of popular ballads in certain back barrooms.

It was most, most frustrating. All, however, was not lost. Fortune favoured the brave, and time the young. As Richard sat in his tiny office in the Welbeck Museum on a stiflingly warm afternoon in early October, he still firmly believed that, Professor Crane not withstanding, his moment would come. Although this particular day, it had to be admitted, hadn't been particularly propitious. You might have expected at least a few visitors to want to view the five high-ceilinged rooms which displayed the major items of the collection he curated, but today not a single one had appeared. Nor had he received any recent letters of enquiry from other researchers, or invitations to speak at some or other academic convention. While the telephone remained frustratingly silent on his desk.

At about a quarter to four, he told his secretary Mrs Marbish—a wizened old bird—that she might as well go home. Then he slid the museum sign to CLOSED and locked the main door with the key he kept on the chain of his watch fob. Of course, curating a museum certainly wasn't merely about *visitors*. Work to be done, always work to be done . . . Beyond a door marked REPOSITORY, a near endless array of potsherds lay in dusty boxes on even dustier shelves awaited his cataloguing according to the so-called Crane Method. But, he told himself as he wandered amid the glass cases in the sun-threaded gloom, there were consolations . . .

There it all was: gold and bronze and silver, gleaming. A woman's locket found still with a strand of her auburn hair. A small iron blade, bereft of its bone handle, but nevertheless beautifully engraved. And here . . . One of his favourite objects; a particularly large and fine example of the broad-bladed weapon characteristic of the finest Anglo-Saxon workmanship, with the hilt's jewelling almost intact and the blade decorated in exquisite silver and gold pattern-weld. Nearly perfect. So nearly perfect, in fact, that Richard often took the sword out to execute a few parrying and stabbing motions.

He opened the cabinet with another of his keys. Holding this weapon, it wasn't so very hard to imagine himself a brave Anglo-Saxon warrior in full gear of battle. What foes would withstand me, he thought as the blade sliced the air like a thickened gleam of sunlight. What lands I might have conquered, what maidens bedded, what battles fought! He was about to the replace the sword in its cabinet when he noticed something which he had never noticed before. The pommel, sadly, had been missing since the item was first catalogued by one of Richard's predecessors back in the

1700s, but now it seemed to him that there might actually be something curled inside the hilt's hollowed metal core. Strange indeed, but Richard's heart only started racing when he used a pair of fine tweezers to draw the object out.

That evening in the murmurous pipefug warmth of the college refectory, as he spooned out beer pie, soggy potatoes and boiled beetroot, Richard Talbot kept himself more than usually to himself. Then, he scurried up to his rooms. Only there, with his door locked and his hands slightly trembling, did he proceed to make a full and proper examination of his find. It was, as he had realised immediately, a scrap of extremely antique parchment, written in the kind of very early Old English which even the Venerable Bede would have struggled to understand.

The parchment referred to a warrior named Cynewald, who the authorities agreed had most probably been King of Mercia in the period between Cnebba and Creado in or around the year of Our Lord 550, although the documentation then current was thin to say the least. Confirmation of Cynewald's existence in this hidden scrap of funerary prose was in itself a significant find. But the scrap then went on to refer to his burial in a place which it described as being at *Fllotweyton*, and beside a *burna*, or clear stream, near to the *brym* or surf, which presumably meant sea. A quick check of a modern atlas confirmed that a small village named Flotterton still existed in Lincolnshire, which would have been a significant part of the Kingdom of Mercia at this time, and also that the village was, indeed, very close to the sea. Richard barely needed to refer to the standard textbooks to know that the place had never been associated with the discovery of any significant Anglo-Saxon remains. At least, not until now.

As to the final portion of text which could be deciphered before the partial document faded, the cursing of a burial site was, for the Anglo-Saxons, fairly standard fare. Rather disappointingly, instead of some fearsome tomb-guarding dragon, this one mentioned a lesser creature from the Anglo-Saxon bestiary known as a *ketta*, which was basically little more than a shadowy cat. The actual curse seemed odd—at least, it did to Richard, who was no specialist in Anglo-Saxon linguistics. It said that the first person to disturb the tomb would find that the *ketta* took *gild nebbhad*. Gild being their concept of value, and *nebbhad* meaning something like identity. Which struck Richard as a peculiarly abstract curse, considering how brutal the Anglo-Saxons usually were.

Merely by heading a few yards down the corridor from his rooms, he could have consulted several experts who had spent the larger parts of their lives studying such arcane threats. Even the great and still absent Professor Crane had considerable expertise in this area—or at the very least had taken someone else's expertise and made it his own. Richard remembered how the subject of burial curses had been raised at one of the professor's famous public lectures when he was an undergraduate. A laughing voice at the back had suggested that such things were, of course, utter rubbish, no doubt expecting the professor, who was as worldly as they come about most matters, to agree. But instead Professor Crane had bowed his long neck and looked momentarily grave, and said in a quiet voice that the wishes of our ancestors were not to be taken lightly.

It was a little odd, Richard had to admit, that this scrap of parchment had never been noticed. Odd, also, that it lay tucked within a sword of entirely different provenance—being at least two centuries less old. Even he, he might have thought, had studied and played with the thing more then enough to have spotted that faded yellow curl hidden within the hilt. But, plainly, he hadn't. Neither had his many predecessor curators. Which to Richard, who had a generally poor view of his fellow toilers across the vast plains of Anglo-Saxon study, both previous and current, was less of a surprise. Things were as they were. And good luck was something he felt he hadn't had anything like enough of during his short academic career. In fact, the opposite. But now, Dame Fortune, had tossed her tresses and beckoned . . .

Richard hardly slept that night, such was his excitement. The next morning, after cramming a few things into his suitcase, he called in briefly at the museum to inform Mrs Marbish about a sudden illness his father was suffering back in Penge, then headed for the railway station. Everyone else at Welbeck College could wonder where he was, for the little it mattered. In fact, they could all go to Hell. They would be looking at him very differently when he returned.

The journey involved several tediously slow trains, and several even more tedious waits on the platforms of otherwise empty stations. Meanwhile, the long Indian summer was finally fading. At first, the sun was merely obscured by a few skeins of cloud. Then an easterly wind began to stir the trees and the wires of the telegraphs. Scattershots of rain were striking the glass of Richard's carriage from out of gloomy skies by the time he took the final leg of his journey across the wide, flat landscapes of Lincolnshire to Flotterton.

The village itself came as a disappointment. He'd imagined somewhere with a few crookedly ancient houses, a decent-sized manor house set amid a still discernible pattern of medieval fields, perhaps a charming pub. But Flotterton, for all its long history, looked as if it had never existed before the age of the railway, the kiss me quick hat, the bucket and spade. To call this desolate settlement a resort, he reflected as he struggled against the wind, past a closed-for-the-season fish and chip shop and a rock emporium which looked to have been abandoned, would be over-dignifying it. The place ran out, as if in shame, at a low straggle of dunes. Still, he told himself, as he espied through the rain a somewhat taller and yet even grimmer building with a sign announcing itself as a hotel, the name Flotterton would soon ring out in the halls of academia, and be writ large across the headlines of the daily papers. As, of course, would that of a certain Richard Talbot.

The hotel lived up to its external lack of promise. The proprietor was a scrawny man of late years in possession of the kind of beard which made you wonder whether its presence was intentional. He looked at Richard as he signed the address book much as one might study the arrival of an unwelcome household pest. The meal Richard ate in the otherwise empty restaurant had been re-heated so often that it was genuinely hard to tell what it might once have been, while the service wasn't so much execrable as non-existent. But he smiled to himself as he climbed into his pyjamas and lay down in the damp grey sheets of his damp grey room. This grim experience would stand up well as a humorous prelude in the many talks he would soon be giving about his discovery. People would smile. They would laugh warmly but respectfully. Even Professor Crane . . .

There, in the darkness, as the sea boomed and rain and wind rattled his window, Richard's smile briefly twitched into a grimace. He was remembering a small, embarrassing interlude which had occurred at the start of the summer recess, not long before the professor had set off on whatever mysterious quest had drawn him. It had been another of those long, slow, afternoons at the museum, and he had sent Mrs Marbish home and locked up early so he could occupy himself with a little sword practice. A few thrusts and parries, and his mind was so far off amid scenes of bloody battle that he hadn't become immediately aware of a watching presence. What presence, in fact, could there have been, seeing as he, as curator, possessed one of only two sets of keys which gave admission to the museum and its precious cabinets?

When Richard had, sweating and breathless, finally finished his pursuit of an imagined Grendel and twirled toward the half-open door where a tall figure was standing, Professor Crane had simply stepped from the shadows and stooped his long neck and announced that he had a query regarding the ground plan of an excavation which had taken place under the college's auspices back in the 1880s. He hadn't even mentioned the fact that Richard had been twirling a near-priceless sword like a child playing at knights-in-armour. Richard, flustered, had at least managed to put the thing away as if he had merely been checking some detail of its making. Then he went to find the papers in question, and the professor pronounced himself much obliged and left. But there was always a sense with Professor Crane that any minor infraction or mistake was carefully noted, analysed and stored until the day when it might prove useful.

Next morning, despite a night of difficult sleep in which a predatory creature seemed to be circling from the shadow-edges of some interminable space, Richard made a hearty attempt at extracting his breakfast of shrivelled bacon and congealed scrambled egg from its pool of cold fat. After all, one must fortify oneself for the work ahead, much as Belzoni surely did before he invaded the pyramids, Schliemann when he discovered Troy, or Carter when he stumbled into the tomb of Tutankhamun. And, yes, the hotel proprietor did possess an Ordnance Survey map of the area, which Richard was allowed to borrow in exchange for an unnecessarily large deposit. There even proved to be a small shop along Flotterton's single street which sold a few items of hardware in the long season when it wasn't purveying buckets and spades. A decent spade, but of a larger and more practical kind, was exactly what Richard had in mind, along with a small lantern and a measuring tape.

The rain, at least, has ceased this morning, but it was nevertheless a particularly bitter and grey day. Wrestling with the map, then briefly peering at the precious scrap of parchment, Richard confirmed to himself that finding the burial mound shouldn't be that difficult. A stream, near to the sea . . . He hunched north around the edge of the pitch and putt course, which somehow felt to be the more promising direction in which to head.

Noontime passed without success. The packed lunch of grey bread and something resembling ham which the hotel proprietor had prepared for Richard, along with a few fragments of his beard, was so poor that he would have tossed it to the screeching gulls if he hadn't been so hungry. North, it appeared, was not the direction he should have chosen, so he retraced his steps toward the pitch and putt course as the wind stung into his face.

He knew exactly what an undisturbed Anglo-Saxon burial mound should look like, but the landscape around Flotterton was so uncertain that he was struggling to make proper sense of it. There were streams winding this way and that toward the shore, certainly. Some of them might even fit the description of being clear. There were also humps and mounds aplenty in the scrubby expanse of grazing land which abutted the dunes and the sea. But there were so *many*, and it was obvious that this whole coastline was forever shifting.

As he trudged past a few desolate bathing huts, then squelched on across a filthy stretch of mud using his shovel as a walking stick, Richard remembered the dreams of his childhood days back in Penge. Then he imagined himself seated in glory at the top table at the Welbeck College Annual Founders Dinner, and in a private first class carriage of a Great Northern express train on his way to collect some award. A plaque, perhaps, outside the museum to commemorate the brief time he had served there in undeserved obscurity? Or an entire new museum devoted to his name. For surely a king of Cynewald's era would have been buried with great riches, which of course was confirmed by that odd little curse. He could expect at very least the man's armour and ceremonial gear, along with—

Richard paused. Darkness was already settling and he would soon have to go back to that ghastly hotel, but for a moment he was almost convinced that he was being studied by a tall and oddly avian-seeming presence from the crest of yonder dune. An actual *bird*? A heron, most probably. Although it did seem unusually large. Were cranes at all common in this part of the world? Richard wondered, as he peered through the thickening gloom and the birdlike figure seemed to puff out in the swelling dusk like a doused candleflame.

Richard shivered. If he stood here any longer, he would probably find himself sinking irrevocably into the mud. Tired and disappointed, he dragged himself back toward the few lights of Flotterton. Taking in what remained of the view as he re-ascended the low rise beside the bathing huts, he was still determined not to give up. And there, over toward the low lands of Lincolnshire, the last of the westering sun flashed briefly toward him through a final gap in the clouds like a final signal of hope.

The effect was briefly beautiful. Richard could almost imagine why the great warriors of that distant and much misunderstood age might have chosen to inter their king here, where the incoming tide roared its grief—

In that moment his gaze caught on something. Such was the clarity of the light thrown by the setting sun that, like a lantern held at an acute angle to reveal the hidden indentations in a sheet of paper, the landscape spoke to him in a language as clear as modern English. In fact, to Richard, it was far clearer. It was suddenly obvious that the many mounds and hillocks which had so confused his day were lumped into their present irregular shapes by the simple forces of nature. But there was one mound which, although relatively small, was different. Astonishing, really, that no one had ever noticed it before—although the fact that it was now part of the pitch and putt course might have had something to do with that.

The sun had vanished, but Richard was in no mood to return to his hotel. Like most things here, the course was closed for the winter, but its peeling picket fence presented no obstacle. After some struggle with the wind, he lit his lantern and inspected the mound, which was perhaps twenty yards across at its base and rose to something like twice head height. The makers of the course had used the mound as a hazard along the fairway of the 18th hole. But standing beside it, Richard was more certain than ever that he had found something ancient and extraordinary.

This was no time for measuring, for trial holes and exploratory trenches. This was his moment alone, and he was determined to take it. He glanced toward the few lights of Flotterton. He was close to what might loosely be termed civilisation, but he doubted if anyone would notice him at work here. Hefting his spade, he started digging.

At first, he struck ordinary turf. Then, he came to a hard-packed aggregation of quartz stones laid in an approximate circle. This placing of an outline of stones being a common characteristic of Anglo-Saxon burial mounds. Next, he began to encounter darker lumps amid the sandy soil. Indicative of burning—funerary incineration also being a common practice. Everything about this mound proclaimed its authenticity. His only fear was that some grave-robber had got to its treasure before him.

Richard laboured. The wind had stilled and a full moon had risen and the scene in which he worked, with the dark earth heaped across the silvered turf of the 18th fairway, acquired the clarity of an old woodcut. The opening on which he was working, a rough trench about two feet wide and three deep cut into the seaward side, became a tunnel. Soon, he was crawling in and out, scooping earth with his hands instead of using the spade. A little dangerous, perhaps, but he felt sure he could manage to scurry out at the first signs of a major slippage.

Unlike Neolithic tombs, he was not expecting to find any solid structure at the mound's core. There would simply be more earth, and then the funerary remains themselves, surrounded perhaps by the bones of those who had been sacrificed in the deceased's cause. So it was a surprise to Richard when his hands suddenly fell through into what felt like empty space. He gasped, and heard the sound re-echoed in a stuttering growl as he wriggled backwards to take hold of his lantern. Then, on elbows, knees and belly, and by now entirely coated in dirt, he wriggled back inside the mound and held the lantern out.

What Richard Talbot saw when light first spilled into the darkness of lost centuries must rank amid the great moments of modern archaeology. The many artefacts which comprised what became known as the Flotterton Horde would surely have gleamed even in that loamy hole. The famous golden-bossed shield. That exquisite dragonfly brooch. The many fine daggers and swords. The great Anglo-Saxon mailcoat. All in all, there was enough here to change the way the world viewed the pre-Christian kingdoms.

As to what else happened in those moments of discovery, there is much that is not entirely clear. Many residents of Flotterton reported being awakened by a ghastly howling, which one described a sounding *like a huge, wounded cat.* The hotel proprietor was, to his credit, one of the first to put on his boots and investigate the horrifying noise, which seemed to emanate from the pitch and putt course. There, he reported that he saw a man staggering about the hillock beside the 18th fairway in the moonlight, seemingly struggling with something which he described as resembling a *blur of shadows.*

By the time the local doctor arrived, and then the police, and despite the horror of Richard's condition, wiser counsel was already starting to prevail. There was, it must be said, some ill-advised speculation that Richard had somehow triggered an ancient form of booby trap when he poked his head into that mound. But any amateur historian of the era would have confirmed that that was not the Anglo-Saxon way. Nor could any device so ancient conceivably have functioned to such terrible effect. No, the general consensus was and always will be that Richard Talbot, perhaps in a spate of madness caused by his excitement and near-asphyxia, somehow managed to claw off most of his own face.

In the circumstances, and with Richard incapable of anything but sobbing screams, it was some hours before the police were able to establish whom they should contact. By next day, however, the first of the dons from Welbeck College were arriving, and they immediately saw the immense value of the discovery their colleague had made. The press came soon after, and the sightseers from the Midland towns not long after that. For the residents of Flotterton—and the hotel proprietor especially, although the man remained strangely subdued—there can scarcely have been better times.

Richard Talbot survived whatever ordeal he had suffered, although he was never again whole or sane. After the immediate medical problems of his loss of flesh, sight and proper speech had been dealt with, he lived his remaining few years at a specialist nursing home at the grateful college's expense. It was, as it happened, at Sutton on Sea, not so very far up the coast from Flotterton. Even there, though, his manner and what remained of his countenance were such that he had to be kept well away from the other residents. Nor was he ever able to tolerate the presence of the establishment's fat and amiable ginger cat. Occasionally, one of the more sympathetic dons would summon the will to visit him, and try to marshal their revulsion at his manner, appearance and continued gurgling screams. One, a junior professor who succeeded Richard as curator of the now much-expanded and enormously popular museum, and an up-and-coming expert in Anglo-Saxon linguistics, took the time to try to decipher the parchment of ever-mysterious provenance which had been found in the pocket of Richard's coat. He was heard to comment how strange it was that the curse contained in the fragment could be best translated into modern English by the term *loss of face*, although this was hardly the type of speculation which would ever reach the academic press.

As for Professor Crane, he reappeared at Welbeck College a week or so after Richard's discovery. For once, he had returned from his researches empty-handed, although his presence and experience was vital in dealing with all the popular and academic interest, which was at fever pitch by then.

Careers blossomed at Welbeck in the years that followed. Several best-sellers were written, Cabinet ministers visited the now-famous coastal excavations and an item appeared on Pathe News. If there was one discovery which forever cemented the college's position in the world of academia, it was that of the Flotterton Horde. But, perhaps oddly given his reputation, this was the one advance in the science of archaeology for which the great Professor Crane, now a Member of the Order of Merit and a Lord, would never take the slightest credit.

AFTERWORD *REJECTION*

HERE'S A STORY WHICH WAS REJECTED WHEN I FIRST TRIED TO SELL IT.
As was "The Cold Step Beyond".

Rejection is something in life we all have to get used to in a whole
variety of ways, from first dates to job applications to our partners turning
the other way last thing at night in bed. Writing is thus no different to a
great many other fields of human activity. If you don't go out there, if you
don't put yourself and often a great deal of you that matters on the line
with dogged persistence, you can expect to make very little progress. All
writers, just like actors who have to go audition after audition, have to
learn to accept rejection, and grow a thick enough skin to put up with it,
and then to push on. For me, I'm pretty sure that my ability to stare at the
rejecting e-mail or letter, and nod, and of course feel furiously disappointed, but then find that feeling somehow turning around into a desire
to write something else, has been a crucial factor in my continuing to write.
A more sensible person would probably have given up.

Rejections hurt far more than acceptances give pleasure. After all,
there's so much more to turn over in your head. But, as I say, you do grow a
sort of skin, and part of you tries to accept that there will be another day,
another short story or five hundred page novel, or that perhaps your feelings and ideas weren't expressed as successfully as you'd thought. Either
that, or the particular editor is an idiot, and you simply need to send your
piece back out into the harsh, uncaring world again.

When it came to "The Crane Method," part of me sort-of knew even
before the rejection arrived that the story started off well enough, but had
been written to a deadline and didn't quite make it all in one piece to the

end. So I went into the sulky fugue which I've come to recognise, and, as is often the case, ended up ditching one or two things and making better use of what was left. My initial idea of having Richard Talbot joining in a monstrous amalgam with all the others who'd sought out the Flotterton Horde over the centuries was just a twist too many. Professor Crane was the real monster, as it turned out.

The re-tweaked story sold easily enough, and now you find it here. "The Cold Step Beyond" also needed some tweaking—but very little—before it sold, and was then, I think, pretty well received. One of the many things about rejection a writer has to learn is that the gap between failure and success can be incredibly small, and that editors are busy people, and they may well fail to spot something that really only needs a few extra touches to work. As for the opinions of "lay" readers, or even other writers, let alone supposed academics, or writers of afterwords in collections of their own stories, I'd strongly advise that you take them all with a lorry-load of salt. At the end of the day, and as I said when I was writing about "The Traveller and the Book," an experienced writers have to try to develop a private sense of the worth and potential of their work, and when push comes to shove, the rest of the world can go fuck itself.

But some rejections deserve a special mention. First of all, there are the ones which all budding writers have to get used to, which tell you nothing at all about why you've been rejected, but maybe include some generalised tips, if you're lucky, about the sort of stuff this particular editor or publishing house or website is or isn't looking for. The first one of these I received came from *The Magazine of Fantasy and Science Fiction* back in the 1960s, and was a standardised printed sheet with a couple of the usual sentences, but had a colour copy of one of the covers of the old magazine printed on the back. Which I thought then, and still think, was a nice touch. I also remember the buzz I got from the first personalised rejection which told me that my writing "showed talent". Even more so, the first rejection I received from an editor and writer whose work I knew and admired. As a developing writer, you have to get used to making the most of this thinnish fare. The best of all, though, was the rejection note from Weird Tales which came when I still hadn't had a word in print, and said they would probably buy the story if I could change the ending. Which they did.

A much less happy kind of rejection, and one which is probably even more common these days than the standard e-mail or pre-printed note, is the one that never comes at all. All you're left with, after perhaps a couple of reminders and six or twelve months, is a sense of hope fading into disappointment and the slow realisation that the chance, if there ever was one, has been lost, finally followed by *What now?* Editors, of course, are busy people, and many of them do their work on a subsistence of little more than enthusiasm and fresh air, but I can't see that not responding to someone's efforts is ever acceptable. If there is a Hell, they deserve a special section where, like the tramps in Godot, they have to wait endlessly for a punishment or pleasure which will never come.

The very worse rejections, though, at least as you get used to selling some of your work, are the seemingly "kind" ones. The ones in which the editor tells you how much they enjoyed reading your piece, novel, story, and how fine it is, and what an excellent example of the writerly species you are, but that the "market isn't right" or, worse still, they're somehow doing you a great favour by not publishing your work. Give me a *pro-forma* sheet any day. Especially if there's a nice picture on the back.

The Decline of the English Ghost Story

O NCE, we used to enjoy being scared. Huddled round the firelight as the trees rattled their branches in the cold dark beyond, it seemed there was nothing better than to curl up with something which would send an even deeper chill through our bones. Everyone loved a good ghost story, and most of us, if pressed or reminded, will admit that we still do. But where are they now? Where did the ghost story go?

Ghosts, of course, are as old as the stones of the hills from which they emerged. They and their cousins, the sprites, demons, familiars and witches of myth, have been around for as long as we have. But, if there was a golden age for the ghost, it began with the Romantic Era and the glorification of all things "gothic", and lasted into a long twilight which extended its coldly evanescent arms deep into the first half of the twentieth century. Dickens, of course, wrote ghost stories. So did Henry James, Saki, Edith Wharton, D. H. Lawrence, H. G. Wells, L. P. Hartley, J. B. Priestly, E. F. Benson and virtually every other double-initialled major author of a certain age (ghosts all themselves, now). Telling tales which dipped the tips of their fingers into the chilly waters of the supernatural was something which most writers simply did back then: and there was certainly a market for their tales. Now, imagine Ian McEwan, John Updike or Zadie Smith writing a ghost story . . .

In a famous article written sixty years ago, George Orwell lamented the decline of the English murder. Now, it seems, the English ghost story has gone a similar way. Not, as Orwell accepted, that people weren't being murdered any longer, but murders, in the wake of the war, the V1, the V2 and the long-range bomber, were becoming less personal. Death as a whole was turning into an industry. The good old, bad old days, when people plotted for years, quietly sharpened their knives, primed their poisons, excavated their basements and filled their bathtubs with lime— when, above all, they knew and cared about, either loved or hated, their murderees—were being replaced by a different kind of carnage. Interestingly, Orwell cites the random killing spree which ex-waitress Elizabeth Jones and US army deserter Karl Hulten went on in 1944 as a sign of the changing times, and he was right. The new beast of terror of the post-war years, the serial killer who kills merely for the sake of killing and has, almost by definition, no true motive, had already escaped its cage.

In this era, we have so many other things to fear. Not just the stranger at the bus-stop, but the rucksack he carries and the bugs he emits when he sneezes. Ghosts appear less *relevant* somehow. So what if Auntie Masie saw Cousin Stan clear as day when he was fighting his last at Slough General? And does it really matter to anyone other than the local tourist board if some gentleman in need of a head wanders the battlements of the local ruin? For most post-war writers, the answer has been no. Serious modern writers, and Ian McEwan is a classic example, certainly trade in fear. But the fear they explore is of every kind but the supernatural. Similarly, Steven King and his many imitators, whose genre of doorstop horror fiction might be taken to be the natural modern home of the sprite and spirit, rarely explore anything so wispy as a mere ghost. Full-on horror, fictional variations of the sort of thing we have streamed live to our screens on the newscasts every evening, has mostly replaced the graveyard murmur of lost voices—unless those voices happen to be attached to the loose jaws of rampaging and irredeemably fleshy zombies. Sitting in the cinema, at home, or reading on the train, we are scared as we have never been scared before. But the scares (with some few, honourable, exceptions) are big and bloody and bone-wrenching. "Are people so numb that they need movies of this intensity in order to feel anything at all?" Roger Ebert asked when reviewing *The Exorcist*. Then and now, the answer would seem to be yes.

But people haven't stopped believing—at least not the kids. In the sessions about creepy stories I sometimes deliver at schools, a forest of arms appears when I ask if any of them wants to share any ghostly experiences. Maybe as adults, many of us are less susceptible to witnessing disembodied faces and feeling strange chills—we look to the alien-infested skies instead, or the latest conspiracy which turns history on its head—but few of us doubt the word of those who claim they have really seen something. Sure, we tell ourselves, the mind is a strange and complex mechanism, and wasn't there that test once which proved that many people who thought they saw things really *were* actually seeing them? We're disappointed sceptics, wary peerers into the veils of a different kind of darkness which is still out there somewhere, but which seems as we reach towards it to float forever farther away.

I, certainly, used to love ghost stories. One of my defining reading experiences was an anthology entitled *Medley Macabre* which I discovered when I was a teenager back in the late sixties. Fat and full, pointlessly subdivided into sections covering premonitions, spirits, witchcraft, hauntings and so forth, and sporting the names of the kinds of authors I'd heard of but would never normally want to read, it opened a door which, both as a writer and a reader, I've been struggling to keep ajar ever since. *Medley Macabre* was a library book, but I came across a copy a year or so ago in a charity shop as I wandered at lunchtime during one of my school visits. I bought it like a shot, although I can't say that rereading it has been a particularly thrilling experience. There are, I soon came to realise, obvious reasons why the traditional English ghost story has faded, and those reasons are pretty much the same ones which explain why few people read Edith Wharton or J. B. Priestley or H. E. Bates unless in response to some pre-digested TV version of one of their works. The book, and, it must be said, much of the genre, creaks with starchy English middle-classishness. Almost exclusively, ghosts only happen to nice people who live, or happen to be visiting, nice friends who live in even nicer houses. If it's a story from the army, the guy who's telling it is an officer from one of the older regiments, and he's probably sitting nursing a brandy in his London club. Governesses, maids, gardeners—indeed, any other kinds of people who actually work for a living, are there either as background, or to be vaguely sinister before stepping back for the real denouement. They rarely ever get the chance to actually do any proper haunting; after all, they're working class, and should have better things to do with their time than lounge around in twilight corridors, even when dead. No, haunting is reserved for the kind of people who devoted their lives to hanging around, looking decorative and doing little productive work, and were thus far better equipped to spend eternity doing much the same. Even when the writers happen to be American or European, traditional ghost stories are often suffused with an Englishness of the kind which tended to dominate much of literature in the days before the world caught on and realised what a small and essentially parochial place England really is. The pieces which still retain some power in *Medley Macabre* and similar collections, tend to be those written by writers who didn't choose to pen the odd creepy story merely to get themselves into the Christmas editions of the posh magazines. They wrote strange and creepy stories because strange and creepy was exactly how they saw the world. Drinking, festering in their garrets, crawling the gutters of their obsessions, American loners like Edgar Allen Poe and H. P. Lovecraft pointed their pale fingers towards a new world, and a terrible century.

So that should be it, then. Ghosts certainly don't exist in any provable scientific sense—if they did, they'd have been found, categorised and hung up for our inspection long ago—and the supposedly classic stories about them are often class-ridden exercises in creating twee thrills. We've moved on. Boo . . . ! No, we're not scared, and you're just being ridiculous. Now, please take off that stupid sheet. But before we give up the genre entirely to the darker corners of charity shops, perhaps we should consider what else—apart from dusty class prejudice—we might be waving away.

The characteristic which comes to mind above all else with a good ghost story is its sheer subtlety. In much the same way that pornography and sexually-loaded advertising have downgraded eroticism, the mundanity and bland universality of the fear which so much of the media pedal has made us forget the quieter, softer, colder sense of chill which comes when something which doesn't quite belong in our world brushes against our thoughts. In literature, in films, in the news and in newspapers, there's so much of *everything* now that the little that isn't there, the things which can't be defined or listed or blown up in digitised slow motion, that we can easily forget, that the unquantifiable can't ever be made to entirely go away.

There are one or two decent recent examples of ghost stories which buck the trend, especially in the movies, of all places (and no, I don't mean Harry Potter; real ghost stories are *never* for children, which is why some children love reading them—or at least, I did). Certainly, the re-working of the classic *The Haunting* turned the film into an exercise in meaningless special effects, but *The Sixth Sense* did manage to chill us until a messy denouement, and *The Others* did so even more successfully through the clever twist of having a haunted house where the ghosts emerged not in darkness, but with the light of day. Even the recent *Skeleton Key*, for all that it pushed the usual southern gothic buttons, managed to recapture some of that old, odd feeling we've all sometimes experienced when we entered a strange and seemingly empty, but not quite empty enough, room. So there is hope. There is some life, or at least, death, in the old dog yet.

The Victorians, who feared God, and had to look death in the eye far more regularly than most of us do now, loved ghost stories. Perhaps they were merely comforted by the idea of presences beyond the grave, and there is undeniably some comfort to be found in stories which reassure us that the world consists of more than that which can be classified and analysed. But mostly, I think, they found in them a way to transform something terrible into something which, while perhaps still terrible, is also rendered beautiful as well. Yes, the Victorians knew what death was, and they experienced fear, and they believed or wanted to believe in some kind of afterlife, but they also understood that not everything could be encompassed in any system of hope, logic or belief. Now, as we teeter at the start of an unnamed age, we balance as well on the knowledge that the world is imperfectible, that knowledge itself is uncertain, and that the matter of which we and this page are made is nothing more than a seething froth of potentiality folded from an impossible number of dimensions, perhaps the time for the shiver which raises the hairs on the backs of our necks is returning. What, after all, is death, and life, and consciousness, and time? Why *do* we cling to the past? And what exactly do we now fear, when there is so much to fear?

Forget the starched collars and quaint locals in their cosy cottages and the cream teas and the parasol-wielding spinsters of the ghost story in its lost English heyday. But don't forget the thing you imagine for a moment as you awake, that appears to be standing at the edge of your bed, and hovers there for a moment longer than seems reasonable as you try to blink it away. Of course, it's just the dressing gown you hung on the door on your way from the bathroom, although you make a mental note, as you drift back towards a changed sleep, not to hang it again on that particular peg again. Life would be lessened without these momentary twinges of illogic. Funnily enough, it would also be sadder, and less hopeful, and probably make even less sense.

There are still some classic English ghost stories which deserve to be read. Anyone who hasn't explored the works of M. R. James such as "Oh Whistle and I'll Come to You My Lad" and "The Stalls of Barchester Cathedral" can't really claim to have a full knowledge of English short fiction, and has an enormous treat awaiting. Dickens still works, W. W. Jacobs' "The Monkey's Paw" remains a classic, and the Irish writer Le Fanu has a cool and sexy detachment which seems untouched by age. Shirley Jackson, of all twentieth century writers, managed to push the ghost story closest towards something which reflects a more modern age, although she was an American. Her novel *The Haunting of Hill House*, upon which one very successful and one less successful films have been based, remains a sparkling, eerie classic. Robert Aickman is also a more modern author whose elliptical tales of terror are well worth investigating. But if there was one story I'd single out from the lost and surely once-golden age of the English ghost story, it would probably be *The Beckoning Fair One* by Oliver Onions, which sets itself in a dowdy London flat and, for all its late Victorian circumlocutions, hits upon one of the creepiest, and loveliest, incorporeal manifestations. Simply, the resident of this damp flat is haunted, and becomes obsessed by, the swishing sound of a woman brushing her hair. Slowly, and as all good ghost stories should, it gets worse, but the subtle pitch is maintained all the way through to a denouement involving something glimpsed in a cupboard which would make even the most hardened aficionado of the streamlined terrors of modern horror want to look away.

Since then, of course, there have been many ghost stories. They are still a staple of the winter season, but they're certainly not the force they once were. Unlike George Orwell's lost English murders, though, we shouldn't quite give up the ghost just yet. If there is scope for something new in this genre, it lies beyond the twee visions of children's fantasists like J. K. Rowling, or even the playfully twisted realities which the Magical Realists once managed to convey; neither of these even attempt to disturb in the traditional English ghost story's coldly subtle way. It probably also lies beyond the cosy idea of *A Ghost Story for Christmas*, or of merely shifting a haunting from the time-honoured stately pile into the chromium kitchen of one of the sheltered flats which was built during the eighties in its grounds. If the genre is to reinvent itself, it doesn't need to strive for relevance or catharsis, but to stumble across these things as it goes about the time-honoured process of making us want to glance back over our shoulder as we read. It's a hit and miss business, the ghost story, but at its best, it can throw the dimmest and eeriest of lights into corners of this world which no other kind of fiction can reach.

LETTER TO WILL

DEAR WILL

That last letter you sent me was the best of all. I know how hard it must be for you, out there in France fighting for your country, but it's good to know that you and your mates in the Worcestershires can take a bit of leave and go somewhere nice and have a few drinks. I know you couldn't tell me where it was, Will—War Office censor and all that—but I picture it as a bit like the painting of the town with the tall steeple and bright clouds that my Nan used to have. Not sure you ever saw it. Nor have I got the foggiest where it was supposed to be, but I always thought it looked a bit foreign.

Not a lot to report here. One thing you can say about this war, though, is that it's been good for Stourport. Time was that things were slow, what with the railways and everything. But I can tell you that trade here at Edwards and Son, Chandlers by appointment to bargemen and boatmen, is going pretty well. Even if the sign over the shop is a bit old and the son is Dad, and with Mum long gone and me being the only Edwards offspring to make it past the crib and not a son at all. As, Will, I think you probably noticed on those evenings when we walked out. There's big loads of coal and iron heading north through the locks to make guns, I suppose, and whatever else this war needs. Pit props from the forest going down the other way for the mines. But lots of other stuff you would never think of that the war seems to need as well. Pots and pans and bricks and whole windows, all ready-made and shining in the sun. And loads and loads of rope, made strong and long in Bewdley, of course, which you know all about, Bewdley being your home town. So much of the stuff I reckon I could tie one end around me and the other end around you and pull and pull until it drew us both back together and there was nothing between us. And maybe then, Will. But the world is full of maybes and what have yous isn't it? And I told you before you went that we would wait until we were properly married and there is no use my bothering about what's never going to happen in a month of Sundays. Although I suppose we can dream.

Enough of this. I'm half a candle down already and I've not said any of the things I wanted to say. Like how I wake up in this room above the shop to the sound of Dad coughing, which hasn't got much better despite the new linctus Doctor Antony's given him, by the way. No time to wait for dawn or cock crow. Not with so much that needs doing. The pump in the yard, and the night bucket, and any new stock for sorting, and the fire to be cleaned and the kettle to be boiled and Dad to have his breakfast fixed seeing as he's not up to doing it himself, and I squeeze in a cup of tea and count the change into the till before I turn the sign on the door from Closed to Open at seven of the clock sharp. Sometimes, a few bargeman will already be smoking their pipes outside and asking me what time I call this. Their sort keep odd hours, and now they've got this God Save the King business to throw at me if I don't have the right colour pot of paint or a new bolt for their tiller on the shelves.

So that's the start of my mornings for you, Will, and I haven't even got around to saying the thing I wanted to say. Soon as I wake up, and despite Dad and his coughing, I feel like you're with me and we really are tied and joined forever by that rope that nothing can ever pull us apart. Then, I turn over and there's your picture. That one you had taken before you went off to France. Looking so smart in your uniform with that smile of yours that makes me feel all warm but I reckon would probably scare the Hun. I lift the frame up and kiss it and I hope that doesn't sound creepy to you, Will. I can see you right now, looking handsome and proud, if I hold up what's left of this candle. And what I really wanted to say, Will, is that my every day begins with thoughts of you.

Usually by about ten, when the early rush is over and Dad's feeling up to it, I sit him on his stool behind the counter and leave him to take care of the shop while I head around the basins to do all the things that need to be done. Now Stourport is so busy again, the scene is cheery enough. That is, if you don't mind all the cursing and the coalsmoke and the smell of horse dung. Bargees and costermongers saying hello Flo, which is what they call me, not Florence like you always do, and tipping their hats. At least some of them. But not so many as used to if I'm honest. I suppose a bit of a cloud hangs over me since word of what happened got out. The groceries to be got and the post to be posted. Maybe a rabbit for me and Dad for supper if I'm feeling flush. A bit of mousetrap and half a cauliflower if not. Sometimes, the way everyone's so busy and smiling, you might think that there was scarcely a war going on at all.

Not sure if I should tell you this Will, but Mrs Bold came up to me yesterday on the High Street with that mole dangling on her cheek like it's got a mind of its own. I've never much liked the woman. Far too Holy Holy Lord God Almighty and looks down her nose and that mole at everything. Anyway, it was still almost nice that she spoke to me when most people these days don't. Not isn't the weather surprisingly ordinary or would you believe the price of potatoes, either. But telling me about you, and how fine and grand it was that you'd volunteered to fight when others have stayed safe at home like the cowards they are. And how proud that must make me feel to have been stepping out with a soldier even though she disapproved of unchaperoned contact before marriage on strong moral grounds. She went on and on like this. All smiley and even grasping my arm as if she didn't know when to stop. And I started to think, poor thing. Maybe she's embarrassed like most people who know we were a couple are. And I'm thinking, is there a polite way I can stop her and get back to Dad at the shop before the trade starts to pick up before lunch? It's only when she starts talking of weddings and babies after the peace when all the nasty Germans have been killed that I finally worked out what was going on. She simply didn't know, Will. Hadn't realised or been told even though your name's been on the lists in the local papers and read out at church. Either that, or she'd forgot.

I don't think you're in Paradise, Will. Or at least not the sort of Paradise that Mrs Bold expects to get to and will probably complain about as she looks down her mole and plucks at her harp. I've no idea where you are, Will. Other than that you're here. Right here with me. Now.

I'm not sure if you soldiers know how these things work, but there was a telegram which came to your Mum. And, fair's fair, she walked down the river from Bewdley that same afternoon to show me, even if it was so crumpled that I could scarcely read what it said. It was like some worn out ghost of you had been killed in action rather than the real William Bishop. Even now it's been in the paper and everyone but Mrs Bold seems to know and people aren't talking to me the way they used to, I could still believe you're alive easy as anything, Will. It's thinking you're dead in some foreign field that's the hardest thing to believe of all.

So I walked back to the shop after Mrs Bold had finally shut up. The name on the door of that imaginary son, and there was the postman with your letter in his hand. If it wasn't for the postmark being three days before the telegram, I could have told myself there'd been some mistake and you weren't dead at all. But the postman, kind of him really, he told me that this sort of thing happens now and then. The telegrams are quick, sent down wires, all light and electricity, and turned into print that gets taken by a lad on a bicycle in no time at all. The whole street stood watching as he comes and hoping he's not going to stop like he did on Lax Lane outside your Mum's. But the letters you lads send us go on trains and boats and wagons and take weeks to come.

It was a lovely letter, though, Will. My name written on the outside in your fine handwriting, and I'd normally have rushed upstairs to read it right away, shop or not. But somehow I couldn't. You'll laugh, I know, when I tell you why it took me a whole day to find the courage to open it up. Thing is, I was worried it might contain bad news. Ridiculous, of course—I mean could any news be worse than what I already knew? It was only when I finished reading it just now, Will, that I worked it out. You see, I wanted more than anything for you to be happy. And you were—having a fine old time by the sound of it with those brilliant mates of yours on your last leave from the front. That, and I wanted to know, to feel in my heart, that you still love me. And you told me that as well.

So here it is, Will. My last ever letter to you in answer to yours. After all, I couldn't not reply to something as lovely as what you sent me, now could I? I wasn't that badly brought up. Posting it in a way that'll reach you could be a bit more difficult. But we'll cross that bridge as and when.

The candle's almost gone now. I must get to bed and then up before cock crow and Dad's cough. You know me, Will. Always in a hurry, and not much of a one for sentiment. I haven't even cried yet. Better to crack on. But there's one other thing I wanted to share with you, Will. You might even think it a bit creepy, although maybe you're past such things. But here goes—

I've been seeing odd things about the town, Will. Started happening, and I know you'll tell me this is sheer nonsense, the day before the lad with the telegram came to your Mum's. Which is the exact day that you became a hero for your country and were lost to me. I felt no foreboding or anything like that. But something a bit odd seemed to happen to my eyes. Things seemed a bit blurry that morning as I walked up past the Tontine. Perhaps the best way of putting it is to say that was like looking though a kaleidoscope, or those coloured windows you get in a church. Oh, I thought to myself, peering around and feeling a bit stupid, why are the buildings shimmering and dancing as if their bricks are on fire?

Ghosts of buildings. I know it's daft. But that was what I seemed to be seeing. And ghosts of people as well. I know they were ghosts because some of them walked right through me. Were talking and laughing, and wearing the most extraordinary clothes. Women in trousers, would you believe? Bare arms and legs and no bonnets. The men with these odd, bright fabrics and funniest haircuts. Up on the High Street, I could still see the horses and the wagons, but there were these sleek machines that looked like bright fish all reflected in the shop windows as they slid past. I'm surprised I didn't get run over by something real, I was so busy trying to avoid whatever else was going on.

It faded soon enough, so I suppose you'd say it was just a bit of soapy water that I hadn't properly washed from my eyes, although it's come back to me once or twice since. And I really don't mind that much when it happens. Sort of brightens up my days. Which, if I'm honest, Will, and lovely though your letter was, could do with a bit of brightening.

I'm feeling stupid now and the last of my candle's going and I'm writing almost in the dark. Even if you were still in this world, Will I think I'd just tear this letter up. What I suppose I should be telling you is how brave you are, and how wonderful it is that you've made the sacrifice you have. But I don't feel ready for that, and there's this theory I have that I want to share with you about the strange things I thought I saw. I don't think they're proper ghosts, Will. At least, not the old-fashioned sort, any more than that's what I think you now are. But who knows how time really works? I mean, your last letter to me proves just how easily it can get twisted around. So, what if I got slipped a bit sideways, and what I was seeing was a blurry vision not of how things used to be, but how they might become?

So there, Will. I wanted to tell you about that, and now I have. And, rather than leave this letter hanging like some old washing, I might as well try to finish it properly off. I *am* proud of you. I really am, even though I know I haven't told so you anything like often enough. And I'm not cross with you, either, because I know that dying for your country is a glorious thing for any solider to do, and really not your fault.

By the way, you might be wondering if I'm thinking about some other boy. But I can't. Not in a month of Sundays or when this war is finally done. It'll always be you and me, Will, and I'll carry those memories of the times we walked out for as long as I live. Sad old maid before my time, then. That's what the people who won't talk to me probably think. And they're almost right. But I'm not sad, Will. Not when I'll always have what we had and your lovely last letter. And I won't give up.

Dad's not up to running the shop any longer. He admits as much himself. But I can. In fact, I already am. Want to know a funny thing, Will? It's the last funny thing, I promise. Those blurry ghosts—the last time I saw them was a few days ago. I went back around the basins, and there were these spinning lights and people laughing with their faces lit up like some giant carnival had dropped down from the sky. And I thought as I wandered through it that this is what heaven should be like, and not Mrs Bold's place with the harps. So if I'd like to think of you anywhere, Will, it would be with your best mates from the Worcestershires in some great, endless fairground where everyone's happy and all the stalls and rides are free. But the scene soon faded, and I somehow knew that was the end of the whole business as I walked the rest of the way back. But not quite, although this was a vision of a different sort. You see, Will, I looked up at that sign above our shop. The one that says, Edwards and Son. And I decided it was about time it was re-painted. And not to Edwards and Daughter, either. But to Florence Edwards, Chandlers.

Now, Will. How does that sound?

Note: The name of Private William Bishop of the Worcestershire Regiment is on the war memorial outside St Anne's Church in Bewdley. The record at www.rememberthefallen.co.uk states: " . . . there appears to be no casualty with these details on Commonwealth War Graves Commission or Soldiers Died in the Great War. Unable to identify this casualty." I have borrowed, I hope respectfully, the name of this nearly-unknown soldier.

AFTERWORD *THOSE WHO CAN'T...*

I MENTION ELSEWHERE IN THIS COLLECTION THAT I'VE BEEN INVOLVED in teaching what's commonly known as "creative writing" for many years. "Dabbled" might be a better word, as I've never held any permanent position, and have dipped in and out of all sorts of levels from professional writers' workshops to rowdy classes in junior schools. Part of me greatly enjoys this work, and part me always feels fraudulent.

Let's face it, the growth of this idea of creative writing as a teachable subject over the last few decades has been good for professional writers. Between novels, scripts, poems, bouts of inspiration, cheques and commissions (and the gaps can be pretty long) it gives us something else to do. You can mark, you can plan your talks and lectures and come up with handouts and fresh themes, you can travel and attend meetings and hang out in collegiate halls. But as to the end product, whether the teaching of writing leads to people becoming good writers, in the way that the teaching of surgery leads to good surgeons—and I suspect that many surgeons might also disagree about that—I feel there's a pretty tenuous link. Sure, many excellent writers have now emerged from the colleges, workshops and universities that claim to teach this subject to an advanced level, but wouldn't they have become writers anyway, and possibly better and more original ones?

The only thing I can really claim to have any knowledge of is my own experience, which got me to publishing well-received novels and short stories without participating in any classes or workshops whatsoever, or indeed gaining any qualifications as a writer to this day. For me, learning about writing was about reading, and trying to write. I did, I admit, seek out a couple of books specifically about fiction writing in my early adult-hood—and I do mean, literally, two—and read many general pieces of the kind of which this afterword is itself an example, especially those written by writers I admired. I'm a loner by instinct, as I think most writers are, and I like to stand back and listen and observe, but I want to make my own mistakes and don't like being told what to do. The idea of the guiding hand, the group opinion, the "useful exercise", the ready-made steps, the preparations and layouts, the term-by-term planning and development, the need to "show your workings" and back up whatever you've produced in the same way that I remember being required to do in maths, still makes me cringe.

What these sort of classes, courses and degrees can provide is the companionship of other writers and would-be writers—in itself a double-edged sword—and a way of gaining some basic competence in the same way that I could learn to become okay at oil painting or golf, but never necessarily be any good, if I took a course. Which is why, although I'm always happy to talk and write about the art and the craft of writing, I generally, prefer to work with kids, especially those who already enjoy writing, because they lack that linear adult sense of "if I do x and y, z will result". In other words, they're interested in writing not because of some perceived end result, but because it's rewarding and fun. They don't want to *learn* about it, any more than a kid out in the park wants to learn about playing football. They want to *do* it.

Which brings me to "Letter to Will," which was prompted by a commission to write a story on a theme decided by my monthly teenage writers' group. Which, as it turned out, was to be about a young woman living in Stourport, where our session was taking place, and set—as the anniversary was already in the air—during the First World War. None of which had been in my mind before we discussed it, although I had this half-remembered thing in the back of my mind about the poignant delays which occurred with the news which came back from the trenches, and the story, after a few weeks of fairly unthinking gestation, pretty much flowed on from that.

ME AND THE MUSHROOM CLOUD

WE all know the future isn't what it used to be. The monorails, the tight-fitting silver suits, the long rows of wardrobe-sized computers with their spinning reels of magnetic tape, have come and gone—if they ever came in the first place. We saw them, if we saw them at all, in fleeting glimpses. They were the yetis of our imaginations, they were the Bermuda Triangles of the newspaper headlines, lingering at the edges of real life; they were the Kirlian photographs of our auras which we never got to see. Such matters awaited—still await—any kind of rational explanation. But the backdrop against which these images were cast was something far more solid. For the larger part of half a century, our whole concept of the future was overshadowed by the chilly thought that, unless you happened to be a cockroach, there might not be any future at all.

I was born in the fifties, grew up in the sixties. My sister loved the Beatles, and the pictures on my bedroom walls were of the lesser beat groups left over from the magazines she'd shredded to adorn hers. Then my brother, who was a little older and apprenticed as a print compositor in the days when such a trade still existed, gave me some magazine pictures he'd accumulated as part of his training. There were cars and there were planes, both of which I was developing an increasing interest in, but the one I remember, the one which immediately drew my attention with something approaching a budding sexual frisson, was a lengthwise colour spread of the mushroom cloud of an atomic bomb. My brother was surprisingly concerned about my choice. "You know what these things can do?" he asked. I nodded my head—of course I knew—and went off to find the Sellotape with which to affix it, in those days before Blu Tack, to my bedroom wall.

There it was. To the left of my bed, so I could see it when I first woke up and last thing before I turned out the light. Immense and somehow god-like, both religious, scientific, and yes, I suppose, phallic. This, it said to me, is what we humans are capable of making. This is what we can do. I didn't then know Oppenheimer's famous words about the destroyer of worlds when he witnessed the detonation of the first hydrogen bomb, but similar thoughts somehow echoed in my mind. Forget about the Bible. Forget about career choices and girls and puberty. Forget about weekdays at school and the long walks I was beginning to take away from my council estate on weekends at home. This was Death, and it was pure, ultimate, world-shattering. I, we all, lived beneath its shadow. And, to me at least, it was sexy and exciting.

A story my mother told me—I have no idea whether it ever happened—was of a couple who'd walked with their child into the sea and drowned themselves back in the Cold War fifties because they couldn't see how human life could continue. Well, we were still here in the sixties, but only just, and it seemed to me that all that effort, all those missiles in their silos in the wild wastelands of Siberia and Texas, could hardly lay dormant for much longer. They were too beautiful, too clean, too perfect. They bore too much purpose. And the end result, that mush-room cloud, was simply too glorious. When the time came for school projects, I lingered long in the local library over soberly jacketed books which detailed, in dense paragraphs and neatly italicised lists, deathrates and afterlifes and megatonnage and final symptoms. From these, and from my aircraft magazines, I learned a whole new terminology. ICBMs and MIRVs. Titans and Minutemen. Ground zero. And it wasn't just mush-room clouds. Even in those days, there was chemical and there was biological as well. The difference was that we weren't just worried about attacks on railway stations and department stores; these weapons would kill us all.

Being a lad of the English Midlands, a shortish bus ride away from the ground zero which I'd seen central Birmingham indicated as on maps, I didn't imagine that I'd survive the first lob of missiles. Although I'd be outside the initial fireball, I was still in the zone of likely 100% casualties. All there would be was a flash, a rumble, and that would be it. Still, there would be some survivors, or so the SF books I was also starting to read led me to think. And those people, as they established monastic communities with liturgies based on discarded shopping lists or fought mutant monsters re-emerged from the Greek myths, generally seemed to have a far better time of it than anything which the prospects of life in the mid-to-late Twentieth Century had on offer. At the end of the day, it was hard for a moderately disaffected teenage lad not to see nuclear annihilation as A Good Thing. Of course it was glamorous! How couldn't it be? Nuclear death was American, for a start, or it was Russian, and both of those countries were far more exciting and mysterious than England could ever be. Sleek submarines prowled the oceans depths while wise men in white suits ignited deserts, and supersonic planes roamed the skies and pushed hard to get into the starry black space above so that it, too, could be claimed for the Arms Race. We in England had the bomb as well, but in a maverick James Bond, Avro Vulcan, Aston Martin sort of way. After all, we didn't want to miss out on the biggest party of all, which was the End of the World.

As I grew older, the prospect of nuclear death faded. I had other fish to fry; a life to grow into. Then, there was détente. The USSR (as people now more commonly called it) turned out not to be quite the monstrous Stalinist beast which we had previously imagined. Indeed, America itself, the USA, with all the cruise and Trident missiles it was trying to sell to poor, bankrupt Britain, was at least as much of a monster. Still, the shadow remained there in the background, not least with the arrival of the concept of nuclear winter. Gone were those glassy desert landscapes where Mad Max and his scantily-clad cohorts could adventure at will. Instead, we were faced with the prospect of gloomy grey skies and endless sleet—a sort of perpetual Manchester in February—engulfing the entire world. Nuclear death was now much less appealing, and this non-sexy image was reinforced by a spate of made-for-TV epics which portrayed the aftermath of a nuclear exchange in terms of blistering, hair loss, starvation and endless wintry misery. No wonder Ronnie and Gorbie were so keen to get rid of their missiles when they met at Reykjavik! After all, who'd want to keep the damned things, when nuclear winter was all they'd achieve? And nuclear power itself, in explosive Chernobyl and leakily incontinent Sellafield, and the fact that other supposedly lesser countries like India and Israel were getting in on the act, was rapidly losing what was left of its glamour. It was like Concorde, or the drip-dry shirt. It had arrived amid much fanfare, we'd got used to it, decided it was probably more fuss than it was worth, and moved on to something else.

In my own personal world, married by now and with a career of sorts in the Civil Service, which gave me the time to write longhand stretches of my first novel, the prospect had faded. I certainly liked the idea of Julie Christie visiting the women camped outside Greenham Common, but then I liked the idea of Julie Christie doing pretty much anything. As someone who regarded himself as intellectual and liberal, I would have argued in favour of unilateral nuclear disarmament, but the subject rarely came up. Like macrobiotic food or animal experiments, it was a trend which had come and gone; it was flared trousers and prog-rock and the spacehopper. I could stare out of my office window at the skyline of central Birmingham for hours without imagining it being engulfed in a white pulse and a shattering blast. Then, through one of the regular moves which are inflicted on government workers once they show any signs of becoming proficient at any particular job, I found myself in a post which included responsibilities for a large safe which contained the details on all types emergency planning.

There were contingencies. There were maps. Here I was, back in the world of my teenage fantasies. It still existed, but only just. I never got the impression (and I have to say that this was quite a long time ago) that anyone in my little corner of government really took the nuclear threat seriously. It was just another paper exercise, like abandoned plans for moving office or a new costing system for stationery. I was a small fish in any case, and certainly wouldn't be going underground, into some dripping cellar filled with old maps and abandoned office furniture, with the senior officials. I'd be up on the surface with all the rest of the world, dead, or slowly freezing and starving as I lost my hair, teeth and what was left of my youthful nuclear dreams. I did, though, once go to a seminar which was brightened by green-cardiganed ladies from the WRVS explaining how they'd be there to ensure that all the straggling survivors were given a nice, warm cup of tea. This, at the far end of that glittering and dangerous technological rainbow which had started in the deserts of Arizona, in the top secret forests of Nazi Germany, in the visionary thoughts of the century's greatest brains, in the click of Leica cameras, in the silky whispers of a thousand high-heeled double agents and that picture on my bedroom wall dangling from its yellowing Sellotape, was what things had come to. Not so very long after that, I and the Civil Service parted company. I became a house-husband, and a writer, and I and the entire world, it seemed, forgot about the prospect of nuclear war.

But it's still there. It hasn't gone away. Even that beautifully named condition of MAD—Mutually Assured Destruction—still exists. Russia, although diminished and no longer the USSR, and with its oil wealth funding one of our major football teams, retains the capability to annihilate most of the western world, and we'd still do the same to them in return, wouldn't we? Nuclear winter isn't like global warming; no one has ever come up with serious calculations which refute it. The world could still die tomorrow, and the men in charge (for there is little reason here to use gender-neutral language) are as mad in the old non-capital letter sense, and in many ways madder, than their predecessors. An American President who believes that the Biblical end of the world is near, anyone? Or how about an aggressive Russian puppet-President who controls, or claims to control, a disaffected, poorly paid and under-resourced military? The missiles may have decreased in number, but they're still waiting in their silos, even if they've gone a little rusty, and the planes are still on the runways, or already circling overhead in case the runways are destroyed, and the submarines are prowling the chill fishless depths. Then there's nuclear proliferation. If all-out obliteration has lost some of its appeal and likelihood, we may nevertheless have to face up to many Hiroshimas. China's nuclear arsenal is growing, the current list of other countries with a nuclear weapons capability includes France, India, Israel, Pakistan and of course Russia, along with the United Kingdom and the good old U S of A. And the list is lengthening, with Iran and North Korea both actively pursuing their own nuclear visions, even if we now know that Iraq's atomic dream was little more than George W's and Tony Blair idiotic catnap.

Nothing was the same after September 11, and I don't doubt that curling posters of the twin towers exploding adorn many teenage bedrooms far beyond Palestine. But, compared with my mushroom cloud, it all seems a little puny. Me, I moved on from reading stories about the future to writing them, although in ways which mostly avoided bare-chested Mel Gibson silliness, or detailing the lives of cockroaches. But my novel, *Song of Time* which I've recently finished begins here and now, where I still live, near Birmingham, and it's forced me to think again about the monorail-less future as something which my characters, and, indeed, I, will still experience. I have to tell you that it's not easy to be cheerful about this new century. There's global warming. There's ecological catastrophe. There are new diseases, and rejuvenated old ones. As ever, there is war and starvation, and the global population (another sixties preoccupation) continues to grow. Then there's terrorism, our current obsession. With that, we've even reached the point of producing leaflets and TV commercials which, no matter how well-intentioned, will no doubt seem as ridiculous in retrospect as that American fifties Duck and Cover film and Norman Fowler's eighties AIDS tombstone commercials. No, the future's not what it once was, but it still has a way of producing events which seem wildly surprising at the time they occur, and yet come, in historical retrospect, to appear entirely inevitable.

These days, I have a family, and a writerly career which I don't have to hide under a government office desk; a whole life which I'd like to hold on to for as long as possible. The last thing I'd want to put on my study wall now, amid my daughter's youthful doodlings and the photos of my wife, is a poster of a thermonuclear mushroom cloud. But the bomb hasn't gone away. To me, it's been like some faithful friend through all these long years, a dark guardian angel, changing, yes, but remaining essentially the same, even when I've neglected it. The bomb's long shadow still hangs over us. And the more we forget, the more we invade impoverished lesser states on flimsy pretence, or create bogy men or false messiahs, or merely worry about congestion charging or the cost of dental treatment or where we're going to go on holiday, the bigger that shadow will grow. Flash. No sound at first, but everything electrical will instantly stop working. Then the shockwave, which will rip up trees and shred flesh and demolish buildings, followed by the fireball which will ignite everything. Then the aftermath, which will be terrible beyond the imagining of all but those who witnessed what happened all those years ago at Nagasaki and Hiroshima. I hope, now, that I never live to see such a thing, and that neither does my daughter, nor her children, nor her children's children. But we're an odd kind of race, us humans; we've always been prepared to think the unthinkable, accept the unacceptable, do the undoable, eat the forbidden fruit, press the button marked Do Not Press. Think of September 11. Think of the Holocaust. Think of the atomic bomb. Eventually, things which can possibly happen tend to happen, even if they're left to nothing but pure chance.

TUMBLING NANCY

AFTER getting my BA in English Lit from a redbrick university back in the early 60s, and with little other idea of what I might do with my life, I started working for the Philip Hobbs Literary Agency as what I suppose an American might describe as an intern, although we in England don't dignify such posts with any particular title. Underpaid jobsbody, though, would have just about covered it.

Don't believe what you now read and hear about the 60s. Even London, which was supposedly at the centre of everything, wasn't that swinging. It was a world which belonged far more to the songs of Rolf Harris and Ken Dodd than it ever did to the Rolling Stones and Jimi Hendrix. London, mostly then as mostly now, was a city full of grey streets, grinding traffic, bickering tourists and limping pigeons. The books that were selling then were as bad as the books which are selling now, although most of their authors, like the songs which really dominated the radio at that time, are best forgotten. I'd gone into the business of books with my head still filled with the works of Proust, F. Scott Fitzgerald and Shakespeare. What I found instead was an industry which subsisted on the outpourings of Barbara Cartland and Dennis Wheatley.

Philip Hobbs was a decent enough old buffer. He cared about his authors, and he cared about books. He was continually bemoaning, through the pipefug of his big old office, the dreadful plight of the publishing industry to anyone who would listen. And listen I did. I'd already worked out that all the stuff I'd learned about great literature was sheer flimflam when it came to the actual business of pushing print. But the publishing industry, I'd somehow decided, was how I was going to make the world sit up and bloody well notice Ros Godby—although a look in the mirror, or a survey of the long nights I'd spent standing in the corner at parties studying the bit on the back of LP sleeves which told you how stereo recordings could also be played on suitably adapted mono equipment, might have had something to do with my decision. In ordinary social intercourse, I know, I'm awkward. Physically, I've never had it. My nose is long and my chest is flat and my legs are bowed and my eyes are set close together and my voice tends to oscillate between a screech and a whisper. Not, of course, that I didn't occasionally manage to get myself involved in sweaty fumbles with boys in doorways or coat-strewn bedrooms back in the day. But the other participant was almost always drunk, and invariably ugly.

In retrospect, I suppose you could say that my one meeting with Edna Bramley was a turning point in my career, although I hadn't planned it that way. Hobbsy simply called me in through the smog of his office one morning—it was by then just me and him and a lady who came in to do what passed for the accounts every other Wednesday—and waved with characteristic dolefulness a letter which had arrived with the rest of the day's meagre post.

"It's Penburys," he said. "The bastards have only gone and pulled the plug on Tumbling Nancy."

"Yes," I said. Neutrally. Everyone of my age and a bit older remembers Tumbling Nancy—although probably without much pleasure. But I hadn't realised that the author was one of ours.

"Poor old Edna. She's put her *life* into those books. I mean, not that they're . . . " He waved the letter again. The grey waves around him stirred and I thought, not for the first time, of Lewis Carroll's fat caterpillar smoking his hookah. "But not to renew the option. After all this time." Hobbsy pushed out his lower lip. He looked genuinely close to tears. There were displays like this almost every other morning. When he wasn't beaming and booming on about some *marvellous new voice, you just wait and see Ros, they'll take the world by storm* that was. Of course, they never did.

"What can you do?" I said. Then; "maybe I could check through the contract. Make sure what Penburys are doing is—"

"No point, my dear girl. Absolutely no point. You know how they tie these things up in small print. But perhaps you could go and have a word with the dear sweet lady? Break the news. Commiserate. Tell her all's not lost. There are plenty of other publishers out there. Plenty of other editors. Tell her it's an opportunity dressed up as an obstacle and we're on her case."

I nodded. Hobbsy had a thousand such phrases. Somehow, he still believed most of them. "Where does she live?"

"Oh, only down in sunny Balham."

All of which found me sitting in a dingy London café just a few hours later opposite a woman who spat at me as she talked. Edna Bramley, I'd quickly decided, wasn't actually either sweet or dear or that much of lady. Was she in her fifties, or older? I pondered, in that way that you do when you're not really listening to what people are saying. A tall woman, once-striking, perhaps, but clumsy and gangling, with long half-grey hair bunched up in an elastic band. She was wearing a frayed old coat with drooping lining, and emitted an odour of BO which competed with all the other café smells in small, sour waves. Talentless old crow, the younger me had thought. Writing those dreadful books, what right does she even think she has to call herself an author? She might almost have been a tramp— what nowadays we'd call a street person—dragging her worldly belongings in a collection of old bags, but she was unwavering in her determination to keep writing more books in the series about the character she called "My Nancy" in the face of Penburys', and most probably the whole world's, disinterest. It was *My Nancy* this and *My Nancy* that, and I leaned as far back as I could from the chipped formica table and waited for the sorry ordeal to finish.

"I'm sure Philip will come up with something," she said as she bent forward to display her unwashed hair's dandruff-clotted parting and spooned more dirty sugar into what was left of her coffee. "He's always worked so hard for me. Over so many years . . . " She scooped up the cup with trembling hands. Then she banged it down again. "He always says that losing a disinterested publisher is the best thing that can happen to a writer. Of course, changes in fashion don't mean changes in quality. And any a writer who—"

"He's dying," I said.

"What?" The cup clattered.

"Philip Hobbs. He's dying. The doctors say it's cancer of the lungs . . . " I extemporised, recalling the office pipefug and showing what was for the time, I think, a surprisingly prescient knowledge of the dangers of smoking.

"Oh! My!" She said it so loud that the other troglodytes in the café glanced around at us. But it was worth it, just to see the miserable look which melted her crinkled old face. After all, it was bad enough having to listen to Hobbsy drooling out this hopeful gibberish day after day. But to have it from this talentless has-been . . . It was really too much. "Is there anything I can do? I must send him flowers, a letter! Perhaps I could—"

"Oh, no." I raised a hand to block the spray. "You know what he's like. Carry on regardless. Every day is a new day."

"So he doesn't want people to even *mention* it?"

I nodded. "Exactly."

She was looking at me in an awed way now. "That's so *right*, isn't it? One has to carry on. Isn't that what we've been saying?"

"Well, *you* have, Edna." I felt as if I was on a roll, and I could get away with anything. "For my part," I sighed, "I really don't know. It's up to you, I guess. You can carry on writing. Or you can give the world a break and stop. To be honest, I doubt if it matters much either way."

"And who will be . . . ?" Her whole face twisted. "Taking over when he's . . . ?"

"It'll be me."

Not long after, her big face still spasming, Edna Bramley blundered between the tables and back out into the grey London streets. But I sat there a while longer. The café, with its crusted tomato sauce bottles and smell of old fat, seemed be suffused in a kind of glow.

It was, I suppose, a small example of the sort of moment Paul experienced on his way to Damascus. I'd realised you could say whatever you wanted, and, at least for a while, people tended to believe you. I mean, Hobbsy himself was a prime example. Although he'd wasted his life on pointless optimism, which had got him nowhere. And I wasn't going to let that happen to me.

I started dressing and acting more sharply after that. I didn't actually tell very many other people that Hobbsy was dying, but I made sure that I gave off the impression—along with a new whiff of Chanel and a better haircut and higher heels which did nothing to improve my looks but at least made sure that people noticed me—that I was in control now, and he was in terminal decline. And as for literature. Fuck literature—and it was unusual in those days for women to swear. What counts is what's going to sell this Christmas, and the fuddy duddies in their ivory towers can go hang themselves. People want to be entertained. They want to be diverted. Or, I came to realise, they probably don't actually want to read much at all. But they still like books, or at least they end up buying some of them, anyway.

Self-help this and that. Pointless lists. Novels which sell solely on the title. Books of inedible recipes that people will never try cooking. Celebrity confessionals. TV tie-ins. The self-justificatory twaddle of ex-politicians. Horoscopes for pets. As the proper bookshops began to close on every high street, this was the breaking wave in modern publishing. Within a few years, Ros Godby had become the kind of agent publishers knew they could always turn to when it came to producing something which would fill a gap in their autumn list. We're looking for something . . . Well, doesn't really matter what it is, Ros, but it's got to suggest shopping and smart hotels. Or gay vampires. Or teenage wizards. Or childhoods and surgical implants gone wrong. Or whatever the current theme was that the sales graph had clustered around, and had thus already been done to death. And I'd ring around, and I'd bully the necessary amount of junk out from some writer's bottom drawer or last night's nightmares which would broadly fit the bill, at least in the sense that it wouldn't warrant a law suit under the Trades Description Act. Good old Ros Godby. I mean, I sure wouldn't want to cross the snarly old bitch, but she's sure as hell pulled the iron out of the fire once again.

I was the voice and presence of PHL, as it was now called, even before Hobbsy retired from the scene and died not long after—of lung cancer, funnily enough, although I don't think I can claim much credit for that after all his years of pipe-abuse. I kept his offices but I had the interior gutted and cleaned out and changed into the squeaky modernist shrine of plateglass and blonde wood which visitors see today. My flat on the Thames isn't dissimilar. I like things new and sleek and clean.

PHL remains a small concern, at least in terms of staffing. Basically, it's just some front office piece of eye-candy. And me. Why would I want to have things done by others which I know I can do better myself? My roster of authors and ghost writers and so-called "celebrity talent" is always impressive, at least in terms of current sales, although in the nature of these things, it changes frequently. In truth, I've long grown tired of those midnight rants and rambling e-mails. If it were possible to be a literary agent without actually having to represent actual writers, I think I would probably go that way. Computers, maybe? They can do so many things these days. But one continuing bonus of the humble origins of PHL in the old Philip Hobbs Literary Agency is a backlist which encompasses some usefully recognisable literary names. A few Latin American magical realists and Lithuanian ex-dissidents may not pay the rent, but they do help to give my company the requisite gloss and keep up the charade that well-written words still matter in publishing. And the best thing of all about almost those Eng Lit Year Two warhorses is that they are all dead.

I *like* dead authors. No objections about marketing and covers. No this-isn't-how-Davina-treated-me-when-I-came-out-of-Big-Brother tantrums. None of those tiresome lunches. A clearly defined catalogue, and only a remote cousin to send a yearly account to. And dying can often be exactly the kind of push that the modern writer needs to get themselves noticed. So one of my first duties when I arrive at work each morning is to log onto *The Bookseller*'s website and check for fresh obituaries.

Which is what drew my attention to a small notice about none other than Edna Bramley. *Once-popular children's writer*, it said. *Mainly known for the Tumbling Nancy series*, it said. *Which she also illustrated*, it added. No mention of representation, but I was up and through the plateglass doorway into the shining space where my current assistant Mark should have been sitting. But Mark wasn't there, any more than he had been a few minutes earlier when I first came in. Sleeping off an over-strenuous session down at the gym, probably. Or with someone he met there. Vain men are even worse than vain women. Time to fire the useless faggot, but meanwhile I would have to undertake the tiresome task of going upstairs to look around in the store rooms myself.

After swallowing an anti-histamine, I keyed in the code for the fireproof door and headed up the creaking stairs. I've already told you that I like things new and clean and neat, and this rambling space full of old files and boxes of complimentary copies is none of these things. Truth is, I hate the upper floor of my offices, and would have the whole mess digitised and put on my Blackberry if it wasn't for the currently ridiculous cost. But I'll have it done, and sooner rather than later, in this day of the Kindle and the MP3. I might even take a trip along to the furnace to watch all the useless crap of lost ages go up in flames.

But there they were; four whole fat files amid the dead bluebottles and letter Bs. I took them down and flapped them out on Hobbsy's old desk, blinking and coughing and sneezing. Nothing but a few dwindling royalty statements after that seminal meeting with yours truly. And then, heaped nearby on the floor like dead seaweed thrown on the shore after a particularly nasty storm, I found a whole stack of the Tumbling Nancy books. Flipping through them, wiping the drips from my nose—bookdust allergy is an occupational hazard literary agents share with spinster librarians—I felt both a sense of repugnance and recognition.

Like most people of my generation, I'd read some of these books. Or they'd been read to me, which somehow brought an unwanted recollection of the sound of boozy arguments which wafted up from below each night in my parent's house. At school, though, was more likely. In one of those lessons where Miss Hall told the class to shut up and read so she can concentrate on staring with bovine yearning at Mister Smith running with the boys out in the playing fields. That itchy sense of imposed quiet came over me again as I flicked through the stiff yellowed pages of those peeling cardbound editions. But part of the feeling wasn't simply mild disgust. Part of it was sheer excitement. My agent's radar was well and truly spinning.

These books were *bad*. Poorly drawn, poorly written. Even poorly bound and printed. Poorly edited, too—I spotted askew words and spellings without even trying. Although perhaps that was just another reflection of the dreadful way they'd been written. Remember *Captain Pugwash*? Remember those ghastly black and white films which were replayed endlessly over the school holidays in one-screen, one horse town cinemas which reeked of cigarettes and toilet block? Remember the patronising, tie-and-twinset-and-pearl-wearing, anciently grown-up presenters with cut glass accents you used to get in the brief moments after the test card on what then passed for children's TV? Remember when there wasn't any TV at all, and girls were expected to do needlepoint and were shocked by their first period, and boys had pass their time trudging through Walter Scott novels and worrying about the perils of insanity brought on by masturbation. A place of brutal haircuts, severe rationing, bad teeth, sexism and clipped phrases—and routine clips, indeed, around the ear. This is the era to which Tumbling Nancy belongs.

The everyday world from which Nancy originated, though, is never delineated with any clarity. All you ever get is the sense of a dark house and bulking adults talking boomingly of incomprehensible things. Nancy, quite understandably, begins every story feeling bored. Does she remember her other adventures? That's not always clear either; they are sometimes referred to and sometimes not. But there is always a darning needle or some other sharp object which Nancy in her frustration starts to play with, and then invariably pricks herself in what a modern psychological interpretation might regard as an early instance of self-harm in children's literature. From that moment, Nancy feels herself shrinking, while a convenient nearby crack in the wall or pavement grows ever-larger until she slips through *lighter than a bob of thistledown*.

So Nancy—now with the Tumbling epithet, although she never actually does much more than blunder vaguely about—enters so-called Splendorland, and lumbers around in her trademark dungarees with her two pigtails sticking ridiculously out from the side of her head, when who should come along but Rarr the Robin or Gordon the Grocer who are invariably *in a most terrible rush* because they've lost something, which, after several pages of conversation so stilted it would shame a speak your weight machine, Tumbling Nancy agrees to help them find. And off they go. And so it goes until, after a sequence of improbable coincidences and occasional weeping rashes of purple prose, something apparently happens which neither Nancy or her friends seem to fully understand, or care that much about, other than that, as they all agree, everything *is just lovely and put back the way it should be.* At which time, Nancy usually remembers her normal life, and flees back home through the crack in the wall where the big, boomy-voiced adults are presumably still waiting.

Have I conveyed to you the full awfulness of these books? The illustrations, for example, have a peculiar ugliness. They're black and white, of course, or rather grey and beige now the pages are so badly foxed. Nancy's face changes markedly from illustration to illustration, and what I imagine are supposed to be appealing freckles shift like bad acne across her face, and there's something invariably wrong about the set of her eyes. If she resembles anyone, of course, it isn't a young girl, but the ratty-coated old bird I met all those years ago in that Balham cafe. And the other people and animals, Nancy's friends, have that dead and snarly look you get from those stuffed-animal displays in glass cases you find in Victorian museums, or in scene of the crime photos of corpses; it really is that bad. You'd think, perhaps, that the bad characters Tumbling Nancy encounters might fare somewhat better than the rest. But that isn't the case. Krago the Dragon with his dreadful snivelling snout doesn't so much snarl as smirk, and some vaguely evil thing called Blighty Blight is depicted as nothing more than a pencil squiggle of the kind toddlers like drawing in books. Really, though, and if you're on anybody's side in the last few confusing pages as they dwindle into defeat, it's theirs.

As for Splendorland itself, it's such a dreary place that you wonder why Nancy ever bothers to crawl through. There are drab shops and lumpy-looking cars and weird patches of clawing trees and narrow terraces stuffed with grim little houses set between grey stretches of wasteland that might conceivably be called fields. Or perhaps they're simply bombsites left over from the Blitz. Then there are the Bumbling People—Splendorland's other occupants—who form a crowd of limbs suggestive of varicose veins encased in pink supportive stockings and wander around mumbling to themselves in a vague and confused way. The phrase *somewhere endlessly in between* which is used repeatedly in the Tumbling Nancy stories struck me as particularly apposite.

In fact, I decided, the Tumbling Nancy books were so spectacularly bad that, if there wasn't something marketable here, my name wasn't Ros Godby. Not the kind of books you'd sell to kids these days—not unless you counted glue-sniffing horror fans. But there would definitely be a kind of frisson in rediscovering just how terrible Tumbling Nancy really was for the adult market which grew up with them. It would be like selling new editions of Little Black Sambo—which has made *someone* a lot of money since it became non-PC—but with a gothic edge. Tumbling Nancy tee-shirts as well? Why not? Even Tumbling Nancy (if it was done badly enough) the Movie.

My imagination was probably running away with me, but I could definitely see a nice line in the gift market for tastefully tasteless reproductions of these books. You could even do straight photoprint copies of the copies I had here and include all the yellowing and foxing. They would make for an edgier variation of the kind of ghastly nostalgia that sells Victorian manners guides and all the other useless crap which people give each other at Christmas. A ha-ha toilet book. Gift-shop promotional stands. Tumbling Nancy dolls, and Krago the Dragon as well, to frighten the kids with, and show them what the world of childhood was really like before it was invaded by all those *Tellytubby* and *In the Night Garden* bad trip goblins. Despite all my years of ingrown cynicism, my mind was already doing somersault sales pitches. Although, even when I reigned myself in, I knew that I was on to some serious money.

I was still leaning on Hobbsy's old desk. For a moment, I thought I caught a lingering whiff of pipesmoke, and glanced up half expecting to see the fat slob slumped there. What, I wondered, would the sad bastard have said? But that didn't matter. This was now and that was then.

The telephone number I found at the back of the files I lugged downstairs with me to my pristine marble desk, and still no sign of Marky-boy, had one of those old London codes; they change them about every ten years now on what's always supposed to be a permanent basis. I'd stabbed at my Blackberry through so many permutations I'd forgotten what exactly it was that I'd dialled when I finally heard a definite ringing at the other end, even though it was crackly and distant. Of course, Edna Bramley couldn't answer it now, but maybe someone else was there, and could point me in the right direction. I wiped a drool of mucus from my nose and tapped my nails. Come on, come *on* . . . Or if there isn't anybody there, if there are no next of kin, then that might mean, subject to all the usual bullshit legalities, that PHW might actually be able to hold any new revenues in their entirety unless and until—

I was almost disappointed when the phone was finally picked up, dropped, and then fumbled around in a dull clatter.

"Er, yes?"

The voice was female and breathy. I pictured somebody running up a set of dark stairs from a cat-smelling hallway strewn with damp final demands.

"Is that, ah, the residence of the author Edna Bramley?"

"Residence?" Another muffly clatter. A giggle from far away.

"I've just read the news," I said. All concern. "I was so terribly, terribly sorry to hear that she'd passed away. I knew Edna over many years. We worked together, but I'd like to think we were also friends. Such a dear, sweet lady. I really am sorry."

"Sorry." Was that an echo down the line? A question? Whatever, the voice had somehow harshened.

"Look," I ploughed on, "My name's Ros Godby and I'm Edna's literary agent. I mean, I represent her books and her interests. I know this must be a difficult time for all involved, but I need to speak to the next of kin. We must discuss how we distribute her continued earnings." That last bit normally got people's interest.

"Involved . . . ?" Another clatter. Another muffled giggle. Or it could have been a sob. In fact, it could have been anything. Then droning silence. I tried hitting redial, but my sodding Blackberry was under the impression that I'd called an unrecognised number. Nothing for it, then. The file address in Balham, of course, was unchanged.

The Northern Line. Lost tourists and foreign students and glum office workers and bag ladies. Gum on the seats and on the grab handles. My eyes and nose still stinging. I sniffled, and stared, with unaccountable fascination, at an old woman's holed and wrinkled pink stockings, and the ghastly bits of mottled yet hairy skin that showed through. Then at a nearby man in a ridiculous tartan flat cap who seemed to have to keep swallowing to stop his teeth from falling out. The Bumbling People, I thought. They're fucking everywhere. Then; how much of what is true about life is expressed through art, even if the art in question is absolute rubbish.

There was a particular Tumbling Nancy story, I remembered now, although I wasn't sure whether that was because I'd just seen it, or it was one of the works I'd somehow absorbed—along with chicken pox, mumps, and the allergy which was still making me feel around for a tissue or handkerchief I didn't seem to have—as a child. *Tumbling Nancy and the Adventure of the Shrunken Treasure*, perhaps, or was I making that singularly stupid name up? But I did have a definite impression that Nancy had actually died at the end of one of the stories. I could see her splayed body, the blood leaking out from her across the blotched page in a dull grey stain. Of course, she'd been up and around and bored as ever at the start of the next adventure. Was this religious imagery some half-arsed tribute to Aslan in the Narnia books? Or had I imagined the whole thing? I swayed with the train and ended up wiping my nose with the back of my hand, and then up and down the sleeve of my midnight blue Bagatelle jacket, which would cost more to dry clean than the other people in this carriage had spent on their entire wardrobes, as I swayed on between seemingly interminable stops. *London Underground regrets*. But not as much as I do, chum . . . Nothing bloody like it.

Some bits of Balham are now gentrified, but this certainly wasn't one of them. Another inconvenience, another sodding glitch in my bloody Blackberry, was that it hadn't even found the road with Edna Bramley's address. So here I was, stumbling through south London along dogshit pavements and fumbling the splayed pages of a London A-Z that I hadn't used for so long it was falling apart. And my nose was still running. But I was still on a buzz. Bad was bad, for sure. But, just a Michael Jackson had once sung when he still resembled someone living, really bad was *good*. I could hear myself pitching it to one of the big editors at some otherwise pointless cocktail evening.

Usually, of course, it's the easiest thing in the world to tell people that something or someone, is past it, old hat, absolute rubbish. People believe that easier than staring down into the toilet bowl at their own shit. It's the positive kind of news—so-and-so's on the up, you wouldn't believe what's happened between the first and the second draft—which is harder to convincingly get across. But this was where Tumbling Nancy already had it won hands down. *No, no, I'm not kidding, it's absolutely terrible . . . But, yes, I represent the old crow's estate, and I'm going to give you first dibs before the bidding war starts as long as you come in with some serious zeros. Absolutely. Deserves an 18 certificate. Sheer trash of the vilest sort. You'd never let modern kids read it, even though they subsist on a diet of internet porn and murderous video games* . . . And they'd turn back towards me, a little wary of course, because I'm Ros Godby and they don't want to piss the old dragon off, but also because I've piqued their curiosity.

But here at last—around a turn and then another turn that looked to be a cul-de-sac but wasn't—was Brook Mews. Greybrick houses with overgrown gutters. The old-fashioned kind of rubbish bins you never saw anywhere now. Exactly what London borough was I *in*? Multiple addresses beside every doorway. Bedsitland incarnate, and not a soul about. I reached number 15, creaked open the gate, and stepped warily over a dead, or possibly slumbering, cat.

No doorbells as such, and the flat labels had been washed out by rain and age. I tried pushing at the front door. Then I gave it a hefty shove. Tumbling inside, I dropped my A-Z, then scrabbled around the greasy carpet amid a spew of old letters to gather it up. Somewhere, someone was talking in a booming voice, or maybe music was playing, but it was far off. The doors ahead had the numbers 1 and 2 screwed into their crackled paint, but the address I had from the file was Flat 3. I grabbed hold of the greasy handrail and hauled myself up the steep stairs.

"Anyone about?"

Nothing, other than those dull, distant voices. I gave the door to Flat 3, which was actually ajar, a little rap.

"Anyone at all?"

It swung open. What can I say about what I found inside—at least, to start with—that you probably can't imagine? A wan little hallway lit by a bare bulb. Cheaply partitioned rooms crammed into what had once been the bigger spaces of a larger house. People lived their whole lives this way. It was a horrible thought. The bedroom might as well have been a wardrobe. Maybe being swung around in here was what had done for that cat outside. The bed was a hollowed mess of off-yellow sheets. I retreated quickly.

The main room had a single bar electric fire, a sagging settee, and a foldout table with a typewriter squatting in the middle of a strew of papers and mouldering mugs. This was where my work in my sacred calling as literary agent lay, so I sat down on the creaky chair and began to pick my way through the papers. Here it all was. More and more Tumbling Nancy in slipping, sliding masses amid the dirty spoons and half-eaten cream crackers.

It was apparent that Edna Bramley had done what she'd said she'd do when she met me at that café, and had continued on down the royal road of her life's work. If Nancy's adventures were dreadful in print, they were even more horrid in these collapsing unpublished drafts. And the illustrations, done in Indian ink using a rusty scatter of artist's pens I pricked my finger on when I found them scurrying around in a drawer, were so crude they should have suggested nothing at all, yet seemed to be working towards some apotheotic vision of the sort which Goya might have recognised. Krago the Dragon was genuinely horrific—a fly-splatter of half-dead wings—while Blighty Blight, no longer a bland scrawl, became a suggestion of something trying to unknot itself from other dimensions. If I'm sounding over-dramatic, all I can say is that you haven't seen those pictures—and that Gordon the Grocer's smile had most definitely acquired a predatory leer as he gazed down at Nancy from over his folded, ham-like arms.

I finally sat back. This was brilliant. This was gold. Tumbling Nancy for the *Saw* generation. Might do to get a photographer in. Get some images. Black and white, of course. No, make that sepia. The same colour as these ghastly woodchip walls. Which only left the issue of who I was now supposed to be dealing with. Was that voice I'd heard briefly at the other end of the line, and whoever it was who'd left that door ajar, a *daughter*? That hardly seemed possible. Distant cousin or niece, then. But where the hell were they? A cold, moist sense of *behind you* touched my neck and I twisted quickly, but of course there was no-one there.

I stood up, and peered and picked a little more. The woman was dead, but I had no idea of what she'd actually died *of*. Squeezing through the sideways doorway into a space which, bizarrely, shared the function of bathroom, toilet and kitchen—and surely that was against planning rules?—my feet crunching dead flies, I was certain that this really would make a fabulously grim photoshoot. Perhaps get it on the news as well. *Famous children's writer dies in squalor.* Play for the sympathy angle to generate some initial buzz. Then build up from that. The bath was scummed and rimed. So was the toilet. Pity she hadn't committed suicide. Unless she actually *had* . . .

I suppose I must have a forensic streak in me, because I was still lifting and peering long after most people would have stopped. Why, for example, would any sensible person want to open the fridge in a dead old lady's bedsit? But doing that almost changed my mind about the photoshoot—maybe we should go for colour after all. I stopped and listened after I'd got my breath back and slapped the door shut. Still, those dull, booming voices were coming from somewhere far off.

Another sound, though, had caught the edge of my senses, and it made me turn back into the foul little kitchen just as I was preparing to squeeze my way out. It was a small sound, thin and scratchy. Insects, most likely. And it seemed to be coming from beneath the sink, which was as stained and ancient as the bath, and filled with a swamp of dirty dishes and more dead flies, while the space beneath it was covered by a piece of gingham cloth strung on one of those lengths of plastic twine. A funny, turny feeling came and went in my stomach. A small bird fluttered close to my heart. My eyes still stung from opening the fridge, and I'd never wear these clothes again, dry-cleaned or not. But it was no use my being squeamish now. Squeamish was other people. Squeamish Ros Godby most fucking definitely was not.

There was no way I wasn't going to tweak aside that little curtain beneath the sink. And if there was something horrible there—say, the author's head with a few beetles crawling in and around it—I'd be kicking myself if I hadn't looked. What I actually saw was therefore a bit of disappointment, for it looked at first like nothing more than a mass of rusty Brillo pads. Or perhaps a ball of coathangers which had somehow got snarled up with old hair. Nevertheless, it was all pretty grim, although I decided after a relatively quick glance that it had no photographic potential for the Channel 5 documentary I was constructing in my mind. I was about to let go of the filthy rag I was pinching between my fingers when the thing beneath the sink started to move.

I stepped back and put my hands to my mouth as the thing flopped out onto the linoleum. It still looked partly metallic, but also like one of those ghastly hairballs you sometimes have to haul out from the drain beneath your shower. It seemed rusty, certainly, and scratchy, especially in the sound it made as it moved. But it also seemed organic, and it was most definitely alive. Nothing which was dead could possibly be hauling itself across the floor like this.

I suppose I could have kicked the thing or tried covering it with a bucket, but I simply stood and watched it go. You might call that a failure of nerve—Ros Godby finally baulked—but I could see where it was intent on going, and I had no desire to get in its way. At the back of the clawfoot bath, there was a crack in the wall, and that was where this damp and clawing mass was heading. All I really wanted to happen as I stood and watched, was for it to hurry up and get there. It left behind dishwater-grey smears. It was alive, but it didn't seem particularly lively. Or cheerful. But who knows what cheer amounts to, when you're a bundle of rotting stuff somewhere between rusted metal and balled-up hair?

Finally, it reached the crack behind the bath. There, it sort-of pulsed amid the old cobwebs. Then it began to claw its way into the crack, which was narrower than the thing itself, but the process was protracted, and looked painful—assuming that, like cheer, the thing could feel pain. It was, I thought, as if the crack was giving birth in reverse. Then, with a final dragging shudder and a bubbling wheeze of greyish fluid—perhaps it was some kind of blood—the thing was gone.

I started shivering from shock, and took my hands away from my mouth and clamped them hard beneath my arms. I had, I realised, just witnessed the passage of Blighty Blight in all his/her/its glory. If only I'd thought to use the camera on my Blackberry. But people rarely do practical things on these occasions. After years of scoffing, and despite some decent sales figures on a few I-was-abducted-by-aliens books, that was something I now fully understood.

I stood there for a while longer, still shivering and staring. The sound of those distant booming voices had faded. It was so quiet I could hear my own breath whistling across my lips. Then, much to my relief, I heard footsteps in the little hall. Pausing only to check myself in the blotched mirror—not that crisp, Godby, and your nose is still dripping and your eyes are red, but it will have to do—I squeezed my way out and through to meet and greet.

"Hello there." I was on autopilot. "I'm Ros Godby. I'm Edna's literary agent. You're probably wondering why I'm ... " The words slowed and thickened in my throat. " . . . Here."

"Wondering?"

Hmmm. This was some strange old bird, even in a literary landscape where you get to encounter more than the occasional loop-the-loop. She was big, broad—brawny even—although the hand that I was still point-lessly trying to shake felt clammy and soft as old dough. She was wearing worn dungarees and her hair was done up in pigtails and her teeth were poor and her eyes were hollowed and her face was covered with what might have been blotches, scars or spots. She smelled the way kids used to smell, back in the time before anyone washed. She looked, of course, a little like Edna Bramley probably would have done when she was a girl. Or, rather, if she'd been trapped in childhood for so many years that every-thing about it had turned to dust.

"You're Tumbling Nancy?"

The snag teeth bared themselves. Nancy giggled. Her hand still hadn't let go of mine, and now she was pulling me towards her with every impres-sion of eagerness, although I really had no desire to come out and play with this monstrous child.

"Can't you talk?" I gave my right hand a more determined tug, this time using the left for leverage. "Can't you *speak*? Can't you even say anything?"

"Talk?"

"For Christ's sake, you sad monstrosity! What the hell are you for? What are you even doing here?"

"Doing?" Nancy giggled. She looked left and right, although there was nothing to see along this narrow hall but yellowed woodchip. "*Here*?"

She was stepping back now, and I was struggling to stop myself falling forward. Then the worn carpet gave beneath my heels. After a horrible moment of stumbling into her stale embrace, my momentum pushed her on into the corridor, and from there, arms spinning and mouth ripped wide, to the lip of the stairs. There, Nancy teetered for a moment, and almost seemed to regain her balance. Then she tumbled back in a series of crashing thumps.

I wiped my sleeve across my face. I think I may have even giggled. Or snarled. Or at least made some kind of noise. I peered down the stairwell, and was less surprised than I should have been to see that, apart from a broad brown stain which could well have been there before, there was no sign of Tumbling Nancy at the foot of the stairs. The fall should have killed her. Or, at the very least, left her crippled. But this is Splendorland, or something like it, where normal life and logic have no place.

Weak-kneed and sniffly and somewhat breathless, I made my way down and out into the street. The houses were much as they had been before, although there were gaps of rubbled wasteland beyond still waiting to be reclaimed. I limped on along the empty roads past lumpy-looking cars beneath scratchy trees. Occasionally, although only in the distance, I hear booming voices and other sounds I have no desire to trace. Every now and then, but so far to no effect, I've tried shouting out Nancy's name. But no response. Nothing. Seems, after what I did to her, that she has no desire to come out and play. It's getting darker now, and I still can't get a goddamn signal on my Blackberry. The battery, as I tap out these words, is down to one eighth. But who knows what adventures await, as I lumber on through this world which really is best described as *somewhere endlessly in between*.

That old witch did have a way with words, and I'm still convinced that her stories could make an absolute packet on the right publisher's list. Soon as I get myself to the office and I've worked out the best spin to use for whatever's currently happening to me and everything's put back the way it should be, I'm going to start ringing round and pitching—maybe even get something viral going on the web. So I hope you'll look out for the Tumbling Nancy books next time you're by the book-bin at the super-market, or get a pop-up when you're browsing Amazon for underwear, or are looking for presents at the local garden centre.

And do buy one.

After all, it isn't as if you actually have to read the horrid thing.

ONE OF THE PROBLEMS WITH DOING SOMETHING YOU LOVE AND sometimes getting paid for it is that, inevitably, the love becomes compromised. Not that the love isn't still there—in fact, I'm continually scraping away the frustrations and the misdirections and moments of pompous over-confidence or equally pompous gloom to try to get back to it—but it's not the pure thing of undiluted joy and ecstatic discovery it once was.

I love books. I love the smell of them and the feel of them, and the look of them on shelves. I might even come to love the electronic versions one day. I love, too, the sense of discovery and surprise I feel when they tell me something new about the world, something which I suddenly realise has always been there. That, or a turn of phrase, or a twist of emotion, or of briefly seeing as someone else might see, or stepping through strange doors into other possibilities and worlds.

Still, there are also other things going on inside my head now when I read. Above all, there's a continued, obsessive hunt for the next new idea, turn of phrase, style or outlook. Many of the books I now love the most, I love not only because of what they are in themselves, but because of what they've led me to write.

Then, there's the question of admiration. Sure, I'll freely admit there are many writers, both past and present, who simply do things I could never hope to do. That's okay. But when it comes to other writers doing something close to something I've written, or would like to write, and doing it well . . . Then, reading can certainly be instructive, even occasionally enjoyable, but it's hard, too. Almost inevitably, an element of competition starts creeping in.

Writing is, and thus reading becomes, an intensely competitive business. Just like a tennis player watching another player, or an artist visiting someone else's exhibition, it's hard not to think how you'd have played that shot, or executed that brush-stroke. Nor should you avoid this feeling, distracting though it can be. Competition is vital to continued creativity. You want to show people. You want to prove something. And, with every story that you write, there's a moment when you feel it will shake things up and make a real impact and well, yes, goddamit, change the world.

I've always identified with something Stephen King once said. Which was, very approximately, that you want every story you write, no matter how slight it might seem, to reduce the reader to a laughing, snivelling heap of forever altered perceptions, and feel disappointed when someone comes up to you and comments that they merely "enjoyed" it, or, worse still, thought it "pretty good". In a way, then, I think I can safely say that Ros Godby, although supposedly an agent, represents a hidden part of the psyche of most writers let loose.

Writing, of all the arts, may well be the one in which the creator solicits the least direct attention, but you still need to have a quietly megalomaniacal streak to want to get your ideas this far into people's heads. And our attitude to other writers, especially the ones who write in something approaching the same areas and, worse still, happen to be still living, is mixed to say the least. For, as Gore Vidal once said with memorable honesty, It's not enough to succeed. Others must fail.

FROST ON GLASS

ON the clearest days, the edge of the mainland was plainly visible from the island's north beach. In that last summer, Boult often went to the stretch of sand and rock which lay near his cottage and around the headland from the village and the harbour. He would stand there for hours, just gazing across the glittering water.

Sometimes, there were pink clouds over the mainland hills. Sometimes, when the sun pricked his neck and the air was clear, there were flashes he took to be the opening of windows or even the passage of cars along the quay of the small town which faced the island: semaphore signals from ordinary life. On other days, and without the slightest hint of fog, the mainland simply vanished. Perhaps the place was afloat and drifting away to warmer climes, happier circumstances, better times. Boult would smile to himself as the waves lapped his ragged canvas shoes. A few years before—more, now, if he was honest—he'd have got at least a poem out of such a conceit.

In the evenings, at night, a few tiny lights would sometimes thread out to him through the dark, but they always died with the curfew.

"I was over there a couple of months ago . . . " Hibbert studied Boult from across the table at the White Tree, the island's only pub. "You remember, for that speech accepting an award some committee or other had decided to give me." He inhaled bubblingly on his cigarette. He wafted a hand. "Things are just as crap as they always where. I slipped my minder—went around the back streets." He took another ruminative drag. Boult was only half-listening. Hibbert's fat body was encased in a wrinkled lanolin-reeking jumper. With the folds of fat distorting the lines of his face, he looked like a wool-encased grub. "The *stink*. The ghastly *kids*. Disease. No shoes. The ruined factories, the wrecked shopping malls and run-down power stations. And the fucking, fucking, women. I wouldn't touch *anything* there, believe me . . . "

It never really got fully dark at midsummer in these high latitudes, and the light was pink through the windows and the perpetual beery fug of the White Tree. On his way here, Boult had walked the north shore in the luminous dusk where the sand lay like bolts of silk, the boulders were sleeping bodies and the mainland was nothing more than a shining haze. He'd barely noticed that he was walking towards the sea until the current had started to tug over his knees. His shoes and trousers were still wet.

Hibbert banged down his empty pint. "Another?"

All it took was Hibbert's raised finger and Clarkie, the publican, put down the glasses he'd been busily polishing and came to lever out the foaming fluid. Dark and woody, better than anything on the mainland, it was fine stuff to get lost in. Clarkie gave Boult a wink as he placed the glasses down. Sympathy? Complicity? But then Clarkie would have been listening to Hibbert's ramblings. It was part of his job.

The other regular inhabitants of the bar pulsed and receded. Over there were the Spinsters: mannish Leticia who wrote light social comedies, and Carla, who had once been a blonde-haired waif of considerable promise and beauty, but she was now putting on weight, a downy moustache, and the blood-threaded glare of the serious drinker. Otherwise, bobbing amid the fog, were a cluster of Young Turks, most of whom had barely been on the island since last winter and were still glorying in the easy joy of getting up each morning to face nothing more than the grinning jaw of a typewriter, the split claw of a pen. Over there, trying hard to be part of the same group with his usual social oiliness, was Kilbracken, who wrote adventures which seemed all the more implausible for the fact that they were apparently well researched. Kilbracken's plump wet lips creased in a grin as he tried to keep up with whatever joke the Young Turks were sharing. Some of them, Boult thought, might even be young enough to be of interest to him, but then again he doubted it. Once in a while, as reward for completing yet another creaking epic, a lad would be quietly plucked from the city slums and borne to the island. They always seemed happy enough, skipping along the high-hedged lanes under Kilbracken's supervision, diving off the rocks into the cold sea. The tragedy wasn't that they were brought here to the island, but that they were banished back to the mainland again.

"One for the weary road?"

Boult noticed that the beer had somehow emptied itself from his glass. "I think I'll go, thanks."

But Citizen Clarkie was already levering out more ale. He gave Boult another wink as he plonked the full glasses down.

Ears roaring, the night air swarming around him like faceted glass, Boult swayed back from the White Tree towards his cottage. Few stars tonight, although his eyes prickled and flashed as he tilted his head towards the sky. The road pitched and rose. The hedges swayed. But Boult's body was like an old horse. Climb aboard it, give it a kick, and it always found its way back to his cottage. Except . . .

A chalky branching of the lane, and the dark headland dipped its shale arms to embrace the ocean. He slid down through the dunes towards his beach. The tide had come and gone. The mainland was flat and black and low and lumpy tonight, coaly and sullen as a dead fire's sweepings, but above it the air was alight. Fingers of flame danced in a silvery, shifting curtain. There were colours as well. Tremulous flashes of ruby and turquoise like flickers of pure joy. Hanging in the spinning dark, seemingly only for his eyes, the Northern Lights gave a ghostly dance.

They caught in the waves. They billowed so close that Boult was tempted to reach out. And the thing of it was that he was happy just to stand there and watch. He felt none of the impetus to trap, control, deceive, recreate, imagine, which would once have filled him. Perhaps that's finally it, he thought as the dancing waves stirred their glorious chilly fingers. At last. I'm done with it. I'm no longer a writer.

The sparkles brightened, hanging against a darkening backdrop of earth and air. A dance of jewels, they winked at him, then faded until there were just two left hanging in a huge well of darkness, close above the sea. Boult waited for them to die, but they remained sharp and clear. Persistent. And slowly, slowly, on the long exhalations of sea air, they seemed to be moving towards him.

The sea shushed and retreated. The lights hung there above the water. Boult waited for his failing senses to correct the illusion, but instead he realised that a shape was coalescing around them, and that it had masts, a hull, a funnel, and was approaching the island.

Boult was washing his breakfast things at his sink next morning when he noticed a small black car crawling through the sunshine towards his cottage. It had to be Roberts, the island's senior watchman.

He dried his hands and quickly inspected the room. A few streamers of smoke from the toast he'd burnt still wafting through the open doorway. The two cracked leather chairs. The collection of old photographic prints of mainland landscapes, which he'd inherited along with almost everything else with his tenancy of the cottage, leaned from the stone walls. It all looked neat, ready for inspection.

A crackle of tyres. Boult cast a final glance at his desk in the corner. The mess of it seemed almost perfect. Piles of sheets here and there weighed down by bits of slate. A scatter of rubbers and pencils. It gave off just the right sense of orderly but intense activity. He just hoped there wasn't too much dust—

But here was Watchman Roberts: red-haired and always smaller and younger than you expected, with those freckles and that nearly-moustache, and that suit which, tailored though it plainly was, still didn't fit him.

"Fine, fine day . . . " He sat down on one of the leather chairs with a squeak of his shoes, placing his briefcase across his lap. "Any chance of a cuppa?"

Boult refilled the kettle and set it on the twin gas hob. The flame, when he ignited it with his fourth match, was nearly invisible in the torrents of sunlight which fell though the window. Boult felt the same. Or like those floating veils he'd seen last night across the mainland.

"Feeling alright? You look a bit peaky?"

"Nothing a good, brisk walk won't cure."

Watchman Roberts subsided into silence. The kettle began to scream. Boult bore a chipped marigold mug across the cottage's rugged slate floor, dribbling so much that Roberts had to shake hot fluid from his fingers. Boult flopped down on the chair facing the watchman. Which was worse, he wondered, to appear as guilty as I do now, or not to seem guilty? For are we not all guilty, just as the ill-advised poor used to believe in the wasted days before the Revolution—stained with the blood of sin and political incorrectness? And who could claim to understand and follow every wish and dictat of the Party? Not Boult, certainly. Perhaps not even Roberts. Guilt, after all, was natural. It was innocence which was suspicious.

The watchman sipped his brew through the thin gills of his moustache.

"Well," he said finally, "how are things going?"

"Pretty well. The characters have started talking to each other. That's always the trick. That, and a few brisk walks . . . Some sea air."

"Good. Good. Resolutions are so tricky, aren't they?"

"They can be."

"Even if . . . " Roberts put down his cup. He steepled his fingers. "Even if they're not the final climax."

A wind stirred, pushing the door farther open. The top sheets on Boult's desk began to flutter.

"I'm so excited." Roberts leaned forward. "That you're so near to finishing. The citizens on the mainland haven't forgotten you, you know. They . . . " He gave a nod at the room around them. "Remain grateful. If anything, the wait's almost been a good thing. You know—anticipation. At last, the sequel to *The Furnace*."

"It isn't a sequel."

"Of course." Roberts sat back again. "Well. Whatever . . . But you're the same writer you always were. Aren't you?"

The door creaked. The topsheets fluttered excitedly. Slowly, the flapping papers were pushing back the stones which were laying on top of them.

"Well, you *did* say, last time we spoke, that that problem chapter was part of the overall resolution . . . "

Boult swallowed. Another few minutes, if this breeze kept up, and the room would be filled with the swirling sheets of everything he'd written these last few years; a dancing snow of gibberish.

"It's nearly finished, actually."

"The chapter?"

"No. The book."

The wind stilled. The papers settled. Had he really said that?

Watchman Roberts drew a breath. "There are timetables and budgets, you know. Precious effort and resources must be set aside. Something like this could throw out a whole five year plan . . . But still, this is marvellous news. Do you have an exact date when you'll have your book ready for proofreading?"

"It's just a few details which need sorting. Things I can easily check up on at the island library." It was almost worth saying these things, just to see the look on Roberts' face: the worried, hurried calculations. "No more than a week."

"Then you have a full synopsis?"

"I'd rather keep that under wraps. As it's so nearly finished."

"So . . . " Roberts stood up. "Would you like a lift?"

"To where?"

"You did just say you had some details to check in the library . . . "

The State offices were in the main square directly opposite the library, and the two buildings, by far the largest on the island, glowered at each other across a stone stump which had once either supported a cross or the statue of a local dignitary. The plinth was debased now, its inscription destroyed in the early frenzies of revolution; it now looked as if a large animal had chewed it. The two opposing buildings, repaired and repainted in a peeling variety of unmatched colours, weren't much better. Still, you could just make out a sign in the arch above the irregular windows on the top floor of the State offices: CIN MA. The one picked out in brick on the side of the library read AMUSEM NTS.

The contents of the library were impressive enough, though. There were publications available in its rickety catacombs which had long ago been banned on the mainland. Foreign authors. Pre-revolution histories. Unblanked maps. Even the occasional erotic text. It was all here. The State accepted that its writers might need to have access to information that its citizens as a whole remained happier and more productive without. Not so that these elements should be included in the writers' finished works, it was understood, but rather that they should be *better excluded*. There was a theory that the mainland authorities used the island library as a repository for all of the information which had been banned on the mainland, but which was considered too sensitive or useful to actually destroy. The place was, indeed, vast. There was another theory that several of the writers who'd vanished from the island in odd circumstances were still somewhere inside this library, lost, living on paper, fungus and bookworms as they continued their endless, hopeless research.

Boult presented his party card at the library turnstile, then took a requisition form over to one of the private booths. During his first few years on the island, he'd been sure that he was being watched from beyond the blank glass which faced him. But the place was too disinterestedly silent, the glass too grubby. Staring back at it, all he saw was his own dim reflection. All he felt was his usual absence of purpose.

"Filled in our form yet, citizen?"

Boult quickly entered his party number, address and date and the subject of his proposed enquiry. The librarian, Styche, sucked his teeth and shook his head as he examined it. His loop of keys jingled. Styche had a huge cyst which dangled over his left eye like a third eyeball. As Boult followed in the little man's sour wake, along lines of bare-boarded corridors, he wondered why the man had never taken a pair of scissors to the damn thing and cut it off.

Styche unlocked and examined the AT-BEs in a set of card index drawers.

"Not here."

"You could try NE-PA instead."

"That's not what you put on the form."

"But you could still try it, couldn't you?"

Styche, wen swaying, keys jingling, shook his head.

"What a pity," Boult mused. "And I was just saying to Watchman

Roberts as he drove me here how important this bit of research was to my finishing my book . . . "

Styche harrumphed and produced the right card. Crisp and immaculately printed, it was so clean and new that it had to be old—pre revolution—and the book it referred to lay unreachably high up on the looming racks. Boult stood back and watched as Styche found and positioned a long ladder and scrambled up it, expertly avoiding its several missing rungs, and released the book from its eyrie in a slow rain of dust.

Settling back in his booth with *Effects of the Upper Atmosphere*, Boult briefly felt the preparatory tingle he always used to feel when he was genuinely researching a project: that trek through the sunny woods of inspiration where every turn you took, each fork and hurdle, always led to the thing you didn't even know you were looking for until you found it. But the book was nothing like the card. The cover was colour-printed, it was true, and so were many of the pages, but the whole thing was so browned and mottled and crinkled and torn that it was hard to believe that the damage wasn't deliberate. It was the same with so many of the pre-revolution books Boult had requisitioned that he suspected it was someone's job to make them seem as unappealing as possible.

But, even then, this book was a dry disappointment. Its contents consisted mostly of equations, charts, graphs, diagrams. There were a few photos of clouds and skylines—and how odd it was to see church steeples and unbroken lines of electric pylons prickling the horizon—but there was no magic for him here, no majesty, not even in the whole last chapter which was devoted to the Northern Lights, the Aurora Borealis. *Ions . . . charged particles . . . geomagnetic latitude . . .* They made as much sense to him as did his own useless scribblings.

"Have we finished with our book yet, citizen?"

Styche was clearly eager to get the thing back on the shelves where it belonged, roosting beyond all possibility of escape for another fifty years. None the wiser, Boult gave it to him, sneezed, returned his requisition form and shoved out through the library turnstile into sunlit midday. The air blown in from the sea across the island was cool and clear and sweet. And there were fresh cherries and unrotten potatoes on sale in the green-grocers along the narrow street which wound down to the harbour, clean new sheets of paper and dark proper ink in the stationers. Not only that, but a dizzy sort of unadmitted capitalism reigned on the island and you could go in and buy any of it with what amounted to real money. One way and another, it was easy to forget just how many and subtle were the ways in which life here differed from that on the mainland.

There was a trawler berthed down in the quiet, sunny harbour. Remembering the lights he'd seen approaching the island last night, Boult picked his way over the rotting ropes to get a closer look. Blackened, paint-peeling, white numbers roughly scrawled on the bow, relics such as this were now used for deliveries and, it was said, to scour the shorelines of the mainland for enemy craft and the flash of furtive signals. It had probably brought the potatoes, the fresh cherries, although it had arrived in the middle of the night which, even by the standards of the island, was unusual. His neck prickling, Boult glanced around him to see if he was being watched. But the town, the harbour, the whole island, lay still and sunned and innocent.

The lunchtime interior of the White Tree was almost as dense and dark as it had been the night before. Hibbert hadn't moved from his bench, and Clarkie, ears cocked as always, was busy behind the bar repolishing what could have been the same glass. But over in the far corner, where the Spinsters usually sat, there was a new group. They could only have come from that trawler.

"I'd ask you if you fancied another. If you'd actually started your first, that is."

Boult glanced down at his untouched pint, then back towards the new group. Most of them were obviously crew; wizened men of that ageless age which the sea seems to engender. But one of them, seated in the sunlit fog of the window and talking animatedly, was young. And female.

"Some new posting, by the look of it. And we all know what that bloody means. Doesn't look as though she's got a book in her, though, does she ... ?"

Boult nodded. The fresh angles of that face; that chin, that mouth. Strangers of any kind were rare on the island, but a new writer arriving generally meant that an old one was heading back to the mainland in disgrace.

"Look on the brighter side. She could be a new Matron . . . "

The Matrons, and a few similar men, lived in the little bungalows clustered down the hill on the island's south side. They were all beyond a certain age, round and solid, big-hipped; as practical and welcoming as farmers about the simple human business of fucking. Easy to like. Easy to confide in. Impossible to fall in love with.

"Or she could be a treat for some once-famous author who's finally finished something . . . "

Boult turned to look at Hibbert. "What have you heard?"

"Oh. The usual. Everything and nothing. That our esteemed friend and good citizen Watchman Roberts visited your cottage this morning and came back mightily pleased—and a bit agitated."

Boult's head was pounding. Perhaps he could do with that drink. Or something to eat. Perhaps—and whatever it really meant—he really did need to get off this island. "I told him that I'd nearly finished my book."

Hibbert chuckled. "You've been telling everyone that for ages."

"I mean, really finished. Apart from a few checked facts, a couple of odd spellings. I told him he could have it for editing in a few days."

"So . . . " Hibbert took a long slug of his pint, paused, and then slugged again until Clarkie left the bar to deal with a minor spillage around the corner. "Finished as in *finished*? So why aren't you buying me this round? Why aren't we dancing around the tables? The sequel to *The Furnace*—"

"—It's *not* a sequel."

Hibbert glanced at Clarkie who, dripping rag in hand, was returning.

"Might as well go and stretch our legs, don't you think, Boult? I hear there's something called daylight going on outside . . . "

The two men headed up across the humped back of the island. The hedges were high. It was always possible that someone was following them on their other side, but the sense of being watched, which had been nagging at Boult since he'd seen that trawler in the harbour, had faded. Sometimes, you just had to trust your instincts.

"So let's get this right," Hibbert was saying. "You *haven't* finished your book, but you've told Roberts that you *have*. I won't bother to ask why."

"Perhaps I just got sick of the whole business. Perhaps I want to leave this bloody island."

"No one who says that ever means it. When was the last time you got off here, anyway?"

"Five or six years . . . " Cavernous hotel rooms filled with a few sticks of old furniture like bones in an empty cathedral. The sounds, the smells, the disgusting food. The taps which groaned and emitted only mud and worms. The pointless lightswitches which he couldn't help testing—just in case. And where would we like to go today, citizen writer? Another trip to the mines? Ersatz tea with an ordinary family? Another ride on an ancient, rickety and over-crowded train? Endless delays. Talks to malodorous crowds in unheated halls. And that was as a dignitary.

"The reason, Boult, that you go to the mainland is to remind yourself how fucking, fucking awful it is there. And then you come back here, where things work the sun often shines, at least in midsummer, and the idea of writing imaginary crap for a readership so dull it couldn't even pick its own nose starts to seem appealing all over again."

Boult had heard it all before; from Hibbert, and from the voices in his own head. Still, nothing but meaningless gibberish would ever come of the pages weighted down on his desk with those slate stones.

"You're not joking? You really haven't finished it?"

"I've barely started. In fact, to be totally honest, I haven't started at all. The only book I've written, the only book I'm ever going to write, is *The Furnace*. So . . . " They'd climbed almost to the highest point of the island. The hedges had fallen away, giving a view of foam-serrated headlands, blue sky. In the north, seemingly so far off across the shining ocean that it hung just beyond the horizon, lay a floating haze which might or might not have been the mainland. " . . . what happens next?"

Hibbert was breathing hard from the climb. A tug of breeze lifted the long lock of hair he combed over his pate. For a long moment, it hung there, upright like the crest of a parrot, before it slipped down over his ears. "You know it's not just back to the mainland if they're disappointed in you, don't you?"

"Of course I do. It's not as if I haven't mentioned to you that I've been stuck before . . . "

"I thought that was the same bollocks we all come up with. Even Kilbracken. One minute he's never going to be able to write a single word in a million lifetimes, and the next, hey presto, another five hundred pages of diarrhoea to fill the people's libraries."

"I'm not Kilbracken."

"We can all rejoice in that one small fact, can't we? But you must have *something*."

"I have this exercise. I write whatever comes into my head. *cat mat maudlin* I used to hope that something would eventually come out of it— a meaningful sentence. I've got reams of the stuff. I've done it for years. Line after line of nothing . . . "

The two men walked on. Roberts would have already radioed the message; the next book by the renowned author of *The Furnace* was finally complete. There would be meetings, timesheets, reallocations of production. Boult could remember how it felt, back in his avid youth, when some long-awaited book finally appeared. The interminable wait as it passed down the Party lists until the precious object, its spine bent and torn, its pages stained and dog-eared, but the words still pristine, finally lay in your hands . . .

"There must be other stuff. After all these years."

"Believe me, there isn't."

"You've always seemed so industrious. So fucking committed. You've still got a few days. How was it when you wrote *The Furnace*? Did it come out all at once, or did it take ages?"

"Funnily enough, it seemed to be both."

"It *is* a long book. Although it doesn't seem so when you're reading it . . . " Hibbert was wistfully studying the landscape. The man was older than Boult. He'd started a proper non-writerly career as a citizen teacher before he made it to the island, and so had had time to appreciate life's true drudgery. No wonder books were so popular on the mainland, with barely an hour of radio each night, and no films showing at any of the remaining cinemas apart from the odd documentary about health and hygiene and how fine life was in the mining communes.

No wonder Hibbert had wanted to get away. Years and years of reeking children, and regular submissions of his kitchen table scribblings to the State competitions. He'd once told Bolt how he'd almost come to resign himself to a lifetime of chalkdust and stale urine when he'd finally got to the top of the library list to read a then-popular book called *The Furnace*. Even before he'd finished it, Hibbert had started to write as never before. One, two novels, and then a third, which he'd submitted to the literary committees with the usual mixture of hope and hopelessness. It was rubbish, as even he admitted, but the ripples cast by *The Furnace* had dwindled by then, and the citizens were anxious to read something similar, and so his time as a teacher had ended, and his career as a writer began . . .

So much history, Boult thought, lies between us. So little of it means anything.

"You could stall Roberts for a while," Hibbert suggested. "Tell him you've realised there are still a few problems with your masterpiece."

"You know what he's like when he gets the bit between his teeth. And once he's told the mainland . . . "

"You handwrite, don't you?"

Boult nodded.

"See, I've got this new book of mine that's almost finished. Of course, it's nothing like *The Furnace* or whatever you might have written to follow it. I'm past all that. But it's words on a page. You could copy it out . . . " They were facing the mid-afternoon sun now, on the far cliff edge of the island. "If you went for it flat out, it would only take a few days." The sea below them was full of comets and stars, wheeling birds. "People would be disappointed, after *The Furnace*. But at least you'd still be here . . . "

Boult shook his head. "I couldn't possibly—"

"—Don't worry. They'll be another book along for me in a few months. There always is."

"It isn't that." Boult couldn't imagine a more generous gesture than this. But the island was floating. He, Hibbert, everything seemed to be receding. The clifftop leaned. Whatever it was this life amounted to, he realised that he'd had enough of it. "Thanks—but I'm sorry."

"I'm not going to say it's your funeral." Hibbert chuckled. The gulls bickered and circled. "But there you are. I have . . . "

———

Boult the ex-writer stood alone on his favourite beach. The twilight was grainy. The land exhaled heat. He'd done, written, nothing. But for his chance remark to Roberts about that finished book, this could almost have been the end of another typical day.

Even as he watched, a luminous curtain was forming above the mainland. Instead of dropping from the stars, it seemed to push out like a misty effusion from some deeper dark beyond. The Northern Lights. Twisting and dancing. The tide had drawn back, and the rippled wet sand spreading before him was laid with the grey shapes of rocks which seemed to twist and move. They reminded him of lovers, and the sea air around him gave off that same briny, erotic scent. Where did you go anyway, when you left this island forever? He wondered. Where did they take you? Surely not simply back to the mainland—and mere death seemed too easy . . .

The Aurora, after playfully drawing closer with a dry electric crackle like silk on flesh, thinned. But the rocks around him were still twisting on the gleaming strand, moving, sighing. Confused, he walked towards them, his sodden feet splashing in deepening rills. One raised itself higher, and he saw a glint of eyes and whiskers before the seals gave their huffing barks and lolloped off towards the ocean.

Boult walked back across the dunes to his cottage. The door, which possessed no lock, swung easily, as if it he hadn't wedged it properly shut. It was too far past curfew now to try the lightswitch. The furniture sat gently seething. Somehow, the air had a charged presence. He went to his desk, touching one by one the heaps of his papers, studying the position of the stones he'd laid over them, feeling them to see if they were cold. He glanced quickly behind him. The pictures hanging from the walls. It was all too neat, too innocent . . .

He pushed open the door to his bedroom, where a rising moon hung at the window, and studied the phenomenon of his bed from every possible angle. The sheets were rucked, pushed, changed. And in their centre, long and indented from the feet right up to the pillow, lay the imprint of a body. Touching that moonlit hollow, Boult found that it was warm.

The coffin turned lazily in the sunlight above the harbour. Boult, the two dockers who were guiding it, and a few circling gulls, were the scene's only witnesses. It wasn't roped particularly well, and tilted down by ten or fifteen degrees. Which is the heavier end of the body? The head, Boult supposed. A shout, a thumbs up, and the coffin was lowered into the rusty shadows of the trawler's hold. Just a long oblong of cardboard stencilled with numbers but no name. After all, what was the purpose of identity when all you were left with could, after some suitably ghastly process in a mainland plant, be usefully returned to the soil of the commune farm. The rest of the trawler's crew were arriving. Those same sun-scarred faces he'd seen in the White Tree. Climbing ladders. Exchanging incomprehensible shouts. The ancient diesel engine started coughing like the near-broken thing it was. The ropes were cast. Boult watched the trawler as it chugged around the headland, leaving nothing but an oily cloud.

This morning, the idea of a visitation at his cottage seemed almost as unlikely as the prospect that he'd write anything when he sat down at his desk. But he'd tried anyway. *escape salt cherries* Another sheet to add to all the others. Then he'd spent a couple of hours tidying, scrubbing the sink, liberating those photos of the lost beauties of the mainland from their patina of dust. It only struck him afterwards that he was giving his cottage a spring clean in preparation for a new occupant.

He walked back up from the harbour and into the village, where the early afternoon shadows were blue against the walls of the houses. He'd come here with the idea of having it out with Roberts, but now he realised that what he really wanted was for things to go on exactly as they were. It wasn't so bad, after all, being here—was it? He was sitting on the chewed stump of the old monument in the main square when the call of a voice started him.

"Citizen?"

It was the girl he'd seen the night before last at the White Tree, and she was heading across the square towards him from the library's swinging doors.

"You *are* Citizen Boult, aren't you?"

"Well, yes."

"I know you must be very busy, but if you have a few moments, there's something in the library I'd like to show you."

Too surprised to protest, Boult stood up and followed her back through the doors and the clacking turnstile into a dusty darkness which whispered with the scattered coughs and sighs of the other writers who had retreated from the sun to pretend to work here. A loop of keys jingled at the polished blue seat of the girl's trousers. Her wrists stuck far out from the frayed sleeves of her jacket as, all jittery excitement, she waved her hands.

"I was checking up some of yesterday's cards. It *was* the Northern Lights you were researching, wasn't it . . . ?" Her voice had dropped to a sibilant whisper which still carried too far. One or two sour looks were aimed her way by the half-roused sleepers in their booths. "I'm afraid there's more than was shown to you by my colleague . . . "

He followed her along the creaking corridors, then up some spiral stairs.

"You're new here?"

The hands fluttered again and she nearly spilled a handful of chits and cards as she nodded. " . . . I'm not sure I'll ever get used to everything. It must be so *marvellous* . . . " Boult somehow felt sorry for her, to be so young, and to be living in these times. Even here. She had dark hair, cut in a short and practical citizenly way that meant she could work a hand lathe or a farm implement safely, and that the delicate curve of her neck could be seen, the small pink lobes of her ears. "I'm Citizen Gloria, and *The Furnace* is almost my favourite book of all time. But don't get me started on *that*."

Only *almost*. There was something else, too, about that smile, those eyes. More than youth. Citizen *Gloria*. Such an old-fashioned and inappropriate and thus unlikely name. Perhaps that was the extra twist of verisimilitude which amounted to reality, that real people in this real world didn't have the names they probably should. Boult's writerly instinct for such things had long left him. All he felt was confused. And what if Hibbert was right, and she'd been brought here to liven up the choice of widows down in their bungalows? Or as a treat solely for him, for supposedly finishing his book? But the trawler had arrived the night before he'd told

Roberts that the sequel—*successor*, dammit—to *The Furnace* was finally done...

Citizen Gloria was climbing a ladder to get to the very upper lip of a huge, gently groaning bookcase.

"You see," she said, looking down at him, her face shadowed by a moss-mottled skylight. "Some aspects of a subject can be correctly categorised in several quite different places. I got special authority to check in something called a microfiche. Phenomena of the higher atmosphere can be regarded as meteorology stroke climatology, or something related to outer space."

"So this is your very first day?"

"Oh yes!" The whole bookcase seemed to sway. She wasn't even whispering now. As Boult blinked and rubbed his eyes, she drew out book after book and somehow hooked them into the crook of her elbow before she descended, almost glided, down the ladder.

"Do you know who it is you've replaced?"

"A citizen called Stick, Styke...?"

"Styche."

"That's it! There was some accident apparently... Not long ago. He fell. Off..." She gestured to the ladder, which she'd left propped against the bookcase, as Styche, for all his many faults would never have done. "...something like this. You can't be too careful, can you, and being a librarian *is* a surprisingly dangerous occupation. But these things sometimes happen, no matter what precautions the State takes."

"I saw Styche yesterday." Boult said. "He brought me a book on the upper atmosphere."

Gloria's eyes, her mouth, widened. "But that means he was still alive when I..." Just like her name, it was impossible to tell if her reaction was fake or genuine. "No wonder people have been so sniffy about me—"

But Boult had already turned from her, the offered books ignored, and was heading for the library exit. Which, long though he'd been here on this island, took him some time to find.

The air smelled of gorse and the sheep were baaing as he stumbled back across the island through the warm afternoon. He felt cheated and drained from that encounter with Citizen Gloria—or whatever her real name was. But she was dangerous to him. He knew that much. Sometimes, you just had to trust your addled instincts.

When he crossed the final rise, he saw that Watchman Roberts' car was parked outside his cottage. If he hadn't felt so tired, he'd have turned and run back toward the library.

"Knew you wouldn't be long." Roberts was sitting inside, waiting in the same chair he'd sat in yesterday, enjoying a cuppa from the same chipped primrose mug. He had his briefcase and a large sheaf of papers balanced on his knees. He smiled at the creak of the door. "I saw you coming out of the library from the window of my office. I thought I'd catch up with you on the road, give you a lift the rest of the way."

"I walked along the coast."

"Obviously." He raised his mug. "Help yourself, by the way. I left enough in the pot."

"I'm not thirsty." Boult tried to flick a casual glance towards his desk, but after the sudden change to the dull interior from daylight outside, all he saw were swarming blotches. He sat down, trying not to shiver, hating himself for this ridiculous nervousness. He'd often felt this way as a child. At school, with the citizen teachers. Sometimes at home with his citizen parents. Always with Party representatives. When you were young, you comforted yourself with the thought that you would grow out of such things. His hands started to sweat as he faced Roberts. It was intensely disappointing. Even as adults, he thought, we still harbour the illusion that the imminence of death will finally bring a loosening of some of the chains which tie us.

"We'll need to go through all of this, I'm afraid . . . " Roberts was teasing out the first of his sheaf of papers. He unscrewed the top of his pen. He flashed another smile. "I'll act as scribe for a change, shall I?"

A state publishing requisition. Pages and pages and pages of it, which, he explained, would be copied and divided and re-copied and sent to all the relevant bureaux, factories, committees, library boards and cultural censorship authorities. Boult had no recollection of anything this complex happening when *The Furnace* was accepted, but that had been more than twenty years ago, and forms and procedures never stayed the same. It was the State's way of making sure that you always had to read every single instruction—and you probably still got things wrong.

The rest of the afternoon ticked by to the sound of the little licks and spits as Roberts and his pen worked through the requisition's many pages. Stupid of Boult, not to have realised this was coming. After all, there were requisitions for everything. Broom handles. Cogs. Shoes. Paving slabs. Cardboard coffins. Anything that the State doled out or took away came wrapped up in its own complex bit of paper. Probably, no undoubtedly, there'd be requisitions for matrons, and for the lads Kilbracken liked to spend his summers with. And for new librarians. They'd do it with clouds, and raindrops and the laughing breath of babies, if only they could identify the correct batch number. Compared to such dreamy things, books were solid and real and ordinary; inky products of the pounding acres of some run-down mainland factory. Name? Address? Party number? It was like call and response, one of the oldest forms of song and poetry. Have you at any time been treated for the following diseases? Boult's problem as a writer, he decided, was that he'd come to this island too early, before he'd had a chance to absorb the oddities of mainland life. This whole process still seemed ridiculous to him when plainly it shouldn't.

"Any special skills and stroke or qualifications?"

"Are you sure this is the right form?"

"Oh, we'll get to the actual book in a minute. Obviously, and as with any activity in life, it's important that the authorities have a full picture of your role and value to the state as a citizen as well as a writer."

"I did attend a people's academy for two years. I gained the appropriate certificate in Understanding Political Analysis . . . No, I think it was Analysing Political Understanding. Or was it The Politics of Analysis?"

Roberts looked up, his moustache twitching, a vague flush of interest in his red-rimmed eyes. Boult—a political animal? It soon faded.

"So you're not sure . . . All that effort and labour by your co-workers to get you to a fine place like that, and you can't even remember what you've studied . . . " This, the vulpine smile which followed assured him, was a joke. "I'm sure we can look that bit up."

Boult nodded. An odd layer of calm had settled on him during this ritual. Death, he imagined, would be a similar process. And the State would never let you go without the right papers. Soon, they were moving into the part of the form which actually dealt with the book Boult had supposedly written. Size and type of paper? Presumed level and accuracy of spelling? Boult wished he'd had a form like this years ago. Broken down to this level of detail, a novel really did seem like something you could requisition like toilet paper. More so, as to produce a few precious sheets of gritty grey paper out of thin air, even over a period of many years, would be an act of genuine magic. Whereas a book . . .

"Number of chapters?"

Boult could picture it. Chapter 1—the crisp proclamation of a story worth telling. Flick through and you came to—Chapter 24? No, too long. Chapter 16? Too short. 18 was too mathematical. A novel, after all, was essentially a flawed thing. It flowed with the tides of passion and grief.

"There are nineteen chapters." A good prime number. Indivisible by anything.

"Good. Good . . . " Roberts' pen ticked, annotated, moved on down the page. "Now, the names of the main characters. Party numbers, it says here, aren't necessary, although suitable dummies can be provided by the census office on submission of the appropriate form."

Boult opened his mouth, expecting nothing to come out. But the one skill he'd acquired on this island was bullshitting about the book he was supposedly writing, and this somehow felt like more than bullshit. Here it was, the book he'd longed to produce, risen from the uncertainties to number exactly 2,100 handwritten pages. Long, of course, but then long was to be expected after all this time. Hero? A young man, yes, and his upbringing is difficult. His father, at an age he can barely remember, is arrested, taken away . . . Robert's eyebrows went up at that, but Boult was in his stride by now, and he knew the nature of every question the book would raise, and how they would all be answered. Every character was clear cut to him. What, he wondered, had happened to those failed efforts of creation which had struggled out of the vats of his imagination with their scarred and seared faces, both nameless and many-named, with their many-coloured eyes, their hair falling out, their waving, changing, limbs and deformities growing and melting like wax?

As twilight settled in, Roberts ticked and signed the form's penultimate page. "Now. One last thing, and I know you'd probably been wondering when this would come up. Although you've had the patience not to ask . . . "

The watchman's freckles, Boult noticed, were more prominent. Like the dots and boxes and lines on the form on his lap, they drifted gently across his face in the failing light.

"We'll need to give the book a title."

Boult was conscious of the cooling air wafting in and out of his lungs like sea from a cave. He'd never been happy with *The Furnace* as a title; it had been the one thing about the book which had never seemed to come right no matter how long he'd agonised and waited. This time, he wanted to get it right. But nothing came.

"That's the one thing I don't have yet."

Watchman Roberts, unconcerned, ticked the appropriate box, squared the many pages of his form and tucked them into his briefcase. The missing title was, Boult decided, as he lifted himself up from the chair's sticky leather, exactly the sort of final twist which made the book seem real.

"Would you like me to take the manuscript now?" Roberts asked. "There's a fire safe in my office."

"I've always felt things were pretty secure here in this cottage."

"Of course. I understand. And it *is* still your baby. I'll come and collect it in a few days. As soon a courier's been organised from the mainland."

A *few* days? How many? But better not to ask.

"Meanwhile, you'll give the title some thought, won't you? But not tonight. We can't let an occasion like this pass entirely uncelebrated. Let me buy you a drink . . . "

Boult sat beside Roberts in his little car with the window down, breathing the night scent of the hedges. When they pulled up outside, the White Tree looked oddly empty. *Looks like a quiet night*, Roberts commented, laying a hand across Boult's shoulder as he steered him across the grey road toward the pub. Noticing that even the lights at the pub's windows were out, Boult suddenly realised what was coming. This, after all, was just another of the island's rituals: the hunched shadows crowded behind the door; the breathless near-silence of here-he-comes; the flags and banners which Clarkie always stretched between the beams of the bar when some major work was delivered—the voices, the faces, the cheers, the sour and arid hugs and kisses from all his fellow writers, which would explode around him as soon as he entered the White Tree.

Boult stood on his northerly beach the morning after the long, beery night of celebrating his achievement. The sun was blazing. So was his headache.

Cold foam swirled around the cuffs of his trousers. The mainland looked soft and green today. The hills tugged a few fleeces of cloud. A window winked at him above the intense glitter of the sea. Something was moving out there amid those sweet, famously treacherous currents. Something long, grey, impossibly sleek . . . A seal, perhaps? But seals were never that big. It let out a plume of water in a sound that reached him on the chant of the waves. Just a whale, but he thought of those old stories of krakens, sirens, mermaids, enemy submarines.

"Citizen? Excuse me . . . "

Even seen as a silhouette against the wet, white sand, it could only be that girl from the library. Gloria, or whoever. Boult took a few more steps farther into the tugging waters, nearly up to his knees. But she waded in after him. For all its practical cut, her hair still snagged at the corners of her mouth. She picked it away.

"You went off so quickly from the library yesterday."

"What do you expect?"

"I know. Poor Stiles. Dead man's shoes . . . " She had a brown paper bag in her hand. "But what can I do? I'm here now, aren't I . . . And I got these." She held it out. "Sorry if they're a bit squishy."

He wanted to refuse, but even citizens on this island had to put up with shortages, and he reached into the bag and took out a hooked bundle of fresh cherries. There was something oddly reminiscent about their soft sweet taste, the contrast with the salt air's harsh brightness. He spat the stones into his palm, then dropped them into the water.

"I think I may be able to find the answer to your problem, Citizen Boult."

"What problem?"

"The title of the book you've just finished. Watchman Roberts had a word with me. He must have been checking the library chits to see what you'd been looking into. Or perhaps he always does that for all the writers. I didn't ask him . . . " She took a cherry, span it around in her cheeks, and spat the stone an impressive distance.

"I'm sure I can help. Please? After all, it's what I'm here for. You will let me, won't you?"

Boult stole occasional glances at Citizen Gloria as they walked out of the waves. She had a pert, plump face, and seemed almost ridiculously young—but then the young always grow younger as you grow older, retreating from you like those mainland clouds. And her lips were impossibly red, which reminded him of some poem. But that was the cherries. Was this, Boult wondered, what death looked like? Sensing, misreading his gaze, Gloria flushed slightly and flashed him a smile. To her, he was probably just a walking copy of *The Furnace*. But oblivion, he supposed, could come in worse forms than on this sunlit beach in the shape of a young female citizen who reminded him so sweetly of all that he'd lost and gained.

"You're not supposed to take those *out*, are you?" he asked when he found her standing outside his cottage door with an armload of books that evening.

"Course I'm not." She breezed past him, cleared a space with her elbows amid the disorder and plonked them down on the scarred dining table.

"You've only just reached this island. Don't you even care about your career?"

"But you're *Boult* . . . Don't you want a title for your book?" She peeled off her frayed coat and dropped it the flagstoned floor. "And it's so bloody *dark* in here. Isn't there any electricity? Isn't that the whole point of living on this island instead of on the mainland, that you can get on with your work in comfort and without distractions and the endless powercuts? Isn't there a lightswitch?"

The tremulous bulb came on. The room seemed odd like this, all the shadows leaning backwards in surprise. Boult hadn't realised how accustomed he'd become to sitting in darkness.

"So that's the famous desk is it?" She lifted a slate, sniffed it, stifled a sneeze, then took up the first page beneath. "Is this a bit of it—the book? How many people have read it so far?"

"No one yet." Boult snapped the page from her fingers and laid it back down beneath the slates. *Through the bicycle wind. Inevitable grin grinding. Fat fart nothing.* The streams of his words, in this yellow light, burned up at him.

"Apart from you, you mean."

"Apart from me."

"But it *is* finished?"

"I did a publishing requisition with Watchman Roberts here only yesterday . . . " He gestured to the chair where the man had sat, beside which her coat now lay like a shed shin. "So. You said you were here to help me?"

It was so very hard to know what to make of Citizen Gloria. The young were so young, and her manner, for that she plainly had read *The Furnace* and seemed to admire it, was always on the edge of disrespect. Not that he deserved respect, Boult supposed. His own younger self would have thought he was contemptible and lazy. And so would his old friends, the ones who'd talked endlessly into the night about writing but had never made it, and were probably now dead or chronically disabled by the grind of lives they'd never been able to escape. *Just imagine . . . To think . . . If we could only . . .* He could still hear the bright cadence of their voices as a hidden counterpoint beneath the words of this strange new creature who had been sent to taunt him.

"There's a theme," he heard himself saying. "It flows in and out of the book. Rising, falling—but always there. Those lights you sometimes see here in the sky at night. For the main character, they mean . . . " Nothing? Everything . . . ?

"So why not just call the book *Aurora Borealis?*" She pulled a face. "But that's stupid. How about simply *Northern Lights?* That sounds good, doesn't it?"

"It needs to be something else, something . . . It's hard to explain. I'll know it when I see it."

Considering that she probably wasn't a real librarian, Citizen Gloria had done her research well. Or someone else had done it well for her. The books she'd carried up here to the cottage were full of useful references and suggestions. The northern lights had many names, many traditions. He particularly liked *merry dancers*, and the *zodiacal shine*. And he liked the way many of the vanished behemoths of capitalist literature, whom this island's library still gave a tarnished sort of half-life, had struggled to find the words to describe this phenomenon. *Streamers. Crowns of fiery rays. Birchbark. Silver clouds*... Yet it was none of those things, and you could tell that these writers knew they'd missed the target even as they wrestled to find it. At least Boult felt that he was in good company.

He glanced at Gloria as she leaned forward over yet another book under the bare-bulbed light of the cottage. She was still full of quick, excited movements. From this close, he could hear the frayed edges of the cheap blue fabric of her uniform brushing against her skin, could see the curve and shape of her neck where her hair fell forward, and the soft whorls beneath. Looking at her like this, he felt sad in a way which was beyond feeling happy; that old ache, which had once sent him scurrying to his pen, his paper, and was now just the thing in itself. He supposed it was called longing. He remembered nights in the local town when he was young and even the revolution and the State itself had felt like something of true purpose and human resolve. He remembered laughter and cherry mouths, and the misting of breath on lips, and the soft urgent pressure of bodies against his own beneath broken streetlamps—and all of it vanishing into the deepening dark, until he was left with only what was here and now, and a hundred books unwritten, a thousand lives unlived...

Somewhere, somehow, his concentration must have drifted as Gloria bared her precious borrowed publications before him. Drifted so far that, instead of muttering nonsense about the supposed title of a book he'd never written, he found himself talking of lost but real things. Just the rantings of some sad old man and unworthy citizen, but Gloria didn't slam her books and stand up in disgust. If anything, she leaned closer to him. If anything, he felt the give and pressure of her breathing pass cool and salt and intimate as the tide against his face.

"You shouldn't be sad," she muttered, her hand across his, her dark eyes searching his gaze. "You're Boult. You're a great man. A genius. The whole world—not just this sorry country that we live in—values everything you are, and everything you've done, or will ever do . . . " And then, as if that wasn't enough, her hand had moved up to caress his cheek, and she kissed him.

For all his pained struggles over the years to recall such an experience and set it down like some oasis on the white deserts of many a blank page, he realised he'd entirely forgotten what it was like to feel a woman's lips against his own. And why, anyway, would anyone want to capture such an evanescent thing, when its whole purpose lay in the moment itself? But still, Gloria's scent and the feel of her lips remained with him long after she'd scooped up her books and pulled on the shed skin of her coat and left. They were still there as he lay in his bed and heard his heart hammering and wondered how it was ever possible for anyone to ever sleep, with the world as wonderful as this surely was.

When he opened his eyes the next morning, Boult almost bounded out of bed. He felt so full of words—brimming with that imponderable something which would only be properly expressed once he'd set it down like the fluttering of a living butterfly upon a page. Only the sluggishness of his limbs and the dizzyingly bright sunbeams threading through his cottage reminded him that he was no longer a young man, was no longer pushing at the doors of recognition and fame, but had somehow stumbled all the way through to whatever lay on the other side—that he'd written *The Furnace* years before, and because of that he was here on this island from which there was only one possible escape. That escape wasn't for him to write something, to suddenly produce the new masterpiece he'd somehow managed to convince Watchman Roberts he'd written. The only escape was death.

He was sitting down on the rickety wicker chair beside his scarred and ink-stained desk in his own cottage. Sheer luxury, of course. There were people on the mainland who'd kill for such privileges, were they not all such good citizens. He would have killed for them himself, or used his own blood to put the necessary words down on the page. He'd had time, opportunity, here on this island even if he'd wasted so much of both that he probably only had one day left.

Boult groaned and covered his aching head. His bladder ached, too. Such had been his eagerness that he hadn't even found the time to piss before he sat at this desk. But now, in the space of however long it had taken him to shuffle across the floor of this little cottage, all the joy of creativity had been transformed into the sheer brick wall of having nothing at all to say. Through kneading fingertips, he studied some of the sheets which he'd filled in all his years of wasted effort. *Train pain rain. System object loose lose lost.* Even as random jottings, they seemed impossibly trite. He groaned again as his other hand went down to press the sour ache of his unemptied bladder through his thin striped pyjamas. Then he heard a scrape at the entrance to the cottage. He started and turned.

The door, already drifting ajar, swung the rest of the way back to let in the bright morning and light poured around the figure which stood there in silhouette. Gloria, surely? It was as if she'd never left. As if the black shadow which streamed over him and blocked the bright sea air also blocked the only possible escape.

He jerked his hands away from his head and crotch. "I was just—"

"None of my business, old fellow." It was merely Hibbert's thick voice. Merely Hibbert's bulky shape. "A man's entitled to do whatever he's entitled. Even on the mainland, the committees haven't taken that away. Not yet, anyway."

"I wasn't . . . " But what did it matter? Clutching the waistband of his pyjamas, Boult stood up and shuffled off toward the toilet, muttering that he wouldn't be more than a minute. Which, of course, he was, seeing as processes far more basic than the act of writing were starting to become a strain.

When he came out again, Hibbert was standing over his desk and shamelessly flicking thorough his manuscript. Page to page to page.

"Well . . . " he sighed. "You weren't wrong when you told me you hadn't exactly finished your novel. I'm surprised Roberts has been so trusting." He resettled the papers, weighing them down with Boult's customary pieces of slate. "When are you actually going to show this nonsense to him and admit that the game is up? Tomorrow? Today . . . ?"

"I don't know." Boult slumped down in his armchair and rearranged the open crotch of his pyjamas. He noted that the offer of borrowing Hibbert's latest parody of something resembling a novel had gone. "Does it matter?"

The frown deepened on Hibbert's face. "There'll be repercussions, you know. And not just for you. They'll set up some new committee and make every writer submit whatever they're working on for inspection and approval on a monthly basis. There'll be rubber stamps and extra forms and we'll all be required to use the same kind of paper and write legibly even in the roughest draft. Things won't be the same after this. This island, it's like the heaven priests used to describe before they were all lynched. We're just so incredibly, incredibly—"

"Yes. I know. Lucky."

"And poor old Roberts. It's not going to look good for him."

"I really don't think—"

"He's still a human being. He's still a citizen. He's doing his job here like all the rest of us. Or most."

"What do you want me to say?"

Hibbert went back to the pages, his face twisted with disgust. "You know what they'll think, don't you, when they read this? They'll think it's some kind of code. That you've been communicating with the enemy."

"But that's nonsense."

"When did that ever matter?"

"Perhaps I should just destroy it." Boult made an effort to get up, but Hibbert glared him down again.

"For God's sake, don't do that! That'll only make it look worse. Whatever it is they think you got rid of, they'll want you to tell them every fucking detail. And they'll make sure you tell them what they want to hear, believe me, irrespective of what's true and what you can remember."

Boult sat dejected in his chair. The idea of death was something he thought he was getting used to, but his mind had stubbornly avoided the obvious fact that he'd suffer prolonged and systematic torture first. "What can I do?"

"You can't do anything." Hibbert's face now bore something resembling sympathy. "What most amazes me is that things have got this far without the authorities realising. Are you absolutely sure they're not on to you . . . ?"

So this was it. Boult had never given much serious thought to how his time on the island would finally end. Confession, confrontation or betrayal had always seemed too *literary*, too *dramatic* a means for a supposed writer, who was actually incapable of writing anything, to be finally condemned. If he'd imagined anything, it had been a slow fading. For the useless words that he wrote daily on those precious and expensively produced sheets of paper to get thinner and fainter, and him with them, until nothing of either was left. Just an empty space in an empty cottage. A final blank page.

But the best, or the least worse, thing he could do in this situation was something straightforward and positive for change. Still, as he walked over the headland towards the village and the changing breezes tugged and fluttered at his clutched manuscript, he still felt pale and faint. He knew Hibbert was right. Prevarication would make this worse for everyone. Going straight to the State offices this morning was exactly what any diligent citizen would do. Assuming—and it was a big assumption—that any diligent citizen would have allowed himself to slide into this ridiculous mess in the first place.

No boats in the harbour. Clouds drifting above their leviathan shadows across a white-flecked, near-turquoise ocean. The mossed slate roofs. The once-white plaster. The cry of the gulls. Would they allow him back to his cottage? Of course they wouldn't. Taking in his last sight of everything, Boult walked down into the village. Clarkie was sluicing out last night's detritus from the White Tree's open door with a mop and bucket. Seeing Boult passing, and no doubt noticing that he had the pages of the famous and much-anticipated manuscript bunched fluttering in his arms, he gave a cheery thumbs-up.

So this was it. Boult entered the main square with the library and the State offices facing each other from across the chewed stump of the ruined plinth. He was glad he'd got here early. The State offices had only just opened, there was no one else about and the building's heavy doors held for a moment, as if surprised that he wanted to enter. Then they gave.

It was so dark inside that he stood blinking for a moment as if he'd tumbled into a cave. Cracked walls, damp-stained ceilings. A sense of strained endeavour, of unrinsed sweat, tired floor polish and poor drains. It all poured around him a slow and greasy embrace. The mainland wasn't just across the water, he decided. It was where it had always been, here on his island, waiting to draw him in.

"Citizen . . . ? Boult . . . ? Is that you?"

He looked around for the source of the voice, along the many corridors which seemed to drop away from him, and cringed as a figure approached.

"I'm sorry. I'm so, so, terribly—"

"Boult—it's me. Citizen Gloria. What's the matter? Why are you here?"

"This manuscript," he stammered, trying to push her away. "You've got to let me deliver it."

"Why on earth shouldn't I? But wait, wait . . . I—I mean you—I mean we—we haven't yet fixed on a title. And why are you suddenly so upset? I thought we were getting somewhere last night with the things you were saying to me. I thought we were nearly there. Can't we just talk about it first?"

Boult was still clutching the manuscript to his chest as she led him out of the State offices and across the bright square.

"Best if we go in here." Another dark doorway, even if it was just the library. "Come on . . . " she eased him over its threshold like a nervous horse, then on past the clank of the turnstile into the more familiar darkness. He obediently followed her along the quiet aisles.

"So," she said matter-of-factly, her hands on her hips as if she was about to tell him off, "this is supposed to be a great day, and I still don't understand what's worrying you. Is it really just the book's title? Has some committee on the mainland decided to come up with one you don't like? I mean, I may be fairly new to this game, but I do know these things happen. The state always fills in the blanks for you, if you ever leave any kind of space on a form, and not always in a good way. Why, I heard of someone who forgot to tick the box which said male or female on a requisition for a cot when they were pregnant, and the next thing was—"

"What were you doing in the state offices?"

She looked around for moment as if searching for inspiration along the lines of cracked spines which slumped along the shelves. She pursed her cherry mouth.

"I was just taking some forms to be collated. Books viewed, number of visitors. Someone has to do it every morning. You know how these things work. Even libraries have five year plans."

"So you *are* a librarian?"

"What else do you think I am?"

He shook his head. "I really don't know. But no, it isn't the title, Gloria, or anything that you said or did last night. It's . . . " He held the manuscript out. "Here."

"Can I *look* at it—your new book?" Her gaze was awed. When she took the pages from him, they trembled in her hands almost as much as they had in his.

"But it's not a book, Gloria. It's nothing. It's just random lines . . . "

She smoothed the ruffled first page with her fingers. He thought she'd just glance at the top sheet, realise what he meant, and glare back at him like Hibbert. But instead she studied the words for some time. He could tell from the travel of her eyes that she was actually trying to read them.

"This is . . . Very interesting and strange . . . " She muttered eventually. "I know it's a lot to ask, but can I have an hour or two to look at it properly?"

"Why . . . ? You mean *now*? In *here*?"

"Why not?" She smiled. "After all, if a great author's new work isn't safe in a library, where is it . . . ?"

Boult sat. Boult stood. Boult waited. Boult wandered the derelict alleys of library shelves. Boult coughed and wheezed like all the other lost and lonely writers who were slowly settling into their accustomed places for another day at the coalface of the strange endeavour of making up things. And what was the need for more of this nonsense, anyway, when so much of it already existed? Boult balled his hands into fists as he prowled past endless titles, tomes, words, fictions, lies. Whole lifetimes of endeavour. And what did it really matter, he asked himself, if a particular novel consisted of nothing but a disassociated jumble of meaningless letters, when it all meant so little anyway? He took down a volume of supposed non-fiction, let it fall open. *Fable.* Took down another, let it fall open in the same way. *Experimented.* None of these books made any sense— not when you studied them in this clear and objective fashion. Just more nonsense filtered down to its citizens by the State. Critics were just critics, and readers were just readers, and committees, when all was said and done, were only committees, and death was just death, and pain was simply pain.

She was taking an extraordinarily long time. He looked along falling aisles—the dusty ruins, the broken pillars, the spills of loose pages which would never be catalogued in this or any other lifetime, lying like heaps of desiccated birds. She was probably reporting him already. In fact, the whole thing was an obvious ruse by the authorities to get him to pass the book into their hands. He was amazed at himself for not having realised. He imagined his pointless words being frowned over, analysed, discussed, until they had lost even their sense of being rudimentary strings of letters conveying thought and sound.

Whatever Citizen Gloria and Watchman Roberts and all the rest of them were now doing, it was bound to turn out terribly for him. Would they really think that those pages were some kind of code, or would they simply decide that he was mad? Code meant that he would be treated as a spy, which was bad enough, but he had no illusions how citizens who had lost the regular habits of a clean and civic mind were treated on the mainland. The cold immersions. The sanitary cleansings. The electric prods. The invasive techniques. The kinds of torture in white rooms he'd feared, until a few moments ago, that his life would soon be ended by, but infinitely prolonged.

He thought of running—fleeing the library. But where could he go? On this island, there was no escape. That was the cleverest thing the State had done to the writers here. It had given those tricky and unpredictable beings all the things that they all claimed they wanted. It had given them peace and quiet. It had given them paper and ink. It had given them time and space and, yes, just a little glory. And it had pushed them all together into the arid vacuum of this bleak paradise, so that they could squabble and bicker and preen and walk and talk and read and drink their beer and fuck their Matrons and do whatever else it was they claimed they wanted until it all lay far beyond their hearts' content.

In his agitated wanderings, Boult had reached the part of the library which he and his colleagues normally avoided, for it contained their own work. There it was, on a middle shelf. A single copy of *The Furnace*. He eased it out, attempted to study the printing history on the first of its splayed pages, then the lending stamps and the library catalogue entry, but too much was obscured by the many stains, marks and creases. He ran his finger along the drift of sand and dark marine matter which had accreted within its wrinkled spine. The thing smelled oddly salty, and felt thickly damp—less a book, more like some ancient, soft-shelled mollusc which had crawled out from the sea.

The person who'd written this book wasn't the same Boult who'd wasted all these years on this island. This was the work of a young, vibrant man who knew less but cared a great deal more about the world. He remembered the cold nights, the struggles to find ink and paper, the aching eyes and fingers, the hopeless hope that he might be creating something out of nothing—then, from the morning bucket, the scratch of the frozen soap across his face. How frail the real world had then seemed! How laughably thin and quaintly pathetic compared to the things he'd felt and witnessed on the page!

The dark corridors of the island library had that same insubstantiality as he looked up at them. So did Citizen Gloria as she approached him.

"I hadn't read this in years." He held out his copy of *The Furnace*.

"That copy rather looks as if it's seen better days. But this . . . " She was holding the heavy sheaf to her breast, and she was smiling. " . . . this . . . "

Boult found himself sinking, falling. Had the pages somehow transformed themselves? Was this some miracle or curse? "You didn't actually try to read it, did you?"

"Well, actually, I did. It's bonkers, isn't it? It's beyond anything that even the most decadent enemy writer would ever dare to create."

To hear her say that was almost a relief. "So you're not pretending to say it has any literary merit?"

"No, but . . . well, it *is* rather hypnotic. I was telling myself for the first few pages that it was just a preamble, an experiment, and the fog would start to clear. But after that, I began to feel disappointed. And then, if I'm honest Boult, rather bored."

Which was, he thought, the kindest review his supposed successor to *The Furnace* was ever likely to get.

"I suppose you could dress it up as some sort of brave experiment, but that won't play with the committees and the censors," she said. "You know how they like their art—simplistically realistic and stupidly linear. Books that read like train timetables—which are, of course, far greater works of fiction over on the mainland than the books themselves. Paintings that should be photographs. Songs you can beat a hammer to so you don't have to hear them. Drama that would disgrace a kitchen sink."

"So at least you see my problem?"

"Yes. You're a great writer who's been blocked for far too long by the petty restrictions and brutal threats."

Boult glanced over his shoulder, then through the gaps in the books at the adjoining aisles. Libraries were notoriously bad places for risky conversation. "You can't say that."

"But I just have. *The Furnace* is a work of genius and is loved the world over."

"You think people read my book beyond the mainland?"

"Of course they do. And better understand and enjoy it for the masterpiece it is. That's what proper freedom means, Boult. You're seen beyond this dreadful country as what you really are—a great man, a great writer. Just like Kilbracken—"

"*Kilbracken*?!"

Gloria smiled. "I'm sorry. I never said that freedom gives everyone perfect taste. But you're the reason I agreed to come here and offer you a chance."

"A chance for what?"

"The chance to escape."

She took his hand and drew him even deeper into the library. Opened what looked to be a cupboard door with one of her keys. Pressed the lightswitch as she beckoned him in, which, somewhat surprisingly, caused many lines of bulbs to glow across a wide, and entirely un-dampstained, ceiling. Not so much a cupboard as a library within a library, lined with shelves in neat array.

"What is this place?"

"It's where all the books which have been deemed unsuitable are stored."

"I thought we writers on this island already had special access to those."

She gave him a pitying look. "That isn't really how you think it works, is it? You lot are given the dribs, the drabs, the leavings. The real stuff is kept in here."

Boult inspected some of the nearby shelves, which were far better ordered than any library he'd ever seen. "But I recognise some of these works. I'm sure they're still available."

"Of course they are, but only in redacted and recensored form. Some books have been through the same process many times, *The Furnace* included. That's often why, when you try to reread something you enjoyed years before, it's nothing like as good as you remember it to be. But that doesn't happen where I'm from, Boult. People are free to read—and write—and say—whatever they want."

"You make it sound very simple."

"It is . . . At least in theory. I'm not pretending everything's perfect— that's what the State does here—but I can offer you that same freedom. And peace and quiet, a pine lodge by a lake in a forest, with endless walks and a decent, proper, library, and big fireplaces and logs to burn in the winter, and air-conditioning in the summer—"

"What's air-conditioning?"

"It doesn't matter. Or you can live in a city, surrounded by noise and life. Eat, buy whatever you want at any time of the day or night. Give talks, travel, write essays, or be a grumpy hermit. It's entirely up to you. The people will love you anyway, just for being Boult, the writer of *The Furnace*, and for getting away from here, for standing up against, this so-called State."

"This is . . . " He shook his head.

"It's what you *deserve*, Boult! And it's why I've risked so much to get here and to try to get you out."

"So . . . " He felt as if he was stepping across a minefield. "What exactly would happen?"

"I just need to send a signal, and we'll be picked up by one of our submarines."

"I'm not a good swimmer, and the currents are—"

"Oh, you don't need to be. An inflatable boat's already been hidden amid the rocks on the north shore. We simply pull that out, row to the rendezvous, and we're both free."

Now he felt as if he was in one of Kilbracken's stupid mysteries. But, impossibly, he believed this was real.

"We'll make it tonight. There's no point in waiting with that weasely watchman creature sniffing around for a glimpse of your finished book. I'll meet you down from your cottage on the north shore at midnight. Meanwhile, you just have to do what you've been doing for decades for a few more hours, and act the part and stall. Now . . . " She was opening the hidden library's door, pushing him out. " . . . *go!*"

Boult said farewell to his cottage in the luminous twilight. The empty chair, the empty bed, his useless manuscript left weighed down by slates on his equally useless desk. He'd achieved something here on this island, after all, which was to escape; it was like some unexpected twist in the final chapter of a novel which seems inevitable once it's occurred. He looked down at his old canvas shoes and his ragged trousers, which would soon be wet. He studied the scuffs on the flagstone floor. More hurriedly now, he left the cottage and stumbled out across the dunes.

The shore. The ocean glinting bright and black as polished basalt. A few stars, a few clouds, and more coming in, borne on the same wind which had ruffled the edges of Gloria's hair as she'd offered him cherries at this shore's edge. The aurora, the northern lights, whatever they might be called, had retreated beyond the hazing dark. So had the mainland. All that was left was him, and his last moments on this island.

But Kilbracken! The idea of Kilbracken being read and admired by people in foreign lands who weren't forced to put up with his contrived, half-literate nonsense left Boult disgusted and dazed. Worse still was the idea that someone like Gloria—but surely not Gloria herself—would someday come to this island to liberate him. Then, of course, the free people of the new lands might imagine that he and Boult had an affinity. Put them in adjoining lodges in the forest, neighbouring apartments in the city, make them sit together on literary panels, give shared interviews about how awful life here had been. Expect them collaborate, even. A horrible, horrible prospect, but perhaps it was no more than he, Boult, deserved. And he'd be deep into his next novel by then. Or the one after that, with some short fiction and a few essays on the simple, complex craft of writing dotted in between. Shielded from the stupid and the mundane, which would surely exist even in this new country of freedom and opportunity, by the balm of knowing he was doing what he was good at, and creating something worthwhile that others might actually care to read.

This world he was about to enter wouldn't be perfect. It was important that he kept that firmly in mind through all the difficulties which he was bound to face. Even more important, though, he must remember what he'd left behind, and why he'd left it. This ghastly State which was its own prisoner, locked in a box of its own creation for which it had long ago lost the key. Which was, he realised, something he'd been wanting to write about through all these seemingly wasted years. Yes—that was it! Suddenly it seemed simple in the way that all good ideas, and the urge to write about them, did when they finally came along. He could use this island as the setting to depict the languid crisis of a writer much like himself. And Gloria, well, Gloria . . . She plainly loved and understood his work, and doubtless she'd keep in touch with him as he adjusted to the challenges of his new life, and whatever air-conditioning was. From that . . . Well, it was probably just an old man's fantasy. But you never knew . . .

Where was she anyway? Boult peered up and down the beach as waves began to wet his feet. And there, at last, was a figure approaching along the shining edge of the strand. He almost shouted. Almost waved. But he didn't, and in another moment he was glad, for it was Roberts, bearing his usual smirk.

"There you are, Boult!" Like all inveterate snoopers, the watchman was good at appearing surprised. "I looked in at your cottage, then up and down here. To be honest, I was getting a little worried. I mean . . . " The smile widened like a crack in a wall. "We can't have one of our best writers just wandering off."

Boult shrugged, wondering if there was still any point in appearing innocent. "Here I am."

"That's . . . Good." As if they might be overheard on this empty beach, Roberts looked around them. "I've been meaning to find you, just to let you know that the publishing requisition we submitted has been formally accepted by the mainland committees."

"Was there any chance it wouldn't be?"

"In my experience it pays not to make too many assumptions. After all . . . " Roberts gave an awkward laugh; almost a seal-like cough. "Here on this island, we can't possibly have a full understanding of all the needs of the State."

"I suppose not."

The two men stood in silence for some time. The stars prickled to greater brightness. The sea retreated, sighed back over Boult's toes.

"There was something else I felt I should mention. It's a kind of warning, really. You see, there's been this new librarian at the library, a young woman. You've probably seen her about. The records may even show she'd found the odd book for you and . . . Anyway, she was arrested in the main square about, oh, noon today. Taken into the State offices for—well, for *questioning*, if you understand what I mean. So, just in case, a word to the wise."

"I see. Is that it?"

"Pretty much." The waves rushed in again, and Roberts took a stumbling step back. "Oh, and I wouldn't expect to see Hibbert around too much in the future."

"He isn't a spy as well, is he?"

"No—nothing like that! It's just that the quality of his work has become so poor that he's been deemed to be no longer a productive unit. He's taking up space, your see, which a better writer could use. So he's going to get sent back to the mainland. I think he used to be a teacher, but he may have to work his way back up to that kind of privilege in one of the commune mines."

"What about Kilbracken?"

"*Kilbracken*? Oh, nothing bad to report there, I'm pleased to say. He's one of our best, one of our greatest. A national treasure. He's right up there with you."

Boult nodded.

"Oh, and I'll be around sometime tomorrow afternoon to pick up your new novel. Assuming it's now finished, that is. Clarkie said he saw you carrying it with you this morning when he was sweeping out, and that you had the air of a man who was ready to hand it in."

"I was. It was just—"

"It's that title, isn't it? I know what you writers are like! You all fret and worry far too much about these things when it's all just ink on a page."

Boult had turned, and was looking north across the water toward the horizon.

"I'm sure you've got something up your sleeve, anyway. Can't have a novel without a title. But don't tell me now—don't spoil the surprise— just let me know when I see you tomorrow, and we'll finish off the necessary forms."

Boult stood watching until Roberts had vanished along the shore, and the water was lapping his knees. That was it then, although he knew enough about the way these things worked to understand that *it* was nothing like it seemed. He didn't doubt that Citizen Gloria had vanished just as swiftly and mysteriously as she'd arrived, for example, but she certainly wouldn't have been imprisoned, let alone questioned, tortured. After all, she was clearly a skilled operative and had done an excellent job, had stripped and gutted him of all the information the State had wanted, and left him waiting here on this shore on the basis of some ridiculous tale that—and at least he'd been right about this part—would have disgraced even Kilbracken's torpid, creaking pages. The whole thing had been a setup, beginning with Styche's unlikely disappearance. Although perhaps Hibbert's initial sympathy and offer of help had been genuine, which would explain why the poor man would never be seen again. Was Styche even *dead*? And just how long had the empty trick of that useless, unwritten novel, which he hadn't even made any proper attempt to hide up in his cottage, been known? Long before stupidity and vanity had suddenly caused him to announce it was finished, that much was sure.

Still, Boult felt oddly grateful to Roberts, or whoever was giving him his orders. He'd had a good innings on this island, far better than he deserved. And now, instead of the hot wires, the drowning baths, the tubes and truncheons and ropes, he was being allowed to do the decent, obvious thing all on his own.

He stepped deeper into the waves, felt their playful nudge and push. After a few steps came a deeper undertow of cold. It lifted him, bore him from the shore and—as if it mattered—he kicked off his canvas shoes. He'd never been much of a swimmer, either here, or back on the mainland in the State's corroded, chlorinous, urinous pools. Still, he found he was striking out with near proficiency and odd urgency, as if it was somehow important that he get as far away from the island as he could. Which, in a way, he supposed it was, seeing as it might upset one of the other writers if they were to find his body washed up on the shore. He was obeying orders, answering the empty call of siren voices, and the north shore had vanished into the gloom when he paused, treading water, to look back.

The water was so very cold, and the pull of the currents now so strong he barely needed to swim to be borne along. Overhead the sky seemed to be as far away as those stupid dreams of good food, uncoarse blankets, lights you could turn off and on without a thought, and that one, brief, kiss. And glinting cities, and deep, dark forests, and roadways filled with purring cars, and work a kind of contentment instead of a dull misery that awoke you trembling and sweating in a room you wished you'd never known. Forget the adulation. Forget the fabulous reviews. The simple peace of doing the thing you knew you existed for would have been enough. Or, if not that, then he'd take this bigger, deeper peace instead.

The grip of the water. The salt, black, incredible cold. But there were lights ahead of him, and voices, and Boult began to laugh until the water choked his throat. It was the biggest joke in the world that he'd somehow managed to swim to the mainland, and surely the island's biggest lie that it couldn't be done. But he knew that was wrong as he somehow struggled back to the surface. He was too far out, too lost, and the lights flickered again, turning, seeking, and the accent of the voices was strange. Boult caught rocking glimpses of something sleek and grey and long as he strove to tread water and raise a hand and drag enough air back into his lungs to shout. But it was hopeless, and the voices had stopped calling, and the lights had gone out with a steely clang. Then, in a hissing sigh and a spume of water, the enemy submarine sank down, and Boult was once more alone.

The swimming was almost easy, if you could call it swimming now. Better, after all, just to submit to the currents and the cold. He was drifting, he was driftwood, and the urge to be what he'd been, Boult the supposed writer, was almost gone. Pain, after all, was just pain, and drowning was simply drowning, and words were only words, and he really did wish this last straining, struggling part of him would just give up. A strange, shuddering combination of absence and urgency. A lifetime wasted, and now almost gone. Along with Gloria's inexplicable bravery, and Hibbert's mild generosity, and Clarkie's warm beer—and even Watchman Roberts, who'd only ever done what he thought was his job . . .

Those useless pages lying under their stones back in his cottage were his only legacy, for the young man who'd once written a book called *The Furnace* had died long ago. *Unabridged abridged destroyed censored. Impossible unlikely smile cherries cheery betrayed ignorance arrogance loss. Cold cold cold cold cold.* But as he struggled up, eyes searing, salt vomit blocking his lungs, Boult saw that the sky above him was pulsing with glorious grey fire. And, as the lights danced, he knew the phrase he'd been seeking before the sea closed over him for the last time.

I MENTIONED IN MY PIECE ABOUT IDEAS THAT THE GENESIS OF THIS story goes back more than three decades. It may be that it takes a degree of maturity for a writer to write about writer's block. I suspect that, at the time I first tried out the idea in my late teens, I regarded it as an almost glamorous state—a struggle between an artist and his muse—rather than the tedious drag it actually is.

I'm lucky enough not to have had too much experience of the type of writer's block that Boult seems to be suffering from, which leaves him unable to produce even a single complete sentence. My own main personal variety of the ailment is what I think of in retrospect as "busy work", where I draft and re-draft and tweak and develop new scenes and seeming insights into a project which often feels okay day to day, but still never gets anywhere.

Not being able to create when it's the thing you most want to do is painful and boring in the way of a dull backache. Not quite bad enough to completely absorb all your attention and destroy your entire life, perhaps, but it upsets the rhythm of your days and, whenever there's a pause in whatever else you're doing, it always returns. Writers, real writers, want to write in the same way that musicians want to play, painters want to paint, or, so I'd like to think, birds want to sing. It's a natural state. It really isn't, or shouldn't be, an either/or thing.

I'm a great admirer of the band Steely Dan, and I used to think it was rather cool that, after the brilliant *Gaucho*, and the equally brilliant Donald Fagen solo album *Nightfly*, he and his co-writer Walter Becker fell silent for the best part of a decade. After all, they surely didn't need the money, and it rather suited their cool, fuck-you image that they should choose to stop at the peak of what they could do. Of course, I learned later that Becker had been plagued by drug, health and personal problems, and Fagen spent much of that "lost decade" trying, and failing, to write new material almost daily.

Apart from my preconceptions about writer's block being cool, which I shed quite a while ago, I think one of the other things which was holding me back from getting "Frost on Glass" to work was my uncertainty about finding a suitable market for a work that barely scrapes in as SF. Now, I'd tell anyone who expressed those sorts of doubts to me to just get the thing done and worry about it afterwards, but it's often the case that, when you're wrestling to get a story right, you're dealing with unexpressed assumptions and thoughts.

In many ways, "Frost on Glass" in its finished state epitomises the sort of piece I love writing above all others, because it blends elements of realistic and fantastic fiction into what seems, at least to me, a pretty convincing yet mysterious whole. The island appears to be somewhere off Scotland, and the culture is clearly British, or even English. Somehow, some kind of communistic state has been established, and the "other lands" Gloria refers to have a ring of the States, and I at least am reminded of Solzhenitsyn's flight from Russia when she talks to Boult of the reception he can expect.

And that, the way the story finally worked out, seemed to be enough. My attempts over the years to expand the piece and explain more about the society beyond the island always floundered. As did those to try to snazz up the kind of technology involved. I toyed on and off with having Boult and his cohorts not producing books at all, but transmitting actual dreams to the mainland instead. Of course, that's what they're doing anyway, and the metaphor works much better at the simpler level of books.

The other thing which was holding me back from getting "Frost on Glass" done was Gloria herself. Her ambiguous role was always part of how I conceived the plot, but does she represent freedom, or hypocrisy? Is she an escape route, or a trap? And so on. But I realise now that what was truly bugging me about her lay deeper than those thrillerish elements, which I was more than happy to play with and leave hanging—at least until the story's end.

The way I see it, Gloria is the agent of a foreign power who has somehow reached the island to facilitate Boult's escape. Which means that she fails to turn up for their rendezvous on the beach not because she's betrayed him, but because she's been arrested by the apparatchiks of the State. Not only that, but she must have held out for long enough during her interrogation to allow Boult time to try to make his escape. I can't imagine, though, that she'd be allowed to live for very long after, or that her last hours would be anything but horrible.

Which, no matter how I choose to look at it, is an unpleasant fate to set up for a character, especially one who plainly doesn't deserve it. Certainly, as I grew conscious of how the end of this story would work, I felt uneasy about what I was doing to this poor woman, who'd risked so much and achieved so little. Gloria had done nothing but step into my story and help to give it life, and here I was giving her nothing but pain, disappointment and death in return.

Obviously, one can get far too sentimental about fictional characters. They come, they go, both for the reader and the writer. After all, they're only made of dreams and ink. But writers must strive to feel something for their characters, and to understand what makes them what they are. To try to bring them to life, in other words. Once I'd got to the point of deciding what was needed to make "Frost on Glass" work, and what would thus have to happen to Gloria, I realised that an unrecognised squeamishness was probably another part of what had been holding me back. Although, and this surely says something about my attitude to other writers, I never felt any qualms about drowning poor old Boult.

ENTANGLED

WHEN she awakes, it seems as if she's not alone. Many arms are around her, and she's filled with a roaring chorus of voices. Consciousness follows in a series of ragged flickers, and the voices fade, and soon she inhabits her own thoughts, and knows that she is Martha Chauhan, and nothing has changed. But the air, the light, the sounds which reach to her room this morning, fifteen floors up in Baldwin Towers, all feel different today . . .

Lumbering from bed, she clears a space in the frost, peers blearily down, and sees from the blaze of white that it's snowed heavily in the night, and that many of the entangled are already up and about. Kids, but adults as well. Either throwing snowballs, or dragging handmade toboggans, or building snowmen, or helping clear the pathways between the tower blocks. The small shadows of their movements seem impossibly balletic.

Still climbing from the fuzz of night, she counts and dry-swallows the usual immune suppressants from her palm. The water isn't entirely cold, the hob puts out just enough heat to turn her coffee lukewarm, and she's grateful she doesn't have to use the commune toilets. In so many ways, she's privileged. Fumbling with yesterday's clothes, she swipes the mirror for glimpses of a woman in late middle age with something odd about the left side of her skull, then she picks up her carpetbag and heads down the pell-mell stairs with other commune residents in their flung coats, sideways bobble hats and unmatched gloves.

Shouts and snowballs criss-cross the air as she crunches to her readapted Mini, another great privilege, which has already been cleared of snow. She clambers in. Shivers and hugs herself as she waits for the fuel cell to warm. Finally, she drives off.

Along with the 1960s tower blocks, there are houses and maisonettes in other parts of this estate that were once occupied by individual families. Now, they have all been reshaped and knocked through, joined by plastic-weld polysheets, raggedly-angled sheds and tunnels of tarpaulin, with the gardens and other open spaces used for communal planting and grazing. Everything's white this morning, but all the roads have been cleared, and braziers already blaze in the local market where the communes come to barter. Strangers smile to each other as they pass. Acquaintances hug. Co-workers sing lusty songs as they shovel the paths. Lovers walk hand in hand. Even the snowmen are grinning.

This isn't how I imagined my life would be.

I grew up in this same city, not far from these streets. Dad was of Indian birth, and came here to England with my brother in his arms and me clinging to the strap of his suitcase and our mother dead from a terrorist dirty bomb back in Calcutta. He changed my name from Madhur to Martha, and Daman's to Damien, and honed his cultural knowledge to go with his excellent English, and had all the certificates and bio-tags to prove he was a doctor, and was determined to make his mark. *Money is important, and so is security, and status is something to be cherished*—that was what Martha Chauhan learned at her father's knee. That, and all the stories he told me as he sat by my bed. Tenali Ramakrishna and the gift of the three dolls who all seemed the same, but only one of which knew how to feel. Artful imps who danced about the flames, to the secret of their own names, in the hidden heart of a forest But maybe I was too cosseted, for I could never get the point. The world was clearly collapsing. You could see that merely by switching screens from the kiddie channels he tried to sit Damien and me in front of in our secure house in our gated and protected estate. A wave of my chubby hand, and the Technicolor balloon things dissolved and you were looking down at people clinging to trees as the helicopters flew on, or at bomb blast wreckage surrounded by wailing women, and then Damien started crying, and that was that.

St James' schoolhouse is like something from Dickensian old times, even without today's gingerbread icing of snow. A great, paternally white oak looms across the trampled playground. Martha heads inside past the tiny rows of dripping coats into a room filled with rampaging four year olds. The walls hang with askew potato prints and cheery balloon-style faces. There's a sandpit and a ballpool and something else that fizzes and buzzes, hovering in mid-air as the kids dive.

Tommy, the teacher, lies at the bottom of a pile of waving limbs, and it's some time before he or anyone else notices Martha's presence. When they do, it's as if she's left the doors open and the kids feel a cold draft on their necks. Once the unease is there, it spreads impossibly fast. Tommy, who's lying on his back like a tickled dog, is almost the last to pick up the change of mood.

He clambers to his feet in a holed jumper and with half the contents of the sandpit bulging his pockets. A dozen kids cluster around him, exchanging looks, half-words, mumbles, grunts, nudges, gestures and silences. Tommy protectively crowds them to him, until he remembers how rude that is.

"It's okay, it's *okay* . . . ! We have a visitor, and I want everyone to simply *talk* when Martha's with us. Right?" Kids give metronomic nods as Martha is introduced as the nice lady who's going to be seeing them individually over the next few hours. Then a hand goes up, then another. "So why . . . " asks a small voice, before a different one takes over until the question finishes in chorus. " . . . isn't she . . . HERE . . . ?" Followed by a rustle of giggles.

After all, Martha obviously *is* here. But, in another, deeper, sense she's clearly not. Martha understands their curiosity, and can remember how she used to stare at fat people and paraplegics when she was young until her father told her it was impolite. She can't help but smile as hands sneak out to touch the snow-melting tips of her boots, just to check she's not some weird kind of ghost.

"I *am* here," she says. "But the thing is, not everyone has the same gift that all of you have. I can *see* you, and I can *hear* you as well. But there was an accident—perhaps you can see where it was . . . " She turns so they can admire the odd shape of her skull. "I lost . . . " She pauses. " . . . part of my mind. Truth is, I'm very lucky to be here at all. What my disability means is that I'm not entangled. Not part of the gestalt. I can't share and feel as you do. But I'm as real as all of you are. Look, this is my hand . . . " She holds it out. Slowly, slowly, tentatively, little fingers encircle her own like new shoots enclosing old roots. Then, and at the same instant, and as if by some hidden decision, they withdraw. As they settle back, the face of one of the boys blurs and tries to reshape itself into Damien's.

Dad always was an industrious man. Not only had he managed to qualify as a doctor back in India, but he'd studied what was then called biome-chanical science. He also had a practical business eye. He'd worked out that the most secure jobs in medicine at a time of collapsing insurance and failing state healthcare were to be found in the developing technologies of neural enhancement.

I remember him taking Damien and me along with him one day to the private hospital where he did much of his work. It was probably down to some failure in the child-minding arrangements that all single parents have to make, although Damien must have been about five by then and I was nearly twelve, so perhaps he really had wanted to show us what he did.

"Here we are . . . "

The rake of a handbrake in his old-fashioned car that smelled of leather and Damien's tendency to get travelsick. We'd already passed through several security systems and sets of high walls, and were now outside this big old castle of a building that looked like something out of Harry Potter or Tolkien—all turrets and pointy windows. Then doors swished, and suddenly everything turned busy and modern, with people leaning down, dangling their unlikely smiles and security passes toward us, to ask who we were—at least, until Damien began to cry. Then we were inside a bright room, and this creature was laid at its centre surrounded by wires and humming boxes and great semi-circular slabs of metal.

Damien sat over in a far corner, pacified by some game. But apparently it was important that I stand close and listen to what Dad has to say. You see, Martha, this patient—her name's Claire, by the way—is suffering from a condition that is slowly destroying her mind. Can you imagine what that must be like? To forget the names of your best friends and the faces of your family? To get confused by simple tasks and slowly lose any sense of who you really are? A terrible, terrible thing. But we now have a procedure that helps combat that process. What we do, you see . . . he'd called up a display which floated between us like a diseased jellyfish . . . is to insert these incredibly clever seeds—which are like little crystals—into her skull that we then stimulate with those big magnets you can see around her head so the seeds slowly take over the damaged bits of her mind . . .

The jellyfish quivered.

Dad doubtless went on in this way for some time, probably covering all sorts of fascinating moral and philosophical questions about the nature of consciousness, and how this withered relic would come to use all this new stuff in her head in much the same way that someone who's lost their hand might use a re-grown one. But not quite. Nothing in medicine is ever perfect, you see, Martha, and bits of people's brains can't be persuaded to regenerate in the way that other parts of their body can, and rejection— that means, Martha, when the body doesn't recognise something as part of itself—is still a problem, and a great deal of practice and continued medication is going to be needed if Claire's to make the most of this gift of half a new mind. Meanwhile, I was staring at the creased and scrawny flesh that emerged from all that steel and plastic like the neck of a tortoise, and thinking, why is something so old and horrid still even *alive*?

Martha's given her usual "room" at the school—actually little more than a cupboard—and says no to an offer of coffee. Then she opens up her carpetbag and puts the field cap, with its dangle of controls and capillaries, on the radiator to warm.

The entanglement virus is generally contracted naturally soon after birth, but it's the job of Martha and many others like her to deal with any problems which may arise during the short fever which follows. She often looks in again on toddlers, but it's at this age, when the children have joined the gestalt as individual personalities, that's the next major watch-out. Then if all goes, as well as it usually does, there are some final checks to be made during the hormone surge of adolescence. In some cultures and other parts of the globe, she'd be thought of as a shaman, priest, imam or witch doctor. But the world had changed, and the differences really aren't that great.

"This is where I . . . Should be?"

Martha looks up, slightly surprised by the way this kid has simply stepped into her tiny room. Most hang around outside and wait to be invited, or rub and scratch at the door like kittens, seeing as, even though her disability has been explained to them, they still find it difficult to believe that she's actually inside.

"Yes. That's perfect. You're . . . " She glances at Tommy's execrably written list. "Shara, right? Shara of Widney Commune. Am I getting your name right, by the way? Shara? Such a pretty name, but I don't think I've heard it much before. Or is it Shar-ra?"

"I think it's just Shara," the girl says as she settles on the old gym mat. She has bright blue eyes. Curly, almost reddish, hair. "Some people say it different but it doesn't matter. The other mums and most of the dads sometimes just call me Sha. I think Shara was just a name they made up for me when I was born."

Shara of the Widney Commune really is an extraordinarily composed creature. Pretty with it, with those dazzling eyes and the fall around her cheeks of that curly hair, which Martha longs to touch, just to see if it really is as soft and springy as it looks. If ever there was a subject for whom her attentions might seem irrelevant, it's Shara. And yet . . . There's *something* about this girl . . . Martha blinks, swallows, kicks her mind back into focus, just as Shara's features threaten to dissolve, and reminds herself that she's taken her usual handful of immune suppressants.

"Are you alright?"

"Oh . . . ? Absolutely, Shara. Now, I want you to put this on."

Shara takes the field cap and puts it on in the right way without the usual prompting, even tightening the chinstrap against the pressure of those lovely curls. She lies down.

"I want you to close your eyes."

Unquestioningly, she does so.

"Can you see anything?"

Shara shakes her head.

"How about now?" Martha lifts the ends of the capillaries and touches the controls.

"It's all kind of fizzy."

"And now?"

"Like *lines* . . . "

"And now?"

This time, Shara doesn't respond. Her fingers are quivering. Her cheeks have paled. The rhythm of her breathing has slowed. Sometimes, although Martha tries to insist that they use the toilet beforehand, the kids wet themselves. But not Shara. The girl's in a fugue state now, lost deep inside the gestalt. Always a slight risk at this point that they won't come back, and Martha's trained in CPR and has adrenalin and antipsychotic shots primed and ready in her carpetbag just in case they need to be quickly woken up or knocked out, but the rigidity fades just as soon as she cuts the signal back. Shara stretches. Blinks. Sits up. Smiles.

"How was that?" Martha helps unclip the field cap and feels the spring of those lovely curls.

Shara thinks. "It was *lovely*. Thank you Martha," she says. Then she kisses her cheek.

It wasn't all famine, tribal wars economic collapse back in the day. Life mostly went on as it always did, and I suppose Dad did his best to try to keep us going as some kind of family as well. I remember a summer West Country beach—it wasn't all floods and landslips, either—that he must have driven us down to from the Midlands in that creaky old car— between regular stops at the roadside for Damien to vomit. There we were, Dad and me, sitting on an old rug amid our sandwiches and samosas while dogs flung themselves after Frisbees and Damien and some other lads attempted to play cricket. Kites stuck like hatpins into a pale sky and a roaring in my ears that could be the sea, but often comes when I chase too hard after memories.

Dad was chattering on as he often did. Trying hard not to be a bore, or talk down to me, but not really succeeding . . . You see, Martha, the work I do on the mind, the brain, the whole strange business of human consciousness, is just the very beginning. The crystals I persuade to grow inside peoples' skulls are almost as primitive as wooden legs. Real, living neurons use quantum effects—it isn't just electricity and chemistry. The mind, the entirety of the things we call thought and memory and consciousness, is really the sum of a shimmer of uncertainties. It mirrors the universe, and perhaps even calls it into existence. But even that's not the most wonderful thing about us, Martha. You see, we all think we're alone, don't we? You imagine you're somewhere inside your skull and I'm somewhere inside mine, that we're like separate islands? But we're not looking at it from enough dimensions. It's like us sitting on this beach, and looking out over those waves toward the horizon, and seeing a scatter of islands. No, no, I'm not saying there *are* real islands out there, Martha because there obviously aren't. But just stay with me for a moment my dear and try to imagine. We'd think of those islands as alone and separate, wouldn't we? But they're not. Not if you look at the world sideways. Beneath the sea, under the waves, all the islands are joined. It's just that we can't properly see it, or feel it. Not yet, anyway . . .

The day moved on, and Dad stood at the driftwood wicket, like any good English or Indian father would, and soon got bowled out. Then he fielded, and dropped an easy catch from Damien as I crunched my through though the last of the sandy samosas. The wind blew colder, and the kites and the Frisbees and the dogs fled the beach, and the last thing I can remember is my lost Dad holding hands with my lost brother Damien as he wandered with his trousers rolled at the edge of the roaring sea.

Martha drives out toward the edge of the motorway system which still encircles much of this old city. The big trucks are out in force now; great, ponderous leviathans that grumble along the rubbled concrete out of a greyness that threatens more snow. Dwarfed by their wheels, she parks her Mini at a transport stop, and stomps up to the glass and plastic counter. It's a regular old-fashioned greasy spoon. The windows are steamed, and baked beans are still on the menu, and the coffee here is moderately strong. Always a difficult dance, getting through a busy space when people's backs are turned, but she clatters her tray to give warning, and they soon share the sense of her oddity and decide not to stare. Mindblind coming through.

She likes it here. The people who do this travelling kind of work far from their communes are still surprisingly solitary by nature. A few are sharing tables and chatting in low voices or quietly touching, but most sit on their own and appear to be occupied with little but their own thoughts. In places like this it's possible to soak up a companionship of loneliness that she can imagine she shares. Sometimes, one of them comes over to talk. Sometimes, but more rarely, and after all the usual over-polite questions, the conversation moves on, and some of the old signs of sexual availability, which to them must seem arcane as smoke signals, waft into view.

There are some rooms at the back of this place which anyone who needs them is free to use. Piled mattresses and cushions. Showers for afterwards—or during. Sex with Martha Chauhan must be something lonely and oddly exotic, and perhaps a little filthy, as far as the entangled are concerned. A weird kind of masturbation with someone else in the room. There's an odd emptiness in their eyes as they and the gestalt study her when, and if, she comes. But Martha's getting older. Mindblind or not, they probably find her repulsive, and whatever urgency she once felt to be with someone in that way has gone.

She pushes aside her plate and swirls the dregs of her coffee. Blinks away the fizzing arrival of her father's reproachful smile. After all, what has she done wrong? But the empty truth is there's nothing she needs to do this afternoon. She could go back to her room in Baldwin Towers and try to sleep. She could go tobogganing, although being with other people having fun is one of the loneliest things of all. This day, the whole of whatever is left of her life, looms blank as these steamy, snow-whitened windows. She could give up. She could stop taking her tablets. Instead, though, she rummages in her carpetbag and studies the list she was given this morning, and sees that name again, Shara of the Widney Commune, and remembers the face of that striking little girl.

I first bumped into Karl Yann during one of my many afternoons of disgruntled teenage wandering. Dad, of course, was full of *You must be carefuls* and *Do watch outs*. Well, fuck that for a start, I thought as I tried without success to slam the second of the heavy sets of gates which guarded our estate. Looking back through the shockwire-topped fence at the big, neat houses with their postage stamp lawns, panic rooms and preposterous names, it was easy to think of prisons. Then, reaching into my coat pocket, hooking the transmitter buds around my ears and turning on my seashell, my head filled with beats, smells, swirls and other sensations, and it was easy not to think of anything at all. Hunching off along the glass and dogshit pavements past the boarded-up shops, dead lampposts and abandoned cars, I'd mastered the knack of keeping my device set so I remained aware enough to avoid walking into things. Until, that was, I found my way blocked by a large, laughing presence that was already reaching into my pocket and taking out, and then turning off, my precious seashell.

The city was supposedly full of piratical presences, at least according to my father, but this guy actually *looked* like a pirate. That, or, with his bushy red beard, twinkling blue eyes, wildly curly hair, be-ribboned coat and pixie boots, like some counter-cultural Father Christmas.

"Give that back!"

He grinned, still cupping my seashell in a big, paint-grained palm. "This is a pretty cool device, you know. Basically, it's mimicking your brainwaves so it can mess around with your thoughts . . . "

My father had said something similar, but this man's tone was admiring rather than concerned. At least, he seemed a man to me; I figured out later that Karl was barely into his twenties.

"I said—"

"Here. Don't want to get yourself tangled . . . " Almost impossibly gently, he was reaching to unpick the buds from around my ears, and already I was hooked. He was asking me questions. He seemed interested in my head-down city wanderings, and where I was from, and what I'd been playing on my seashell, and what I thought about things, and even in my Indian background, although I did have to make most of that up.

"This is the place. Don't snag yourself . . . "

Now, he was holding the wire of the fence that surrounded one of those half-finished developments that the dying economy had never finished. Maybe shops or offices or housing, but basically just a shrouded, rusty-scaffolded, concrete frame. A few floors up, though, and this place he called "the waystation" became a different world. In many ways, it was a glimpse of what was to come.

People stirred and said hi. The waystation's inner walls were painted, or hung with random bits of stuff, or fizzed with projections that drifted to and fro in the city haze. Old vehicles, bits of construction material, expensive drapes, blankets and rugs that looked more as if they had come from gated estate communities such as my own, had all been cleverly re-used to shape an exotic maze. Everything here had been transformed and recycled, and it was plain to me already that Karl was an artist of some talent, and at the heart of whatever was going on.

The Widney Commune is based around a grand old house, with icicled gates leaning before a winding drive. Some long-dead Midlands industrialist's idea of fine living. Shara and the other commune youngsters will still be down at the schoolhouse, and most of the adults will be out. This place could almost be deserted, Martha tells herself as she edges her Mini up the drive and clambers out. The main door lies up a half-circle of uncleared steps. Something tinkles deep within the house when she gives the old bellpull an experimental tug.

Even with all the indignities which have been inflicted on it—the warty vents and pipings, the tumbling add-ons—this is still a fine old sort of a place to live. Especially when you compare it to Baldwin Towers. No fifteen floors to ascend. No concrete stalactites, or rusting pipes, or a useless flat roof. The entangled might claim that they can see the wrongness of things, and feel disappointment and envy. But they clearly don't.

Martha starts when snow scatters her shoulders.

"Hello there," she shouts up with all her usual yes-I-really-am-here cheeriness. "Just trying to see if there's anyone at home."

"Oh . . . " A pause as the head at the window above registers that she's not some odd garden statue. " . . . I'm sorry. The front door's been stuck for years. If you can come around to the side . . . "

This pathway's been cleared, as even a mindblind moron should have noticed, and leads to a side entrance which leads down brick corridors into what was once, and still mostly is, a very great hall.

The space goes all the way up and there are galleries around it and a wide set of stairs. Live ivy grows up over the beams and there's a hutch in the corner where fat-eared rabbits lollop, and it's plain that the woman who's sashaying over to greet Martha is the source of at least half of Shara's good looks.

"I'm Freya . . . " After a small hesitation, she holds out a hand. It's crusty with flour, as are her bare arms. Her shoulders are bare, too, and so are her feet. Which, like the tip of her nose, are also dusted white. She's wearing holed dungarees that show off a great deal of her lithe, slim figure. Dirty blonde hair is done up in a kind of knot. " . . . you're . . . ?" Confused by the difficulties of introduction with someone of Martha's disability, she hesitates with a pout.

"Martha Chauhan." Martha lets her hand, which by now is floury as well, slip from Freya's. "I'm guessing you're Shara's birth mother?"

"That's right." Freya squints hard. "You were testing Shara? Today? At school?"

Martha nods. "Not that there's any cause for concern."

"That's good." She smiles. Hugs herself.

"But I, ah . . . " Martha looks around again, wondering if this is how social workers once felt. "Sometimes just like to call in on a few communes. Just to . . . Well . . . "

"Of course," Freya nods. "I understand."

Somehow, she does, even if Martha doesn't. The entangled live in a sea of trust.

"Most people are out, either working or enjoying the day. But I've just finished baking . . . so what can I show you?"

The entangled are relentlessly proud of their communes. They'll argue and josh about who breeds the fluffiest sheep, puts on the cheeriest festival or grows the best crop of beets. As always, there's the deep, sweet, monkey-house reek of massed and rarely washed humanity, but it's mingled here with different odours—of yeast, and the herbs that seem to be hanging everywhere to dry, and yet more of those rabbits. Each commune has its own specialities which it uses to exchange for things it doesn't make, and this one turns out to be rabbits, which are raised to make warm blankets and coats from their skins, as well as for their meat. This commune's bread is something they're particularly proud of, as well. Down in the hot kitchen, Freya tears some with her hands, takes a bite, then offers Martha the rest, dewy with spit. She doesn't have to lie when she says she isn't hungry.

Many of the rooms look like the scenes of some perpetual sleepover. The entangled mostly sleep like puppies, curling up wherever they fancy, although Freya's slightly more coy about one or two other spaces, which reek of sex. Another smell, sourer this time, comes from some leaking chairs and sofas set around a big fire where the old ones cluster, basking like lizards, tremulous hands joined and rheumy eyes gazing into the tumbled memories of a past forever gone.

"And this is where Shara sleeps with the rest of the under-tens . . . "

Another charming, fetid mess, although this one's scattered with toys. There's a spinning top. There are rugs and papier mache stars. There's a one-eyed, one-armed teddy bear. A few story books and piles of paper, as well, along with newer, stranger devices that make no sense to Martha at all.

"Shara's your only birth child?"

Freya nods. She looks at least as proud of that as she is of most things, even if parenting is shared in a loose kind of way that involves the whole commune and no one gets too possessive. Knowing exactly who the father is can be difficult. In this era of trust, mothers are surprisingly coy about who they've fucked. Women often wander out to visit other communes—driven either by biological imperative or the simple curiosities of lust—and births are often followed by versions of the *he's got Uncle Eric's nose* conversations that must have gone on throughout human history.

Freya's showing drawings and scraps of writing that Shara's done, then lifting up pretty bits of clothing she's resewn herself for all the kids to use and share.

"No new babies at the moment," she adds. "Although we're planning, of course . . . Soon as the commune has the resources. And Shara's been such a joy to us all . . . That I'm rather hoping . . . " As she puts the things back, her hands move unconsciously to her breasts.

"And Shara's father? Somehow, I'm guessing he's a fair bit older than you are . . . ?"

"Oh? That's right." Freya smiles, not remotely insulted or surprised. "Karl's hoping, as well. We all are. Would you like to see the studio where he works?"

Martha blinks, swallows, nods. A falling feeling as she follows Freya down a long corridor then through a doorway into what's clearly an artist's studio. Rich smells of oil and varnish. Linseed oil squeezed out over a press. Pigments from the hedgerow, or wherever it is that pigments come from. Half-finished canvases lean against the walls. The room is a kind of atrium, lit from windows on all sides and high up. The colours and the shadows roar out to her even on a day as wintry as this.

"He's probably out helping in one of the greenhouses," Freya says. "That or sketching. He tends to paint in short, intense bursts."

The canvases are part abstract and part Turner seascape. They're undeniably accomplished, and recognisably Karl Yann's, although to Martha's mind they've lost their old edge. The entangled are good at making pretty and practical things, but proper art seems to be beyond them. Still, as Martha stares at the largest blur of colour, which looms over her like a tsunami in a paint factory, it's hard not to be drawn.

Freya chuckles, standing so close that Martha can smell the grease in her hair. "I know. They're lovely, and they barter really well . . . But Karl doesn't like to have them up on display in our commune. Says all he'd ever see is where he went wrong."

I never did get my seashell back, but I got Karl Yann instead. He had a bragging mix of certainty and vulnerability which I found appealing after my father's endless *on-the-one-hand-but-on-the-other* attempts at balance. Karl was clever and he knew what he thought. Karl was an accomplished artist. Karl *cared*. He'd read stuff and done things and been to places and had opinions about everything, but he also wanted to know what my views were, and actually seemed to listen to me when I told him. Or at least, he had a roguishly charming way of cocking his head that made it look as if he was listening. Maybe it was a little late in the day for this whole hippy/beatnik/bohemian revolutionary shtick, but these things come new to every generation—or at least they used to—and they felt new to me. Karl used real paint when he could, or whatever else came to hand—he found the virtuals fascinating but frustrating—but what he really wanted to create was a changed world. No use accepting things as they are, Martha. No use talking about what needs to be done. At least, not unless you're prepared to act and make the necessary sacrifices to help bring about the coming wave of change. The forests dying. Whole continents starving. The climate buggered. The economy fucked. So, are you with us, Martha, or not?

They called them performance acts, and Karl and the other inhabitants of the waystation were convinced they were contributing towards bringing about a better world. And so, now, was I. People had to be shaken out of their complacency—especially the selfish, cosseted rich, with all their possessions, all their *things*—and what was the harm in having some fun while we're doing so? Right? Okay? Yes?

We used my credit pass to gain access to one of those exclusive, guarded, gated, palm tree-filled, rich-people-only, air-conditioned pleasure domes they still called shopping malls to which my father had occasionally taken me and Damien as a birthday treat, and pulled on balaclavas and yelled like heathens and flung pigshit-filled condoms at the over-privileged shoppers and their shit-filled shops, and got out laughing and high-fiving in the ensuing mayhem. We climbed fences and sneaked through gardens and around underlit pools to hang paintings upside down and spraypaint walls and mess with people's heads. Then, often as not, and young as Martha Chauhan still was, she went home to her gated estate.

The Mini seemed to know the way from the Widney Commune, but time and entanglement haven't been kind to this part of the city. Martha's boots press through new white drifts to snag on the rusted shockwire and fallen sensor pylons that once supposedly protected this little enclosure. The houses, haggard with smoke, blink their shattered eyes and shrug their collapsing shoulders as if in denial. Is this really the right place? Even the right street? Martha struggles to make sense of the layout of her lost life as she stands at what was surely the heart of their neat cul-de-sac where an uprooted tree now scrawls its branches until she's suddenly looking straight at her old home and everything's so clear its as if her eyeballs have burned through into ancient photographic negatives. The roof of the old house is still intact, even if Dad's old car has long gone from the driveway, and she almost reaches for her key when she steps up to the front door. But the thing is frozen solid by age and perhaps even the fancy triple-locking that once protected it. *You can't be too careful Martha* . . . She looks around with a start. The other houses with their blackened Halloween eyes stare back at her. She shivers. Steps back. Takes stock. Then she walks around to the side past an upturned bin and finds that half the wall is missing, and pushes through, and everything clicks, and she's standing in their old kitchen.

Over there . . . Over *here* . . .

She's an archaeologist. She's a diver in the deepest of all possible seas. She scoops snow, dead leaves and rubble from the hollow of the sink. She straightens a thing of rust that might once have been the spice rack. Many of the tiles with their squiggle pattern of green and white that she never consciously noticed before are still hanging. And all the while, the thinning light of this distant winter pours down and in. So many days here. So many arguments over breakfast. She can see her father clearly now, quietly spooning fruit and yoghurt onto his mueseli with the flowerpots lined on the windowledge behind him and the screen of some medical paper laid on the table and his cuffs rolled back to show his raw-looking wrists and his tie not yet done up. Damien is there as well, chomping as ever through some sugary, chocolaty stuff that he'll waste half of.

"I had a visit from some police contractors yesterday," he's telling her as he unfolds a linen handkerchief and dabs delicately at his mouth. "Apparently, they're looking for witnesses to an incident that happened at the Hall Green Mall. You may have heard about it—some kind of silly stunt? Of course, I told them the truth. I simply said you were out."

Now, as he refolds his handkerchief, he turns his guileless brown eyes up towards her, and the question he's really asking is so padded with all his usual oblique politeness that it's easily ignored. Anyway, time is moving on—Martha can feel it roaring through her bones in a winter gale—and now she's back home from her first term at the old, elite university town that her father, ever the supportive parent, has agreed to finance her studies at. Politics and Philosophy, too, and not a mention of the practical, career-based subjects she's sure he'd have much preferred her to take. Even as he spoons yoghurt over his mueseli, she can feel him not carefully mentioning this. But he seems newly hunched and his hand trembles as he spoons his yoghurt. And here's a much larger, gruffer-sounding version of Damien, as well, and sprouting some odd kind of haircut, even if he is still half-eating a bowl of sugary slop. All so very strange: the way people start changing the instant you look away from them. But that isn't at the heart of it. What lies at the core of Martha's unease is, of all things, a dog that isn't really a dog.

"*Of course* he's a dog, Martha," my father's saying as his suddenly liver-spotted hands stroke the creature's impossibly high haunches and it wags its tail and gazes at me with one eye of brown and the other of whirring silver. "Garm's *fun*. We take him for walks, don't we Damien? The only difference is that he's even cleverer and more trustworthy, and helps bring us a little bit of extra safety and security in these difficult times. Some worrying things have occurred locally, Martha, and I don't just mean mere destruction in unoccupied homes. So we do what we can, don't we Garm? Matter of fact, Martha, the enhancement technology that allows him to interact with the house security systems is essentially the same as I use to help my patients . . . "

But this is all too much, it always was, and Martha's off out through the same stupid security gates and on along the same cold, dreary streets with more than enough stuff roaring around in her head to make up for her missing seashell that Karl never did give back to her even though all property is, basically, theft. That's dumb sloganeering and there are many new ideas Martha wants to share with him. But even the waystation seems changed. Sydney's been arrested, and Sophie got her arm burned on some stray shockwire, and different faces peer out at her through the fug. Who *is* this person? Martha Chauhan could ask them the same. Then up the final level, squeezing past a doorway into some windy higher floor which already looks like the aftermath of a battle in an art gallery, with ripped concrete walls, flailing reinforcing bars and blasted ceilings all coated in huge swathes of colour. Clearly Karl's experimenting with new techniques, and it's all rather strange and beautiful-ugly. Forget regurgitated abstract expressionism. This is what Bosch would have painted if he'd lived in the bombed-out twenty-first century city. But hadn't they agreed that art for art's sake was essentially nothing but Nero fiddling while Rome burned?

"So," he gestures, emerging from the dazzling rubble with the winter sun behind him like some rock star of old. "What do you think?"

"It's . . . incredible . . . " So much she wants to tell him, now that she properly understands the history and context of their performance acts and sees them as part of a thread that goes back through syncretic individualism, anarcho-syndicalism and autonomism. But Karl is already scuttling off and returns holding something inside a paint-covered rag that she momentarily assumes as he unwraps it is some new artistic toy he's been playing with—a programmable paint pallet or digital brush. But, hey, it's a handgun.

Snow blows in. Martha's breath plumes. It's growing dark. The old family house creaks, groans, tinkles as she shuffles into the hall and brushes away ice and dirt from the security control panel beneath the stairs. But everything here is dead—her own memory of the night when she lost half her mind and more than half her family included. Just doubts and what-ifs. Things Karl had said, questions he'd asked, about her Dad being a doctor, which surely meant access to drugs and money, and about the kind of security systems employed in their gated estate, and ways to circumvent them. That, and the strange, dark, falling gleam of that handgun, and how those performance acts of old had never been *that* harmless. Not just ghastly artwork hung up the wrong way but taps left running, freezers turned off, pretty things smashed. Precious books, data, family photos, destroyed or laughingly defaced beyond all hope of recovery. Pigshit in the beds. Coy carp flopped gasping on Persian rugs. Treasured bits of people's lives gleefully ruined. In a way, she supposes, what Karl did to her here in her own home was a kind of comeuppance.

With numb fingers, she picks out the thumbnail data card that once held the house records and shoves it into her coat pocket, although she doubts if there's anything that would now read it, the world having moved on so very far. The rotten stairs twitch and groan as she climbs them. The door to poor, dead, Damien's room is still closed, a shrine, just as it was and always should be, but the fall of the side wall has done for most of Dad's room, and she's standing almost in empty air as she looks in.

Amazing that this whole place hasn't been ransacked and recycled, although she's sure it soon will be. Her own room especially, the floor of which now sags with the rusty weight of the great, semi-circular slabs of polarised metal and all the rest of the once high-tech medical equipment which encircled her bed.

My father pitted all his money and energies toward healing his injured daughter in the aftermath of the terrible night of Damien's death. All I can recall of this is a slow rising of pain and confusion. Instructions to do this or that minor task—the blink of an eye, the lifting of a finger—which seemed to involve my using someone else's body. My thoughts, as well, seemed strange and clumsy to me as the crystal neurons strove to blend with the damaged remains of my brain and I dipped in and out of rejection fever. In many ways, they didn't seem like my thoughts at all. I wasn't *me* any longer.

Sitting watching bad things happen on a screen with my baby brother crying. Or being on a beach somewhere with crashing waves and the dogs, the Frisbees, the cricket. These were things I could understand and believe in. But the uncooperative limbs and wayward thoughts of this changed, alien self belonged to someone else. A roaring disconnect lay between the person I'd been and the person I now was, and the only way I could remain something like sane was to think of this new creature as 'Martha Chauhan'.

"I'm so grateful you're still here and alive," a tired, grey-haired man Martha knew to be her father was saying as he spoon-fed her. "Is there much . . . " The offered spoon trembled in age-mottled fingers. " . . . you can remember of how all this happened?"

Martha made the slow effort to shake her head, then to open her mouth and swallow.

"There was a break-in, you see, here at our house. I don't know how the person got in, nor why the systems didn't go off, or why poor Garm wasn't alerted. But he wasn't. Neither was I—I'm too old, too deaf—and I think it was your brother Damien who must have heard something, perhaps the glass of the back door being broken, and got you to go downstairs with him. And then I believe the intruder must have panicked. After all, it can't be easy, to be standing alone in the dark of someone else's kitchen. A gun going off—that was what woke *me*, and by the time I got downstairs the intruder had fled and poor Damien was past any kind of help, although at least I know he didn't suffer. And poor Garm, of course, proved to be no use at all, and I had him reformatted and sold. But then, you never did like him much, did you? I thought you were lost to me as well for a while, Martha, what with the damage that bullet had inflicted to your head. But you're here and alive and so am I and for that I'm incredibly, impossibly grateful . . . We've spilled a bit there, though, haven't we? Hold on, I'll get a cloth . . . "

Eventually, Martha learned how to sit up unaided, and to spoon, chew and swallow her own food. It was a slow process. Through several sleepless years, as her father grew withered and exhausted from wiping her arse and changing the sheets and tending the machines, she learned how to walk and talk and returned to some kind of living. He never left her. He never let go. He never relented. He was a sunken smile and tired eyes. He was the stooped back that lifted her and hands which were always willing to hold. He never spared the time or energy for any feelings of rage, or such abstract concepts as retribution, although he surely knew who was responsible for the destruction of his family, and had sufficient evidence to prove it, even in the days when justice was about as reliable as the power grid and the police were privatised crooks. Karl Yann slunk off toward the sunrise of this bright new world, while Martha Chauhan's father's heart gave out from grief and exhaustion, and she was left empty, damaged and alone.

———

She rams the old car into gear and thumbs on the headlights. The tyres slide. The black-edged, glittering night pours past her. She can hear laughter over the roaring in her ears as she parks and kills the Mini's engine at the far edge of some trees outside the Widney Commune. She rummages deep in her carpetbag, picks off the fluff and dry-swallows the few immune suppressants she can find loose in the lining. Not enough, but it will have to do. Then she takes out a primed antipsychotic syringe and shoves it into her coat pocket.

Her feet are dead and the house's fire-rimmed shadow leaps over a field of untrampled snow as she crunches toward it. There's no one about apart from pigs sleeping in their pens until she turns a corner and hits a blaze of bonfire. Then there's life everywhere, and dancing to the accompaniment of discordant shouts and bursts of clapping.

Amazing, how well this useless brain of hers still works. How it can devise and dismiss plans without her even realising she's thought of them. The paintings inside the house, for example. She could walk in and slash, burn or deface them. But that wouldn't hurt Karl Yann. At least, not enough. He'd just pronounce it a fresh phase. Even burning this whole commune to the ground wouldn't be sufficient. What about that child, then, Shara—who Martha can see twirling at the shimmering edge of the flames? Or the lovely Freya? He'd feel *their* loss, now, wouldn't he? But Martha's mind slides from such schemes, not so much because she finds them abhorrent but because they lack the brutal simplicity she craves. It has to be *him*, she tells herself as she stands, ignored at the edge of the light, searching the shining, happy faces. Has to be Karl Yann. Draw him away to some quiet spot—he might recognise her, but the entangled are impossibly trusting—then knock him senseless with the contents of this syringe. Drag him to the Mini, drive him to some as-yet undefined place . . . In this world where no one steals and no one hurts and everything is shared, all these things will be ridiculously easy.

The straps of the field cap can be easily adjusted. Its settings are incredibly flexible. You could kill someone, fry their brains, if you really wanted. That, or turn them into a gibbering vegetable. Appealing though these options are, to Martha's mind they lack the simplicity of true retribution. So why not destroy just enough of his thalamus to break the quantum shimmer of entanglement? Then, he'd be alone, just as she is. He'd be lost, and he'd know what it really is to suffer. The final performance act in a world made perfect.

But where *is* he?

"Hey, hey—look who it is! Its Martha!"

A familiar male voice, but it's Tommy the teacher who comes up to embrace her. Perhaps this is his commune. Perhaps he's looking for new friends to dance, laugh or fuck with. The entangled are like bonobo monkeys. Smell like them, as well. Others are turning now that Tommy's noticed her, mouths wide with surprise and sympathy. Poor, dear Martha. Sweet, old Martha. Standing there at the cold edge of the dark, when all of us are so very warm and happy. You don't need to be entangled to know what they're feeling.

She's swept up. She's carried forward. She lets go of the syringe in time just as her hands are hauled from their pockets. The entangled don't do booze, or other drugs—most of them frown at Martha's liking for coffee— but the stuff that steams in the cracked mug that's forced into her fingers is so sweet and hot it must be laced with something. Then there's the rabbit: tender, honey-savoury—a treat in itself, meat being something that's reserved for special occasions. They're so happy to see her here at the Widney Commune it's as if they've long been waiting for her, and their joy spills out in hugs, giggles and touches. The kids flicker like elves. The old ones grin toothlessly.

Come on, Martha! Now, they're clapping to some offbeat she can't quite follow. A circle forms, and she's at the heart of it, where the snow's been cleared and the fire roars. *Come on, Martha! Come on, Martha!* They think they're not taunting her. Think they're not drunk. But they're drunk on this hour. Drunk on the future. Drunk on everything.

Martha does an ungracious bow. Stumbles a few Rumpelstiltskin steps. She's the ghost of every lost Christmas. She's the spirit of the plague from that story by Poe. And everything, her head most likely, or possibly her body, or this entire world, is spinning. Poor Martha. Dear Martha. They stroke the lumpen shape of her skull like it's an old stone found on a beach. And this isn't even her commune. Isn't her world.

"Hey, Martha . . . " Now, Freya and Shara emerge from the glowing smoke. "So great that you've come back to see us again!"

"Oh, yes . . . " Shara agrees. "We all love you here, Martha. We really do."

"Where's Karl?" Martha yells over a roaring that must be mostly in her head.

"He's . . . " One starts.

" . . . out." The other finishes.

"Right," Martha says. "You don't have any idea *where*, do you? I mean . . . You see . . . "

She trails off as these two elfin creatures, one small and one fully grown and both entirely beautiful, gaze at her with firelight in their eyes.

"Oh, somewhere," Freya says with a faraway smile. "Your birthfather likes to wander, doesn't he, Sha?"

For Martha's benefit, Shara gives an emphatic nod.

"Oh? Right. Good . . . You see, I think I used to know him . . . Long ago."

"Oh, but you *did*!" Freya delightedly confirms. "I said you'd come to see us, and Karl instantly knew who you were, didn't he, Sha? Said you went back a very long way."

"And then . . . He went out again?"

"Of course. I mean . . . " Freya shrugs her shoulders. Gazes off, as if nothing could be more welcoming, into the freezing dark. "Why not?"

After her father died—a feat he managed with the same quiet fortitude with which he'd done most things throughout his life—Martha Chauhan found herself living in a place with Harry Potterish turrets and pointed windows that could have been the one she and Damien had visited when they were kids. A kind of commune, if you like. But not.

Still a youngish woman by many standards, but she fitted in well with these wizened and damaged creatures who cost so much money and technology and wasted effort to keep alive. She learned how to talk to them, and show an interest. She got better at walking. She learned to how play mah-jong. And outside, beyond the newly heightened shockwire and the sullen guards, the world was falling apart. The tap water was brown with sewerage. The winters were awful. The summers were shot.

But wait. The big screens they sat in front of all day were showing something else. There was a virus—a new mutation of a type of encephalitis that attacked a part of the brain known as the thalamus. The fever it triggered was worrying, but very few people died from it, and those who survived were changed in ways they found hard to explain—at least to those who hadn't yet become whatever they now were. Some said the virus wasn't just a random mutation, but that it was down to terrorists, or space aliens, or the government. Or that it was awakening something that had long been there, buried deep inside everyone's skulls, and that this was a new kind of humanity, a different kind of knowing, which was triggered by a form of quantum entanglement which joined mind to mind, soul to soul.

Others simply insisted that it was the Rapture. Or the end of the world.

Of course, there were riots and pogroms. There was looting. There were several wars. Politicians looked for personal advancement. Priests and mullahs pleaded for calm, or raged for vengeance. People walked the streets wearing facemasks, or climbed into their panic rooms, or headed for hilltops and deserted islands with supplies of food and weapons to last for years. A time of immense confusion, and all Martha Chauhan knew as things collapsed was that the few staff who were still working at Hogwarts laughed as they saw to the catheters or mopped the floors. Soon, many of the wizened and damaged ones were laughing as well.

The day the shockwire fell—her own personal Berlin Wall—Martha Chauhan stumbled out into a changed world. It was as she'd long expected. There were the bodies and the twisted lampposts and the ransacked buildings and the burnt-out cars. But people were busy working in loose, purposeful gangs, and *clearing things up*. Stranger still, they were singing as they did so, or laughing like loons, or simply staring at each other and the world as if they'd never seen it before.

On she stumbled. And was picked up, cradled, fed, welcomed. Then, as the fever passed by her and nothing changed, she was pitied as well. Eventually, she got to meet people who could explain why she could never become entangled, but she already knew. There was nothing that could be done to replace the dumb nano-circuitry that took up vital parts of her skull without destroying this construct known as Martha Chauhan as well. Still, the commune at Baldwin Towers were happy to have her. Like the blind piano tuners of old, she was even given special work, along with some privileges, to reflect her odd status and disability. And so it went, and so it still is to this dark winter's night, and now Martha Chauhan's back in her Mini, driving lost and alone through a fathomless, glittering world.

She's stopped. The little car's engine is quiet, and the cold is incredibly intense. She fumbles in her carpetbag with dead fingers, but whatever immune suppressants she has left—carefully made somewhere far from here at great but unmentioned expense—must all be back at Baldwin Towers, and the roaring in her head deepens as she breaks the car door's seal of ice and tumbles outside.

Another day is greying as she looks up at the waystation. Superficially, nothing much has changed. It's still an abandoned ruin, although the snow and these extra years of neglect have given it a kind of grace. Even the dead shockwire Karl once held up for her remains, and shivers like a live thing, scattering rust and ice down her neck as she crawls beneath.

All the old faces seem to peer out at her as she clambers in through concrete shadows and icicle drips. Who *is* this person? She could ask the same of them. Not that she ever really belonged here. Or anywhere. Creaks and slides as she climbs ladders and crawls stairways until she claws back her breath and finds she's standing surprisingly high, overlooking a greened and snowy landscape that seems more forest than city in the sun's gaining blaze. For all she knows, the entangled will soon be swinging tree to tree. But that isn't how it will end. They're biding their time for now, still clearing things up as this damaged world heals, and the icecaps, the forests, the jungles, the savannahs, return. But the gestalt will spread. Soon, it will expand in a great wave to join with the other intelligences which knit this universe. Martha Chauhan hears laughter and realises it's her own. For a dizzy moment there, standing at this precipice at the future's edge, she almost understands what it all means.

The whole sky is brightening, and she's starting to realise just how beautiful this high part of the old waystation has become. Blasted rubble and concrete and a sense of abandonment, certainly, but everything covered in the glimmer of frost and snow and old paint and new growth. Colours pool in the icemelt. Then, something bigger moves, and she sees that it's a ragged old man, a kind of grey-bearded wizard, half Scrooge and half Father Christmas, who seems to belong in this grotto in his paint-strewn clothes.

"It's me, Martha," Karl Yann says in a croaked approximation of his old voice as his reflections ripple about him. "I just wish I could share how you feel."

"But you *can't* can you? You're here and I'm not." Martha Chauhan shakes her head. Feels her thoughts rattle. That isn't what she meant at all. "You think you know everything, don't you? All the secrets of the fucking universe. But you don't know what it is to *hurt*."

He winces. Looks almost afraid. But there's the same distant pity in his old eyes that Martha's seen a million times. Even here. Even from him. She tries to imagine herself dragging the syringe from her pocket. Running forward screaming and stabbing. Instead, her vision blurs with tears.

"Oh, Martha, *Martha* . . . Here, look . . . " Now he's coming toward her in a frost of breath, and holding something out. "This used to be yours. It *is* yours. You should have it back . . . "

She sniffs and looks despite herself. Sees her long-lost seashell nestling in his craggy hand. She gabs it greedily and hugs it to herself. "I suppose you've got that other thing as well—another bloody souvenir?"

He looks puzzled. "What thing?"

"The gun, you bastard! The thing you killed my bother with—and did this to me!" She slaps the slope of her skull so hard it rings.

But he just stands there. Then, slowly, he blinks. "I think I see."

"See what?" The entangled are useless at arguing—she's tried it often enough.

"You think, Martha, you *believe*, that I broke into your house and did that terrible thing? Is that what you're saying?"

"Of course I am." But why is the roaring getting louder in her head?

"I'm sorry, Martha," he says, looking at her more pityingly than ever. "I really am so very, very sorry."

"You can't just ... Leave ... "

But he is. He's turning, shuffling away from her across this rainbow space with nothing but a slow backward glance. Dissolving into the frost and the shadows, climbing down and out from this lost place of memories toward his life and his commune and a sense of infinite belonging, before Martha Chauhan even knows what else to think or say or feel.

Full day now, and Martha Chauhan's sitting high at the concrete edge of the waystation.

It's freezing up there, despite the snowmelt. But she doesn't seem to be shivering any longer, nor does she feel especially cold. She sniffs, swipes her dripping nose, then studies the back of an old woman's hand which seems to have come away coated in blood. That roaring in her ears which is much too loud and close to be any kind of sound. Although there's no pain, it isn't hard for her to imagine, with what brains she has left, the wet dissolution of the inside of her skull as the immune suppressants fade from her blood. If she doesn't turn up back at Baldwin Towers soon, she supposes help will probably come. But the entangled can be astonishingly callous. They let their old and frail die from curable diseases. They kill their treasured pets for clothing and food.

She inspects her old seashell. A small glow rises through the red smears when she touches its controls. Something here that isn't dead, and she hooks the buds around her ears and feels a faint, nostalgic fizz. But the stuff she liked back in the day would surely be awful, old and lost as she now is. A different person, really. In fact, that's the whole point ...

She feels past the syringe in her coat pocket, finds the data card she took from the house security system and sniffs back more blood as she numbly shoves it in. It's still a surprise, though, to find options and menus hanging against the clear morning sky. Files as well, that she thought Dad would have deleted. But then, he never liked destroying things—even stuff he never planned to use. And perhaps, the thought trickles down through her leaking brain, he left this for her. After all, and despite his many evasions and protestations, he always had a strong regard for the truth.

She waves a once-practised hand through ancient images until she reaches the very last date. The end of everything. The very last night.

And there it is.

There it always was.

She's looking into the bright dark of their old kitchen through the night-sight eyes of that stupid not-dog. Fast-forward until a window shatters in a hard spray and the door opens and something moves in, and the not-dog stirs, wags its tail, recognises . . . Not Karl Yann, but a much more familiar shape and scent.

Martha rips the buds from her ears, but she still can't escape the past. She's back at this waystation, but she's young again, and the colours are brilliant, and she's here with Karl Yann, full of Politics and Philosophy and righteous anger at the state of the world. And he's got this handgun that he's merely using as a prop for all his agitprop posturings, when she has a much clearer, simpler, cleverer idea. The final performance act, right? The easiest, most obvious, one of all . . . Come on, Karl, don't say you haven't *thought* of it . . . And fuck you if you're not interested. If you're not prepared, I'll just do the damn thing myself . . .

Martha flouncing from the waystation. Into the darkness. Hunching alone through the glass and rubble streets. The gun a weight of potentiality in her pocket and the whole world asleep. She feels like she's in the mainstream of the long history of resistance. She's Ulrike Meinhof. She's Gavrilo Princip. She's Harry Potter fighting Voldemort. A pure, simple, righteous deed to show everyone—and her Dad especially—that there is no way to keep the truth of what's really happening away from these prim, grim estates. Not this shockwire. Not these gates. Not anything. Least of all the glass of their kitchen door which breaks with a satisfying clatter as she feels for the old-fashioned handle and turns. Not that this isn't a prank as well. Not that there isn't still fun to be had. After all, that fucking thing of a dog isn't really living anyway, it's nothing but dumb *property*, so what harm is being done if she shoots it properly dead? Nothing at all, right? She's doing nothing but good. She's shoving it to the system. She's giving it to the man. The darkness seethes as she enters, and she feels as she always feels, standing right here in the kitchen, like an intruder in her own life.

That roaring again. Now stronger than ever, even though the seashell's buds are off and its batteries have gone. After all, how is she to tell one shape from another in this sudden dark? How could she know, when she can barely see anything, that the thing that comes stumbling threateningly out at her is Damien and not that zombie dog? It's all happened already, and too quickly, and the moment is long gone. A squeezed trigger and the world shudders and she's screaming and the dog's howling and all the backup lights have flared and Damien's sprawled in a lake of blood and the gun's a deathly weight in her hand—although Martha Chauhan doubts if she could ever understand how she felt as she turned it around so that its black snout was pointing at her own head and she squeezed the trigger again.

Her father is with her now. Even without looking, and just as when she lay in her bedroom surrounded by pain and humming equipment, she knows he's here. After all, and despite her many attempts to reject him, he never really went away. And, as always, he's telling her tales—filling the roaring air with endless ideas, suppositions, stories . . . Talking at least as much about once-upon-a-times and should-have-beens as about how things really are. Using what life and energy he has left to bring back his daughter. And if he could have found a way of sheltering her from what really happened that terrible night, if he could have invented a story that gave her a reason to carry on living, Martha knows he would have done so.

She sniffs, tastes bitter salt, and feels a deep roaring. It's getting impossibly late. Already, the sun seems to be setting, and the beach is growing cold, and the cricket match has finished, and that last gritty samosa she's just eaten was foul, and all the dogs and the kite flyers have gone home. But there's Dad, walking, trousers-rolled and hand-in-hand with Damien as the tide floods in. Martha waves cheerily, and they wave back. She thinks she might just join them, down there at the edge of everything where all islands meet.

IN A WAY, THE LAST STORY IN THIS COLLECTION GOES BACK TO THE FIRST. Instead of the near future of "The Discovered Country" where the world is wrecked and the dead rule, this is one where the living have triumphed and everyone is happy. Not that even I would describe it as a happy story. But then, one of the most useful things I ever discovered about writing about changed worlds came from a comment made by James Blish, which went along the lines of, when you come up with a new discovery or innovation, you next have to ask yourself is "Who will suffer as a result?"

The route to Martha's changed world came via a BBC Horizon episode called *Are You Good or Evil?* which looked at the work of researchers who were seeking the genetic and personality traits which would allow psychopaths to be identified—perhaps while they were still children, and certainly long before they'd committed any crimes. This is a trope SF writers have been using for years, *Minority Report* being the most obvious example which springs to mind, but it wasn't one I'd ever tried. As I mulled it over, something like the nurse who I remember used to look for nits in our hair at St James' Infants' when I was a kid began to evolve. From that, the idea that she might encounter the child of someone who had once committed a crime against her seemed an interesting way to go.

But I couldn't reconcile this seemingly dystopian world of thought-crime and mind control with all the happy people who kept buzzing around Martha as she went about her work. I even had problems with the snow. Which, as I discovered, might bring joy to everyone on the morning it falls, but tends to cover over and distort much of the landscape you want to describe. Although, and rather like Martha, I somehow managed to plough my way through.

The premise of the finished story has very few links with that Horizon programme. The dystopia and the mind-control are gone, or remain as faint shadows which only Martha really sees thrown across the snow. Still, it does involve a mind-changing virus, quantum entanglement, robot dogs and artificial brain-enhancement, and thus explores some pretty hard-core scientific and technological themes by my usual low-tech standards.

Now and then, some people, including a few writers, have expressed surprise at my lack of any proper scientific background. After all, don't I write SF, and isn't SF supposed to be about science? Of course it isn't, or it shouldn't be, any more than good crime fiction is about forensic and legal minutiae, or historical fiction is a rigorously detailed and accurate portrayal of the past. All fiction, wherever it's set and whatever it's supposedly about, is really about people, and their concerns, and what it's like to be alive in the world of now. Still, it has to be admitted, science and SF are obvious bedfellows, and the mirror that the genre, not to mention science itself, can hold up to the world can be thrillingly fresh and askew.

I've been fascinated by science from the first day I turned up at infants' school and was disappointed to find out we were expected to shape letters and play in a sandpit instead of learning about dinosaurs and volcanoes. I'm not sure my sense of disappointment with the education system ever quite recovered from that initial blow. Science, when we finally got around to it, seemed to be mainly about giving things names rather than discovering why they existed, and how they worked. But by then, I starting to read and find things out for myself. And, as a bright kid who, as a result of what would now be diagnosed as dyslexia, along with a singularly disruptive attitude, was graded as below average and shunted into a bottom form, that's pretty much how it's been ever since.

My maths is functional, and I've never been able to grasp equations, although I sometimes have odd flashes of insight which no one else seems to be able to follow, and I struggle to explain even to myself. Even when it comes to English, and no doubt in part as a combined result of my dyslexia and low achieving academic environment, my knowledge of grammatical structure remains shaky and instinctive to this day. The technical terminology of English is something I've had to study when I was required to teach it, but it remains a rickety afterthought to the way that I see language, in that it ever enters my thoughts at all. And as for spelling—again, that's something I've studied as an adult so I can explain it to others, but I can still get the most obvious things wrong.

But back to science, and a fascination which was, of course, fed by my teenage reading of SF, and has never gone away. Not to mention a feeling of disappointment with the real world, a sense that it somehow isn't enough on its own, and could be improved and made stranger and more wonderful—both darker and brighter—which has driven me to write. And, somewhere in me, I'm sure there's still that little boy, excitedly pushing things around in a sand pit as he waits to find out about volcanoes and dinosaurs.

Ian R MacLeod is the critically-acclaimed author of six novels and more than fifty short stories. His work has been published in many languages and dramatised on television, and he has received many major awards, including the Arthur C. Clarke Award for *SONG OF TIME* which PS published in 2008. PS also published not only one of the author's previous collection — *Past Magic* — but also a vampiric novella entitled *The Réperateur of Strasbourg,* and the novel *Wake Up and Dream*, described as "Film Noir with Technicolour Wraiths." He lives in the riverside town of Bewdley.